Electronic Signals
and Systems

The English Language Book Society is funded by the Overseas Development Administration of the British Government. It makes available low-priced, unabridged editions of British publishers' textbooks to students in developing countries. Below is a list of some other books on electrical and electronic engineering published under the ELBS imprint.

Bannister and Whitehead
Fundamentals of Modern Digital Systems
Macmillan

Clayton
Operational Amplifiers
Butterworth

Havill and Walton
Elements of Electronics for Physical Scientists
Macmillan

King
Integrated Electronic Circuits and Systems
Van Nostrand Reinhold (UK)

Lewin
Design of Logic Systems
Van Nostrand Reinhold (UK)

Ramshaw
Power Electronics
Chapman & Hall

Ritchie
Transistor Circuit Techniques
Van Nostrand Reinhold (UK)

Seymour
Electronic Devices and Components
Longman

Watson
Analog and Switching Circuit Design
Adam Hilger

Electronic Signals and Systems

PAUL A. LYNN

MACMILLAN

First published 1986 by
MACMILLAN EDUCATION LTD
Houndmills, Basingstoke, Hampshire RG21 2XS
and London
Companies and representatives
throughout the world

ISBN 0–333–39164–0

Printed in Hong Kong

Reprinted 1986, 1991

Contents

v

List of Computer Programs

The following BASIC programs appear in the main text

All programs have been developed and tested on an Amstrad personal microcomputer. They use relatively few of the available BASIC instructions, and should run on a wide range of other machines with only minor modifications.

Most programs include both a *plot option* and a *print option* for the output. The relevant program lines may be included or omitted, as required. The plot options use the Amstrad BASIC instructions CLS (clear screen), PLOT (plot pixel at stated X, Y coordinates), and DRAW (draw line to stated X, Y coordinates). They are based on a screen resolution of 640×400 pixels. All plots have been kept simple, and it should be straightforward to produce equivalent graphical outputs on other computers.

In most cases programs are based on mathematics developed in the accompanying text. Their structure and content should therefore be clear to the reader. The only exceptions are program no. 5 and program no. 8. These are presented without detailed explanation, and used to illustrate important techniques described in more general terms in the text.

Preface

This book is designed as an introductory text in electronic signals and systems for the early stages of degree courses in universities and polytechnics. Its level and scope should make it suitable not only for electronic and electrical engineering courses, but also for those covering other branches of engineering, physics, and computer studies. The initial pace of the book is deliberately gentle. Students with very little previous knowledge of electronics should find its first few chapters quite easy to follow.

Pressure on the electronic and electrical syllabus continues to grow. New material, particularly in microelectronics and computing, constantly competes for the student's time. Yet most lecturers (and employers) are reluctant to see important topics such as linear circuit theory, communications, and control seriously reduced. A partial solution to the problem is to teach Signals and Systems early in the course, using it as a foundation for much that follows. This can substantially reduce double-teaching. It also has the great intellectual advantage for the student of emphasising links between the many branches of electronic engineering.

Quite a number of Signals and Systems textbooks have appeared in recent years. However, in my view these are often too difficult for the early stages of an undergraduate course. Furthermore, many use a 'black box' approach. Students get much of their initial motivation from practical work with circuits, and they appreciate a Signals and Systems approach which illustrates ideas with circuit applications. I have decided to meet this need by including many examples based on operational amplifier techniques. These have the advantage of requiring no detailed understanding of active devices or circuits.

The book offers a number of features

A unified treatment of continuous-time and discrete-time signals and systems.
A thorough introduction to time and frequency domain analysis.
Circuit examples—passive and active, analog and digital—to illustrate the text.
Worked examples in the text, problems at the end of each chapter, and solutions at the end of the book.
BASIC computer programs, integrated with the main text, to illustrate important concepts and applications.

The last item deserves a little explanation. Digital computers are becoming more and more important in teaching, and many students now have the use of a personal microcomputer. All programs in this book are suitable for such machines, and I believe that most readers will gain a lot by using them. I should add that the programs are included as aids to understanding signals and systems, *not* computer programming. I make no claims at all for them in this latter respect.

In slightly more detail, the first two chapters are intended as a gentle introduction to the background and scope of the subject. I have, with some misgivings, decided to summarise the basic circuit ideas needed for this book in chapter 1. The aim here is to make the book self-contained. I have emphasised in the text itself that these sections are in no sense to be regarded as a course in circuit theory! Chapters 3 to 6 offer a fairly conventional account of the basic tools of signal and system analysis. Convolution is covered *before* frequency-domain transforms, because discrete-time convolution is so straightforward and illuminating. If the student understands it well, such notions as the transient and steady-state response of a system, stability, causality, and so on, present very little difficulty. I hope that these first six chapters form a coherent and readable introduction to linear signal and system theory. I have tried to suggest and include plenty of applications, and have commented on some of the practical problems of design. The chapters contain many cross-references, and should preferably be studied in the correct sequence.

Chapter 7 consolidates and extends ideas about feedback, and introduces a number of important applications. I have tried to show how the major characteristics of negative and positive feedback are put to use in a variety of practical systems—analog and digital. Chapter 8 on signal processing first covers signal sampling and reconstitution with some care. It then outlines the processes of signal truncation and windowing, and introduces analog and digital versions of the widely used Butterworth and Chebyshev filter families. These last two chapters are independent of one another, although each relies heavily on material in chapters 1 to 6. They may therefore be included, or omitted, as required.

It would be impossible to list all the sources which I used, consciously or unconsciously, in the writing of this book. I have referred to numerous books on signal analysis, system theory, circuits, and filters. I have also drawn on personal experience, lecture notes generated over a number of years, and unrecorded conversations with colleagues. I gratefully acknowledge all these contributions. I also wish to make a few more specific acknowledgements. Dr W.A. Atherton's excellent book on the history of electrical and electronic engineering, *From Compass to Computer* (Macmillan, 1984), suggested the use of the photographs and historical material in chapter 1. I am grateful for permission from the Bell Laboratories, the Siemens Museum, the Marconi Company, and *Punch* magazine, to include them. I should finally like to record my thanks to Jeana Price for all her work on the typescript; and to express gratitude to those, near and far, without whose support this book would not have been completed.

4 Kensington Place   Paul A. Lynn
Clifton
Bristol BS8 3AH

1 Introduction

"It is a good thing to have two ways of looking at a subject, and to admit that there are two ways of looking at it."

James Clerk Maxwell (1831–1879),
whose electromagnetic theory
predicted 'wireless' communication

1.1 Historical perspectives

The early pioneers of electronics and telecommunications would surely be astonished to see the variety of uses of modern electronic engineering. Even as late as 1950, the impact of electronics on the average household in the industrial world was limited to a telephone, a radio receiver, and perhaps a gramophone. We now also have televisions, home computers linked to data and communications networks, pocket calculators, video and audio tape recorders and electronic watches—and we increasingly use electronics in our domestic appliances, for the control of heating systems, and in our cars. Such uses are apparent to everyone. But of course electronics has also entered schools and universities, offices, factories, and hospitals. Ships and satellites navigate with it, aircraft cannot fly without it. Government departments and business organisations rely upon it, in the form of digital computers, for information storage and retrieval. The list seems endless, and grows longer every year.

The reasons for all this are not hard to discover. Electronics can detect, measure, control, process, and communicate. It does all these things quietly, cleanly, and very quickly. It is also becoming increasingly cheaper. The valve receivers used by amateur radio enthusiasts in the 1920s cost, in real terms, perhaps 50 times as much as their modern solid-state counterparts. The digital computers of the 1950s used hundreds or thousands of expensive thermionic valves, gave off large amounts of heat, and were very unreliable. Essentially research machines, they were so expensive that only large organisations could afford them. Today the same computing power is available to the individual for less than the price of a pair of shoes. The same story is repeated with a wide variety of electronic systems—as a result, of course, of the very rapid development of semiconductor and microelectronic technology since about 1960.

1

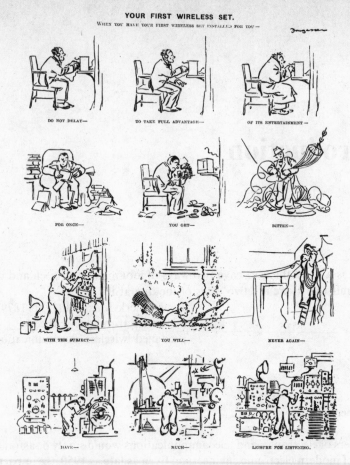

YOUR FIRST WIRELESS SET.

Figure 1.1 The cumbersome technology of early radio: a cartoon from *Punch* magazine, 1924 (courtesy of *Punch* magazine).

This book is about electronic *signals*, and electronic *systems*. And to put the present situation into a fuller historical perspective, it is helpful to consider the early development of telegraphy and telephony.

Optical transmission and coding of signals and messages—mainly for the purposes of warfare and defence—were current in antiquity, and the idea of a binary code had already been mentioned in the early 17th century. However, it was the systematic development of the electric telegraph in the 19th century which really laid the foundations of so much of our present electrical and electronic technology. Much of the early work stemmed from Oersted's crucial discovery, in 1820, of the magnetic effect of an electric current. More than 10 years were then to elapse before Gauss and Weber in Germany, and Henry in the USA, demonstrated electromagnetic signalling systems working over cables a kilometre or two in length.

Subsequent commercial development of the telegraph in Britain is associated with the names of Wheatstone and Cooke, and in the USA with that of Morse, who remarked to his friend Professor Gale of New York University in 1837 that if he could work his telegraph through ten miles of wire, he could work it round the world. Ambitious though the claim was, it rested on two very sound ideas: that a signal or message coded into just two basic types of symbol or

Figure 1.2 An early example of communication technology: the Siemens needle telegraph of 1847 (courtesy of Siemens Museum, Munich).

character (such as 'dot' and 'dash') was inherently immune to electrical disturbance during transmission; and that even if such simple symbols *were* degraded to some extent, they could readily be regenerated at various 'repeater stations' spaced along the cable route. It is essentially these same two notions which underpin the massive development in our own time of what we now call digital communications systems.

The early telegraph engineers realised that, as cable lengths increased, a pulse signal such as a dot or a dash became spread out and delayed in time at the receiving end, because of the presence of resistance and capacitance in the cable. This meant that closely spaced symbols could not be separated at the receiver, and the message was lost. Kelvin's famous paper to the Royal Society in London in 1855 established the mathematical basis of such effects, which were of particular relevance to the development of a successful transatlantic telegraph. We now see Kelvin's work as an important example of the analysis of the effects which a *system* can have on the *signals* which it transmits or processes. Engineers are supposed to be ingenious, and it soon occurred to them that it might be possible to alleviate the undesirable 'spreading effect' of a long cable by modifying the receiver. Heaviside, writing in the *Philosophical Magazine* of 1874, showed that a valuable improvement in pulse shape could indeed be obtained by placing capacitors in parallel with the receiver. Since each pulse was now less spread out, more dots and dashes could be successfully transmitted in a given time, thus increasing the message capacity of the cable.

Further important developments in the theory and practice of telegraphy by pulse code took place in the later decades of the 19th century. However, we now turn to the direct electrical transmission of speech by a continuously varying, analog waveform—initiated by Bell's famous patent of 1876.

CITY HALL, LAWRENCE, MASS.
Monday Evening, May 28

THE MIRACLE

TELE P HONE

WONDERFUL   DISCOVERY

TELE P HONE

OF THE AGE

Prof. A. Graham Bell, assisted by Mr. Frederic A. Gower, will give an exhibition of his wonderful and miraculous discovery **The Telephone**, before the people of Lawrence as above, when Boston and Lawrence will be connected via the Western Union Telegraph and vocal and instrumental music and conversation will be transmitted a distance of 27 miles and received by the audience in the City Hall.
    Prof. Bell will give an explanatory lecture with this marvellous exhibition.

Cards of Admission, 35 cents
Reserved Seats, 50 cents
Sale of seats at Stratton's will open at 9 o'clock.

Figure 1.3 A publicity notice for one of Alexander Graham Bell's demonstrations of the telephone, 1877 (courtesy of AT & T Bell Laboratories).

The analog principle, exemplified by the Bell telephone, seemed at that time nearly ideal for speech transmission, since the rate at which pulsatile dots and dashes could be transmitted over even very short cables was severely limited by the available technology. Further developments were greatly stimulated around the turn of the century by Marconi's experiments in radio, providing a practical sequel to the earlier theoretical studies by Maxwell and the pioneering investigations of Hertz. Other major contributions were made by Fleming and Lee de Forest, who developed the first vacuum valves for detecting and amplifying the very weak signals entering a radio receiver. By the 1920s, however, it was realised that electrical interference or 'noise'—arising not only along the transmission path but also, inevitably, in the receiver itself—formed a fundamental limitation to the rate at which messages could be sent through any communications 'channel'. The separation of a wanted signal from such noise using electrical filters became, and has remained, an important application of electronic systems.

In the early years of telephony, its underlying engineering principles seemed clearly different from those of telegraphy, concentrating as they did on continuous analog waveforms rather than 'digital' pulses. However, during the Second World War telephony in certain applications became, in a quite literal sense, a form of telegraphy. In modern terminology, the system underwent an analog-to-digital conversion, whereby the speech waveform was sampled, coded into digital pulses for transmission, and reconstituted into analog form in the receiver. We shall have more to say later about this approach, which is now called Pulse Code Modulation (PCM) and is widely used by telephone authorities around the world. At this point, we merely note that

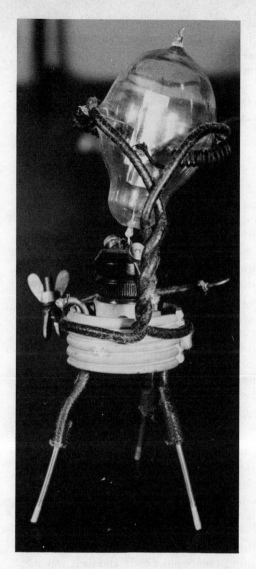

Figure 1.4 One of Fleming's experimental diodes, 1906 (courtesy of the Marconi Company Ltd).

its major advantage is immunity from noise and interference—as noted by Samuel Morse back in 1837! So the modern view is that telegraphy and telephony, formerly seen as distinctive types of communication, are inextricably linked in both theory and practice.

The last 50 years or so have seen an enormous expansion in the practical applications of signal and system ideas. For example, the development of radar before and during the Second World War initially drew upon, and in turn made major contributions to, the theory of signals and communications. Another major application area is Automatic Control, which also developed rapidly in the 1940s out of the need to design effective systems for such tasks as automatic gun-laying and anti-aircraft tracking. Also the field of Signal Processing, which is concerned with the modification of signals in a whole variety of ways by electronic circuits and computers, has found important applications in such diverse areas as communications, seismology, biomedicine, and the enhancement of pictures and images.

The application of signal and system concepts has now become so widespread that we should no longer think of the word 'signal' as necessarily representing a message to be sent from one place to another. It can just as well represent almost any type of information, data, or physical variable—the variation of bank interest rate, the midday temperature at a certain place, or the blood velocity in an artery. Provided such 'signals' may be converted into electrical waveforms, or entered as data into an electronic computer, we may use the ideas of signal and system theory to analyse and process them in a wide variety of valuable ways.

1.2 Continuous and discrete signals and systems

The ideas and applications of electronic engineering often seem to fall into two rather distinct camps. On the one hand, there are analog circuits, composed of elements such as resistors, capacitors, inductors, and amplifiers; on the other hand, there are digital circuits and computers, built up from a number (and often a very large number) of logic gates. Analog circuits deal mainly with such continuous waveforms as mains voltages and currents, or the voltage output from a microphone. Digital circuits appear to be concerned with what are essentially switching or control problems, such as the sequencing of a set of traffic lights.

It is a major aim of this book to show the reader that such distinctions between the applications of continuous and discrete electronics are in many ways artificial. A large number of engineering design problems can be, and indeed are, solved by either analog or digital methods, or by a combination of the two.

We have already seen how the history of telegraphy and telephony underlines the fact that speech messages can be transmitted either as digital pulses or analog waveforms. Let us consider two other practical examples of this essential equivalence between the analog and digital approaches.

(1) For almost exactly a century following Edison's invention of the phonograph in 1877, records of music and speech for home entertainment were based exclusively on analog techniques. During replay, a needle or stylus followed a fluctuating groove on the record's surface. This analog movement was transformed into a corresponding sound pressure variation—in the early years by a flared horn, later by a loudspeaker driven by an electronic amplifier.

In about 1982, however, digital records also became available. In this PCM method, the music or speech signal is first converted into a binary pulse code, and then impressed on the record as a series of minute indentations representing '1s' and '0s'. It may be read off the disc by laser. Of course, the pulse code cannot be interpreted by the human ear, so must be converted back to analog form before delivery to loudspeakers.

(2) In hospitals, electroencephalograph or EEG signals (sometimes popularly referred to as 'brainwaves') are often recorded from the surface of the scalp; for example, in patients with epilepsy, or for monitoring the effects of drugs and anaesthetics. These electrical signals are amplified, processed, and displayed, often on a multichannel chart recorder. It is sometimes valuable for diagnosis to separate the signal into certain frequency ranges, or bands, before display.

For many years, such 'frequency analysis' was performed by analog wave filters, consisting of such circuit elements as resistors, capacitors, inductors, and amplifiers. However, these filters were bulky, expensive, and hard to calibrate. With the advent of cheap computers it has become common to achieve equivalent filtering by digital means.

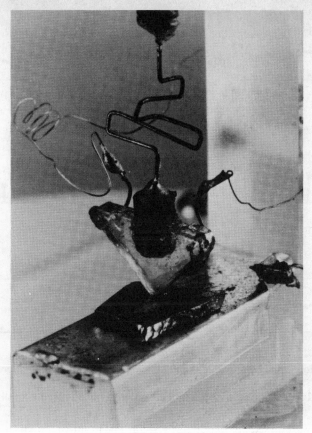

Figure 1.5 Bardeen and Brattain's first point-contact transistor, 1947 (courtesy of AT & T Bell Laboratories).

The EEG signal is first sampled and converted into a binary code, and then fed into a computer and processed.

Of course, we must not assume that because a digital solution to a particular problem is possible *in principle*, it is necessarily preferable *in practice*. There are many factors involved in the design of an electronic system to solve a particular engineering problem. These include technical performance, speed, cost, equipment volume, availability of components and spares, ease of maintenance, and so on. It nevertheless remains a very important idea that many design problems may in principle be solved by either analog or digital methods.

The above ideas are summarised by figure 1.6. Part (a) shows an analog, or continuous, system fed by a continuous input $x(t)$ and producing a continuous output $y(t)$. The system might be a cable or other transmission medium, or a unit designed to process or modify the signal in some way. In this particular case it has the properties of a *low-pass filter*, that is to say a unit which passes the low-frequency (that is, the slowly fluctuating) components of the input signal, but suppresses high-frequency ones (which might here represent rapid unwanted disturbances or 'noise'). In figure 1.6(b) is shown a digital, or discrete, system which processes an input signal $x[n]$ composed of a set of discrete sample values. We may normally think of these as simply representing the numerical value of the input at equally spaced instants of time. The output $y[n]$ is also in sampled form. The system may well be a digital computer, programmed in this case to

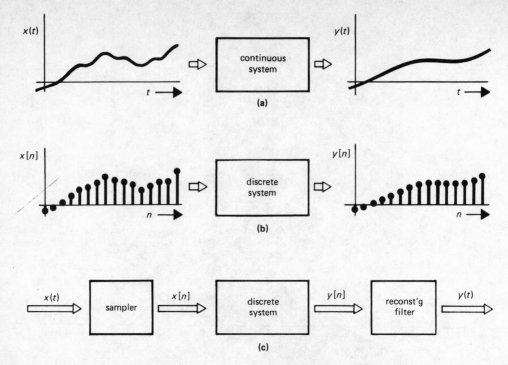

Figure 1.6 Continuous and discrete signals and systems: (a) continuous, (b) discrete, and (c) mixed.

act as a low-pass filter. The sample values at its input and output are normally represented by a binary code.

Figure 1.6(c) shows a mixed analog/digital system. The input signal $x(t)$ is continuous, but is sampled to produce a set of values $x[n]$. These are generally processed or transmitted digitally. The output $y[n]$ from the discrete system, already converted back from a binary code into a set of sample values, may be changed back into an equivalent continuous signal $y(t)$ using a 'reconstituting filter' (its details need not concern us yet, although it is in fact another example of a low-pass filter).

The sampling and binary coding of a continuous signal may both be accomplished by a device called an analog-to-digital converter (ADC). The decoding and reconstitution of a continuous waveform from a set of binary pulses require a digital-to-analog converter (DAC). Since these processes and devices are very important for many of the ideas covered in the rest of this book, they will be described in some detail in the following section.

1.3 Analog-to-digital and digital-to-analog conversion

Suppose a continuous signal $x(t)$ is to be represented by a set of sample values $x[n]$ spaced at equal time intervals. The obvious question which arises is: how often must it be sampled? An intuitive answer is suggested by figure 1.7. Part (a) shows a signal sampled at a rate which is clearly too low to pick out the faster waveform fluctuations. In part (b) of the figure, however, the sampling is much faster. Although this gives a very accurate representation, the number of sample values which must be stored, transmitted, or processed seems unnecessarily large. It therefore seems that there must be some intermediate sampling rate which is adequate, but not excessive.

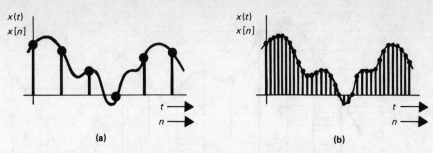

Figure 1.7 Sampling a continuous signal.

Assume, for the moment, that $x(t)$ represents a speech waveform from a microphone. Then it will typically contain a range of significant frequencies between about 300 Hz and 3 kHz—the range catered for by many telephone systems. Since the fastest fluctuations in the waveform must correspond to the highest frequencies, it is clear that these are the ones which will be lost if sampling is too slow. This important intuitive deduction is expressed quantitatively by the famous *Sampling Theorem*, which will be covered more fully in chapter 8. We merely state it here, asking the reader to accept it for the time being.

"A continuous signal containing frequency components up to some maximum frequency f_1 Hz may be completely represented by regularly spaced samples taken at a rate of at least $2f_1$ samples per second."

For various practical reasons it is normal to sample somewhat faster than the minimum specified by the theorem. For example, a speech waveform with $f_1 = 3$ kHz is commonly sampled at about 8000 samples per second. Such a rate would represent a situation somewhere between parts (a) and (b) of figure 1.7.

As already mentioned, sampling is normally carried out by an analog-to-digital converter (ADC), which then transforms the stream of samples into a binary code. The second important decision concerns the number of binary characters ('0' and '1') or *bits*, which the ADC must allocate to the coding of each sample value. It is simple to show that a binary code of N bits allows 2^N separate numbers, or signal values, to be represented. For example, if we allow 3 bits, we may encode 2^3 or 8 values as follows.

Value	Binary code
0	000
1	001
2	010
3	011
4	100
5	101
6	110
7	111

The right-hand character in the code is called the *least significant bit* (LSB); the left-hand one is called the *most significant bit* (MSB). Note that this 3-bit code could be used to represent *any* 8 previously agreed values, or indeed messages; but there cannot be more than 8 of them.

Continuous signals generally take on a wide range of values, so a 3-bit code is almost bound to introduce substantial errors at the coding stage. This is illustrated by figure 1.8. The signal $x(t)$ is assumed to occupy the amplitude range 0 to 7 units, and is sampled at an appropriate rate.

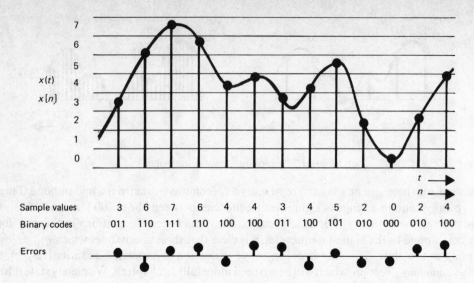

Figure 1.8 The conversion of a continuous signal into a binary pulse code.

Each sample falls within one of the 8 discrete amplitude slots, known as *quantisation levels*, and is allocated the corresponding binary code. This sequence of coded values now represents the original waveform, and may be stored, transmitted, or processed as a digital signal.

The maximum error introduced into each sample value by this process is plus or minus half a quantisation level. With a 3-bit code this equals $\pm 1/16$ of the total available amplitude range. The magnitudes of successive errors, also illustrated in figure 1.8, are often more or less independent between one sample and the next. They may therefore be regarded as unwanted 'noise' introduced by the coding process. This cannot subsequently be removed. For obvious reasons, it is referred to as *quantisation noise*.

Analog-to-digital conversion therefore always involves some degradation of the original signal. This may at first appear to be a serious drawback. But we must always bear in mind two things. Firstly, if the quantisation noise is unacceptably large, the number of bits in the binary code may be increased. Secondly, any practical analog signal has *some* noise or uncertainty associated with it anyway, so the addition of a certain amount of quantisation noise need not cause further significant corruption.

Note that the effects of quantisation become more serious if the signal fluctuations are of low amplitude. To keep the *signal-to-noise ratio* (SNR) as high as possible, the signal should therefore be made to occupy more or less the full input amplitude range of the ADC.

It is interesting to consider how many bits are allocated to coding each sample value in some practical engineering systems. Broadly, we may expect that the more unreliable or 'noisy' the analog signal which is represented, the fewer bits will be needed to code it adequately. A 7-bit code is commonly used for encoding speech signals for commercial telephony, giving 2^7 or 128 discrete amplitude levels. The quantisation noise is then a maximum of plus or minus about 0.4 per cent of the available amplitude range. Radar signals, representing echoes from distant aircraft or other targets, are often represented by 9 or 10-bit codes. Digital records for home entertainment typically use a 16-bit code, giving 65 536 distinguishable levels. This is clearly very 'high-fidelity'! As a general guide, most applications require between 6 and 16-bit coding. Although the details need not concern us here, we should note that extra bits may be included for control purposes, including automatic error detection.

When both the sampling rate and the length of the binary code have been decided, the *bit-rate* of the signal or message is specified. Thus for ordinary telephony with a sampling rate of 8 kHz and a 7-bit code, the bit-rate is 56 kbits per second. For digital records, not only is the code much longer, but a sampling frequency of about 44 kHz is commonly used—allowing audio frequencies up to over 20 kHz to be represented according to the Sampling Theorem (20 kHz is often taken as the highest frequency audible to the human ear). Thus the bit-rate is about 700 kbits per second. These figures do not allow for any additional control or error-correction bits.

A wide selection of ADCs is available in integrated circuit form. The binary code used is not necessarily the normal, 'straight', code described above. There are, for example, several possible ways of representing negative numbers. A more basic consideration, however, is whether the ADC is fast enough for the particular application—how long it takes to complete a conversion. Slow devices taking a millisecond (1 ms) or more are cheap. But the price increases considerably for conversion times of less than about one microsecond (1 μs), especially when the number of bits in the code is large. This makes the digital representation of, for example, television video signals rather expensive. They typically contain frequencies up to several MHz, and therefore require a conversion time of less than about 0.1 μs.

We next consider the problem of converting back from a binary pulse code to an equivalent analog signal, using a digital-to-analog converter (DAC). This is a much simpler device than an ADC, and fast, accurate operation may be achieved quite cheaply. DACs are also widely available in integrated circuit form.

DACs normally require the complete binary code to be presented at their input at the same instant. For example, if an 8-bit code is to be converted, 8 input terminals are provided, and these must be fed in parallel. In many practical applications, the binary code is transmitted in *serial* fashion—one bit at a time along a single cable or path. Therefore it is often necessary to perform an initial *serial-to-parallel conversion*. However, this is a relatively simple procedure.

Although we have not discussed the detailed circuits of ADCs, which are rather complicated, we can readily consider the type of circuit used in a DAC. This gives some additional insight into the whole digital–analog interface problem. A commonly used circuit is the so-called *R–2R* ladder network illustrated in figure 1.9. The length of the 'ladder' depends on the number of bits

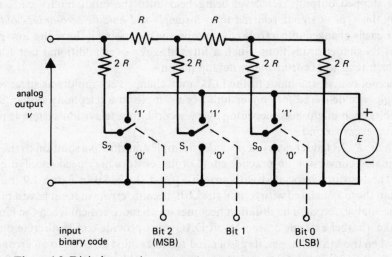

Figure 1.9 Digital-to-analog conversion using the *R–2R* ladder network.

in the code. For convenience it is shown here for just 3 bits (although, as we have seen, this would be too few for almost all practical applications). Note that, whatever the length of the code, there is an extra terminating resistor of value $2R$ at the LSB end of the ladder.

The incoming binary code controls switches S_2, S_1, and S_0. These are high-speed electronic switches based upon transistors or other active devices. Whenever a given bit is high ('1') it causes a proportion of the DC voltage E to be delivered to the output terminals on the left-hand side via the resistive network. This proportion is larger for the MSB and S_2 than it is for the LSB and S_0, because the voltage reduction effect of the ladder network is less. Using Thévenin's theorem (discussed in the following section), and assuming that negligible current is taken from the output terminals, it is fairly easy to show that the voltage v reaching the output is $E/2$ if only bit 2 is high, $E/4$ if only bit 1 is high, and $E/8$ if only bit 0 is high. This result does not depend on the absolute values of the R and $2R$ resistors used in the network.

We may now see how the DAC decodes any 3-bit binary number delivered to its input. Since this is a *linear* network, the *Principle of Superposition* may be used (these terms will be discussed further in the next section, and more thoroughly in chapter 2). In this case, it implies that the output voltage v due to any combination of switches being set high is equal to the sum of the voltages produced when those same switches are set high individually. Thus we may draw up the following table for all 8 possible binary codes.

Code	Switches set high	Output voltage (v)
000	none	$= 0$
001	S_0	$= 1(E/8)$
010	S_1	$E/4 = 2(E/8)$
011	S_1, S_0	$(E/4) + (E/8) = 3(E/8)$
100	S_2	$E/2 = 4(E/8)$
101	S_2, S_0	$(E/2) + (E/8) = 5(E/8)$
110	S_2, S_1	$(E/2) + (E/4) = 6(E/8)$
111	S_2, S_1, S_0	$(E/2) + (E/4) + (E/8) = 7(E/8)$

We therefore see that as the input goes through all 8 codes, the analog output changes in a series of equal steps of $E/8$ volts, taking on 8 discrete amplitude levels. Digital-to-analog conversion has been accomplished. Actually, this statement should be slightly qualified, because the DAC produces a stepped output, each level being held until the input binary code is changed. Fortunately this type of signal, referred to as a *sample-and-hold* or *zero-order-hold* waveform, can be quite easily changed into a truly continuous one by passing it through a low-pass filter to smooth out its sudden transitions. Such a filter also removes additional fast transients, or *glitches*, which tend to occur at the switching instants.

In practice, of course, the input to the DAC may change very rapidly as successive binary-coded samples are delivered for conversion. For example, in a telephony system 8000 binary codes of 7 bits each might need decoding every second. In a television system it might be 10 million codes every second.

Although the R–$2R$ ladder network provides a simple and effective solution to the problem of digital-to-analog conversion, in practice some of its resistors may need specifying with great precision. The resistors associated with switch S_2 and the MSB in figure 1.9 must be more accurate than those associated with S_0 and the LSB, because errors in them have a much greater effect on the analog output. The situation becomes much more critical when the binary code is long. To take a rather extreme case, a 16-bit DAC must provide 65 536 discrete output levels. Therefore when the MSB changes, its associated resistors must give rise to an error of less than about 1 part in 65 536. This implies resistor tolerances considerably better than ± 0.01 per cent.

If we recall that even high-quality discrete resistors rarely have a tolerance better than ± 1 per cent, it is clear that the practical design and manufacture of DACs can be demanding. Fortunately the required tolerances are not too hard to achieve using integrated circuit techniques.

1.4 Review of continuous circuit concepts

We next summarise some important ideas used in the analysis of continuous electrical and electronic circuits composed of discrete, or *lumped*, components—resistors, capacitors, inductors, power supplies, and amplifiers. The treatment will not be rigorous, but will concentrate on illustrating some important concepts by simple examples. Furthermore, we will cover only a fairly narrow range of topics necessary to understand later chapters, in which circuit applications will be used to clarify various aspects of signal and system theory. This short review is designed to make the book self-contained. It should not in any sense be considered as a substitute for a proper course in circuit theory. Furthermore, the reader who has already taken such a course may now safely proceed to chapter 2.

The work in this section is restricted to the *steady-state analysis* of DC and AC circuits, and operational amplifiers. A further major aspect of circuit theory is *transient analysis*. However, this is such a central part of our story that we will deal with it in a fuller and more systematic way in chapters 3 to 6.

1.4.1 *DC circuits*

Some of the key ideas of DC circuit analysis can be conveniently illustrated by a simple example. Suppose we need to find the steady voltage V developed across the resistor R_6 in the circuit of figure 1.10, which is energised by a DC source or battery E. There are various ways of solving this problem. The reader may be tempted to use the 'potential-divider' principle; but this can

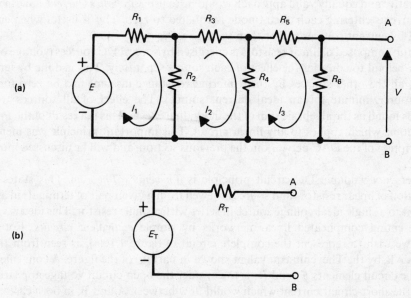

Figure 1.10 A DC circuit and, below, its Thévenin equivalent.

easily lead to mistakes in all but the simplest of circuits, and is not recommended. One satisfactory approach is to use *Kirchoff's Voltage Law*, which states that the sum of voltage drops across the passive elements in any closed circuit loop equals the sum of applied voltages (which may, of course, be zero). Therefore if we label circulating currents, I_1, I_2, and I_3 in the three circuit loops, we may write the following equations

$$E = I_1 R_1 + (I_1 - I_2)R_2 \tag{1.1}$$

$$0 = (I_2 - I_1)R_2 + I_2 R_3 + (I_2 - I_3)R_4 \tag{1.2}$$

$$0 = (I_3 - I_2)R_4 + I_3 R_5 + I_3 R_6 \tag{1.3}$$

$$V = I_3 R_6 \tag{1.4}$$

These equations could, of course, be solved algebraically; but, for simplicity, let us assume $E = 1$ volt and that all resistors are of value 1 ohm. Then

$$1 = 2I_1 - I_2 \tag{1.5}$$

$$0 = 3I_2 - I_1 - I_3 \tag{1.6}$$

$$0 = 3I_3 - I_2 \tag{1.7}$$

and

$$V = I_3$$

It is now easy to deduce that

$$I_3 = 1/13 \text{ amp}$$

Therefore the required output voltage is

$$V = 1/13 \text{ volt}$$

An alternative and equally valid approach would be to use *Kirchoff's Current Law*, in which the sum of currents entering each circuit node is equated to zero. This is useful when circuits are energised by current sources rather than voltage sources.

If a circuit composed of linear resistors is energised by several DC sources (voltage or current) it is often helpful to consider the effect of each source separately. This is done by temporarily replacing all the other sources by their internal resistance (assumed to be zero for an ideal voltage source, infinite for an ideal current source). The effect of all sources together is afterwards found as the algebraic sum of the individual effects. This is a result of the *Principle of Superposition*, which applies to any linear circuit. This important principle was mentioned in our description of the DAC network in the previous section, and will be discussed more fully in chapter 2.

Another very valuable DC circuit principle is *Thévenin's Theorem*. This states that any combination of linear resistors and sources, viewed from a given pair of terminals in a circuit, is equivalent to a single ideal voltage source in series with a single resistor. This idea is very useful for representing complicated linear networks by simple *equivalent circuits*. For example, suppose we wish to represent the complete circuit of figure 1.10(a), as seen from the output terminals AB, by the Thévenin equivalent shown in part (b) of the figure. A convenient way of finding the circuit elements E_T and R_T is to consider the open-circuit voltage appearing across AB, and the short-circuit current which would flow between A and B, in both cases. We have already found the open-circuit voltage across AB in the actual circuit to be 1/13 volt. Hence this must also be the value of E_T. Let us now find the short-circuit current. If a short-circuit is placed across AB, then R_6 is effectively reduced to zero, and equations (1.3) and (1.7) above become

$$0 = (I_3 - I_2)R_4 + I_3 R_5 \qquad (1.8)$$

and

$$0 = 2I_3 - I_2 \qquad (1.9)$$

Assuming again that $E = 1$ volt and all resistors are 1 ohm in value, it is simple to show that I_3 is now 1/8 amp. This must therefore be the short-circuit current. In the Thévenin equivalent circuit, the short-circuit current would clearly be

$$I_{SC} = E_T / R_T$$

But $E_T = 1/13$ volt, so that

$$R_T = \tfrac{1}{13} \div \tfrac{1}{8} = \tfrac{8}{13} \text{ ohm}$$

We have therefore replaced the whole of the circuit to the left of AB in figure 1.10(a) by just two elements.

The resistor R_T is often referred to as the *internal resistance* of the circuit, seen from terminals AB. If A and B are output terminals (as in this example), it is also known as the *output resistance*. If A and B are input terminals, to which an input voltage or current is to be applied, it is known as the *input resistance*. The idea of associating a single value of resistance with a pair of terminals is of the greatest importance when discussing complicated networks or systems.

1.4.2 *AC circuits and the j-notation*

It is fortunate that many of the ideas and theorems of DC circuit theory may be applied to the steady-state solution of linear AC circuits energised by sinusoidal waveforms of voltage or current. This is possible because any measurable waveform in such a circuit must be sinusoidal in form, with the same frequency as the excitation. All that such a circuit can do is modify amplitude and phase—not frequency. If similar circuit equations to those used for DC circuit analysis are written in terms of the *impedances* of the various elements, then the normal rules of complex algebra give a solution which contains both amplitude and phase information.

We again illustrate the essential ideas with a simple example. Consider the series *RLC* circuit shown in figure 1.11, which is energised by a voltage source

$$v_1(t) = A \sin \omega t = A \sin 2\pi f t$$

where A is the peak value or amplitude of the waveform, ω is the angular frequency in radians per second, and f is the frequency in cycles per second or hertz (Hz). Using the *j-notation*, we

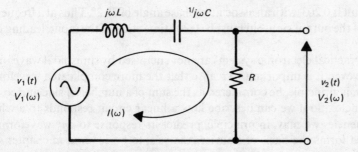

Figure 1.11

may write the impedances of the passive elements as R, $j\omega L$, and $(j\omega C)^{-1}$ respectively. Note that these impedances are frequency functions, not time functions. We have, in other words, used a *frequency-domain* description. We must therefore also consider the applied voltage as a frequency function $V_1(\omega)$ when analysing the circuit.

The inclusion of the term j in the impedance expressions for the inductor and capacitor denotes a 90° phase-shift between the voltage across, and current through, either of these elements. The voltage leads the current by 90° (or $\pi/2$ radians) in the inductor, but lags it by 90° in the capacitor. The symbol j is best thought of as a *phase-shift operator*. Note also that multiplication by j^2 is equivalent to a phase-shift of 180° (π radians), representing an inversion; hence $j^2 = -1$.

Let us next derive an expression for the voltage appearing as an output across the resistor R. Such an output might be monitored on an oscilloscope, or passed on to a further circuit. Note however that the convention is to assume (unless otherwise stated) that the output terminals are effectively open-circuit. In other words, negligible output current is drawn. We may then write

$$V_1(\omega) = I(\omega)\{j\omega L + (j\omega C)^{-1} + R\}$$

and

$$V_2(\omega) = I(\omega)R$$

Hence

$$V_2(\omega) = V_1(\omega)\frac{R}{j\omega L + (j\omega C)^{-1} + R}$$

or

$$\frac{V_2(\omega)}{V_1(\omega)} = \frac{j\omega CR}{1 - \omega^2 CL + j\omega CR} \tag{1.10}$$

The last equation shows how the output voltage is related to the source, or input, voltage in both magnitude and phase. Let us insert some values. For example, suppose that $R = 20$ ohms (Ω), $L = 0.01$ henry (H), $C = 1$ microfarad (μF), and that the input frequency is 1000 Hz ($\omega = 2000\pi$). We then obtain

$$\frac{V_2}{V_1} = \frac{0.126j}{1 - 0.395 + 0.126j}$$

which rationalises to give

$$\frac{V_2}{V_1} = (0.0416 + 0.199j)$$

The magnitude of this result is 0.203, with an associated phase angle of 78.2°. Thus at a frequency of 1 kHz, the amplitude of the output sinusoid must be 0.203 times that of the input, leading it in phase by 78.2°.

The great majority of practical electronic systems are not energised by sinusoidal waveforms at a fixed frequency. However, it is important to realise that the more complicated waveforms often met in practice may, in principle, be considered as the sum of a number of sine and cosine waves of different frequencies. So if we can describe how a linear circuit responds to a whole range of sinusoidal frequencies we may, in principle, predict its response to *any* waveform or signal. This powerful idea forms the basis of Fourier Analysis, to be covered in chapter 4.

Let us therefore consider the frequency ω in the circuit of figure 1.11 to be a continuous variable, and look at equation (1.10) again. At very low frequencies ($\omega \to 0$), we have

$$\frac{V_2(\omega)}{V_1(\omega)} \to j\omega CR$$

Therefore the magnitude of the output becomes proportional to frequency (assuming a fixed input amplitude), and leads the input by 90°. If ω is now increased to the value $(LC)^{-1/2}$, the condition known as *resonance* occurs, and

$$\frac{V_2(\omega)}{V_1(\omega)} \to \frac{j\omega CR}{j\omega CR} = 1$$

At resonance, the impedances of the inductor and capacitor are equal but opposite, and the circuit 'appears' purely resistive to the source. Finally, when the frequency is very high ($\omega \to \infty$), we have

$$\frac{V_2(\omega)}{V_1(\omega)} \to \frac{j\omega CR}{-\omega^2 LC} = -\frac{jR}{\omega L}$$

Thus the output amplitude becomes inversely proportional to frequency and lags the input by 90°.

These conclusions are illustrated by figure 1.12. This shows the variations in amplitude and phase of the output, compared with the input, as the frequency varies. The circuit values used are those quoted above: $R = 20\,\Omega$, $L = 0.01$ H, $C = 1\,\mu$F. Note that, in general, the sharpness of a resonant peak depends on the amount of resistance in the circuit. If the resonant peak is very pronounced, the circuit is said to be *sharply tuned* and to possess a high *Q-factor* ('Q' standing for 'quality'). Circuits with a high degree of frequency selectivity find a great variety of practical applications as *filters*. One well-known example is the filter used to select the required signal at the input to a radio receiver. This is normally done by varying the capacitance of the circuit, thereby altering its resonant frequency.

Thévenin's Theorem may also be used to derive an equivalent of an AC circuit, provided we

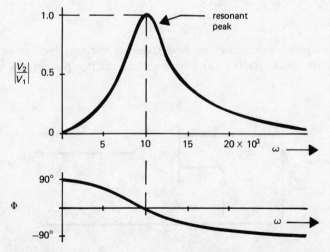

Figure 1.12 The amplitude and phase response of an *RLC* circuit as a function of frequency.

think in terms of internal impedance rather than resistance. Of course, the situation is more complicated than with a DC circuit, because an impedance does not have a unique value, but varies with frequency. Fortunately, the reactive (that is, the inductive or capacitive) component is quite often negligible in practice, so that an impedance may be assumed resistive and independent of frequency. For example, the input and output impedances of many amplifiers used for speech or music are quoted as particular values in ohms, and may be taken as more or less resistive over the full audio-frequency range.

1.4.3 *Operational amplifier circuits*

An electronic amplifier is a unit designed to increase the amplitude of a signal or waveform delivered to its input, without introducing significant distortion. Amplifiers are also used in a wide variety of less obvious ways, and form important 'building blocks' for applications in such fields as communications, signal processing, and automatic control. Practical amplifiers work satisfactorily only over a limited range of signal frequencies: for example, an audio amplifier may work up to 20 kHz, and a video amplifier up to 5 MHz.

The term *operational amplifier* was originally coined to describe amplifiers designed to carry out particular mathematical 'operations' in analog computers. Now that such computers have been very largely superseded by digital ones, operational amplifiers are rarely needed for their original application. However, they have proved extremely versatile and useful devices over a wide spectrum of analog electronics. Provided one is working at frequencies below about 1 MHz, cheap and reliable operational amplifiers are readily available in integrated circuit form. They are, generally speaking, quite simple to use.

From our point of view, 'op-amps' have the added advantage of behaving in an almost 'ideal' way at low enough frequencies. The circuits in which they are employed may be easily analysed using a few simple equations. This makes them very useful for illustrating a number of important signal and system applications.

Figure 1.13 shows the circuit symbol used for an operational amplifier. It has two input and one output connections: one of the inputs, labelled (+), is known as the *noninverting input*; the other, labelled (−), as the *inverting input*. If fluctuating signal voltages v_+ and v_- (both measured with respect to the earth or reference potential) are applied to the two input points as shown, then the output signal voltage is given by

$$v_2 = A(v_+ - v_-) \tag{1.11}$$

A is the voltage amplification factor, or *voltage gain* of the amplifier. Since it amplifies the difference between the signals applied to its noninverting and inverting inputs, it is often called a

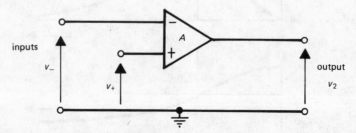

Figure 1.13 The operational amplifier.

differential amplifier. In practice, as we shall see, a signal is often provided for only one of the input points, the other being connected directly to earth.

All operational amplifiers require a DC power supply (often a twin-supply of between about ± 5 V and ± 15 V with respect to earth). However, the power supply connections are generally omitted from a circuit diagram, for the sake of clarity. The connections shown in figure 1.13 are the essential ones, and are adequate for our discussion.

The nominal voltage gain A is usually very large—say between 10^4 and 10^6. However, this impressive figure is only available at low frequencies (including zero frequency, or DC). In cheap devices the gain may start to fall off above about 10 Hz. Furthermore the value of A may vary quite widely between devices of the same nominal type, because of manufacturing tolerances. For these reasons, operational amplifiers are invariably used with one or more external passive components or connections, which provide *negative feedback*. Such feedback (the theoretical details of which need not concern us yet) greatly reduces the voltage gain from its nominal value A; but, at the same time, it *stabilises the gain* at the lower value, and extends the available *frequency range*. The overall amplifier (including its external components and connections) is now a very stable and versatile active circuit, with a host of practical uses.

We concentrate here on three particular operational amplifier circuit configurations: the inverting amplifier, the noninverting amplifier, and the voltage follower. We shall see that the performance of all three may be analysed quite easily by making a few simple (and normally valid) assumptions about the performance of the integrated circuit 'op-amp' which forms the heart of each unit.

The standard *inverting amplifier* configuration is shown in figure 1.14(a). A feedback resistor R_2 is connected from the output terminal back to the inverting input. An input resistor R_1 is also provided, and the noninverting input is earthed. We now make the following assumptions about the integrated circuit

(1) Its voltage gain A is very large.
(2) Its input impedance, 'seen' between the inverting and noninverting input terminals, is also very large. Thus it takes negligible input current.
(3) Its output impedance is very small. Thus any reasonable value of output current can be accommodated, without significantly affecting the output voltage.

Using assumption (1), we infer that the differential input voltage $(v_+ - v_-)$ must always be very small, for any reasonable value of the output voltage. But since the noninverting input is earthed, v_+ is zero and hence v_- must also be very small in amplitude (in practice it may well be in the range microvolts to millivolts). The inverting input is therefore said to be at *virtual earth*.

Since the inverting input is close to earth potential, the input signal v_1 must give rise to an input current v_1/R_1, by Ohm's Law. Using assumption (2) above, this current, arriving at node X, *must* flow through the feedback resistor R_2 and generate a voltage across it equal to

$$\frac{v_1}{R_1} R_2 = v_1 \frac{R_2}{R_1}$$

However, one end of R_2 is also at virtual earth, so its other end—which is also the output point—must assume the above voltage fluctuation. In fact, if v_1 is instantaneously positive, the output point must be instantaneously negative, and there is an inversion. We therefore infer that

$$v_2 = -\frac{R_2}{R_1} v_1, \text{ or } \frac{v_2}{v_1} = -\frac{R_2}{R_1} \tag{1.12}$$

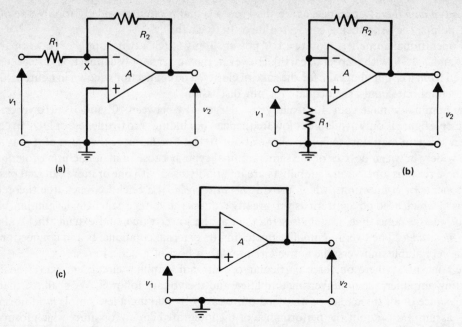

Figure 1.14 Three widely-used operational amplifier configurations: (a) inverting amplifier, (b) noninverting amplifier, and (c) voltage follower.

The voltage gain of the overall circuit is therefore negative (this implies inversion), and is simply equal to the ratio of two external resistors, whose values are normally very stable. In practice, we might use resistor values between say, a few hundred ohms and a few megohms. For example, if $R_2 = 100 \, \text{k}\Omega$ and $R_1 = 1 \, \text{k}\Omega$, the voltage gain would be 100, with an inversion.

At first sight the above explanation, which is rather intuitive, seems hardly to depend on the properties of the operational amplifier at all. Indeed, the reader may be tempted to suggest that it could be removed from the circuit altogether! However, we must remember that it has the essential role of maintaining node X at virtual earth. Without this, the above argument would not hold good.

It must also be emphasised that the above derivation is approximate. It would of course be possible to do a more exact analysis, taking into account not only the finite values of the integrated circuit's voltage gain—and input and output impedances—but also their frequency-dependence. However, provided we operate with low-frequency signals, the above result is quite accurate enough for most practical purposes.

We have spent some time on the inverting amplifier configuration. We will now analyse two further configurations rather more quickly.

The standard *noninverting amplifier* is shown in figure 1.14(b). Once again a feedback resistor R_2 is used, but the input signal is applied directly to the noninverting input point. Using assumptions (2) and (3) above, we may write the following equations

$$v_2 = A(v_+ - v_-) \tag{1.13}$$

$$v_- = \frac{R_1}{(R_1 + R_2)} v_2 \tag{1.14}$$

$$v_+ = v_1 \tag{1.15}$$

Substituting for v_+ and v_- in equation (1.13), it is simple to show that

$$\frac{v_2}{v_1} = \frac{A}{1 + \dfrac{AR_1}{(R_1 + R_2)}} \tag{1.16}$$

But A is very large (assumption (1) above), so that, to a good approximation

$$\frac{v_2}{v_1} = \frac{A}{\dfrac{AR_1}{(R_1 + R_2)}} = 1 + \frac{R_2}{R_1} \tag{1.17}$$

The voltage gain of the overall circuit is therefore positive (no inversion taking place), and is once again determined by the ratio of two external resistors. For example, if $R_1 = 10\ \text{k}\Omega$ and $R_2 = 1\ \text{M}\Omega$, then the gain will be 101.

Whether an inverting or a noninverting amplifier is chosen depends upon the application. One factor in favour of the noninverting amplifier configuration is that it generally has a much higher input impedance than the inverting one. So it draws much less current from the input signal source.

Part (c) of figure 1.14 shows a *voltage follower* circuit. We may think of this circuit as a special case of the noninverting configuration, with $R_1 = \infty$ and $R_2 = 0$. Hence its voltage gain is given by

$$\frac{v_2}{v_1} = 1 + \frac{R_2}{R_1} = 1 \tag{1.18}$$

At first sight this may not seem a useful result, since the output signal is just the same as the input and is said to 'follow' it. The essential point, however, is that the input impedance of the voltage follower is very high indeed (typically much greater than 1 $\text{M}\Omega$), whereas its output impedance is very low (often much less than 1 Ω). It demands almost no input current, but can supply a substantial signal current to a load or further circuit connected to its output terminals. It therefore offers a large current gain, or power gain, even though its voltage gain is only unity. It may be used to 'isolate' a signal source from the current or power demands of a load. In this important role it is widely referred to as a *buffer amplifier*.

Before leaving the topic of operational amplifiers, we should emphasise, once again, that the above simplified analyses are only valid over a limited frequency range. All three circuits perform as required only when the input signals applied to them (which can, in principle, have any waveshape) contain frequencies below a certain upper limit. This limit depends upon the particular operational amplifier used, the circuit configuration, and the amount of negative feedback. Typically, it may fall in the range 10 kHz to 10 MHz. However, this restriction does not preclude a wide variety of practical applications, as we shall see later.

A note on worked examples

Subsequent chapters contain much more quantitative material than chapter 1, and will include a number of worked examples illustrating key points in the text. Here we limit ourselves to just one such example, designed to summarise some of the main quantitative results in this chapter.

Example E1.1

(a) Speech signals in a high-quality PCM telephone system are represented by a 10-bit

binary code, and sampled at 16 kHz. How many distinct amplitude levels are represented
and what is the bit-rate of transmission? If an R–$2R$ ladder network is used for digital-to-
analog conversion in the receiver, approximately what percentage tolerance would you
expect the most critical resistors in the network to have?

Solution

The number of distinct amplitude levels, or slots, provided by a 10-bit code is $2^{10} = 1024$.
The bit-rate is

$$10 \text{ bits} \times 16 \text{ kHz} = 160 \text{ kbits/s}$$

The DAC must offer an accuracy of better than about ± 1 part in 2048. Hence the tolerance
of the most critical resistors in the ladder network (which are those associated with the
MSB) is expected to be about $\pm 1/2048$ or ± 0.05 per cent.

(b) In the circuit shown in figure 1.11 of the main text, $R = 2 \text{ k}\Omega$, $C = 100 \text{ pF}$, and
$L = 100 \,\mu\text{H}$. What is the resonant frequency in hertz? If the input voltage amplitude is
10 mV, what are the magnitude and relative phase angle of the output voltage at a
frequency of 500 kHz?

Solution

The resonant frequency is given by

$$\omega^2 LC = 1 \quad \text{or} \quad \omega = \left(\frac{1}{LC}\right)^{1/2}$$

Hence

$$\omega = \left\{\frac{1}{(100 \times 10^{-6})(100 \times 10^{-12})}\right\}^{1/2} = (10^{14})^{1/2} = 10^7$$

Thus the resonant frequency is $10^7/2\pi$ Hz $= 1.59$ MHz. The input and output voltages are
related by

$$\frac{V_2(\omega)}{V_1(\omega)} = \frac{j\omega CR}{1 - \omega^2 LC + j\omega CR}$$

At 500 kHz, we have

$$\omega CR = (2\pi \times 500 \times 10^3)(100 \times 10^{-12})(2 \times 10^3) = 0.628$$

and

$$\omega^2 LC = (2\pi \times 500 \times 10^3)^2(100 \times 10^{-6})(100 \times 10^{-12}) = 0.0987$$

Hence

$$\frac{V_2(\omega)}{V_1(\omega)} = \frac{0.628j}{1 - 0.0987 + 0.628j} = \frac{0.628j}{0.9013 + 0.628j}$$

$$= \frac{0.628j(0.9013 - 0.628j)}{(0.9013 + 0.628j)(0.9013 - 0.628j)} = \frac{0.566j + 0.394}{0.812 + 0.394}$$

$$= \frac{0.566j + 0.394}{1.206} = 0.469j + 0.327$$

The magnitude of this result is $(0.469^2 + 0.327^2)^{1/2} = 0.572$.

The phase angle is given by

$$\tan \phi = \frac{\text{imaginary part}}{\text{real part}} = \frac{0.469}{0.327} = 1.434$$

Hence $\phi = 55.1°$.
Since the input voltage amplitude is $10\,\text{mV}$, the output voltage amplitude is $10(0.572) = 5.72\,\text{mV}$, lagging the input by $55.1°$.

(c) Using the standard operational amplifier circuit configurations of figure 1.14, estimate the value of R_2 required for an inverting amplifier and for a noninverting amplifier, if the required overall voltage gain is 50 and $R_1 = 1\,\text{k}\Omega$ in each case. The operational amplifier may be assumed ideal.

Solution

We may use the expressions derived for voltage gain in the text (eqs (1.12) and (1.17)). Thus for the inverting amplifier

$$\frac{v_2}{v_1} = -\frac{R_2}{R_1} = -50 \quad \therefore R_2 = 50R_1 = 50\,\text{k}\Omega$$

Whereas for the noninverting amplifier

$$\frac{v_2}{v_1} = 1 + \frac{R_2}{R_1} = 50 \quad \therefore R_2 = 49R_1 = 49\,\text{k}\Omega$$

Problems to chapter 1

Section 1.3

Q1.1. A continuous (analog) TV signal is to be coded by an ADC for transmission through a PCM system. The signal contains significant frequencies up to 5 MHz. The quantisation error in any one sample value, introduced by coding, must be less than 1 per cent of the total amplitude range of the ADC.

What is the minimum bit-rate of the PCM transmission, assuming the Sampling Theorem is obeyed?

Q1.2. The TV signal in Q1.1 fluctuates in amplitude, occasionally filling only 20 per cent of the available amplitude range of the ADC. If the amount of quantisation noise, *relative to the signal*, is to be no worse than before, what minimum bit-rate is now required?

Q1.3. Using Thévenin's Theorem and the Principle of Superposition, satisfy yourself that the DAC network shown in figure 1.9 of the main text works as outlined. What is the output resistance of the network (as seen from the analog output terminals)?

Section 1.4

Q1.4. In the DC network shown in figure 1.10 in the main text, $E = 1$ volt and all resistors are of value 1 ohm.

(a) What resistance is 'seen' by the source E when the output terminals are open-circuit, and when they are short-circuit?
(b) What voltage appears across resistor R_4 when the output terminals are open-circuit?
(c) What current would flow through a 1 ohm resistor connected across the output?

Q1.5. The AC circuit shown in figure 1.11 of the main text has the following values: $R = 100\,\Omega$, $L = 0.04\,\text{H}$, and $C = 1\,\mu\text{F}$. Find the ratio of output to input voltage magnitudes, and their relative phase angle, when the input frequency is (a) 500 Hz, and (b) 2000 Hz. Also find the resonant frequency of the circuit.

Q1.6. The circuit shown in figure Q1.6 is energised by a sinusoidal voltage source. Using the j-notation, derive the relationship between $V_2(\omega)$ and $V_1(\omega)$ as the frequency ω varies. Assume that the output is open-circuit.

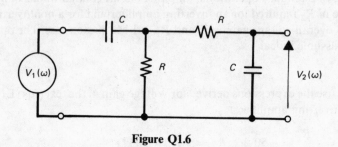

Figure Q1.6

Sketch the magnitude of $V_2(\omega)/V_1(\omega)$, and the relative phase angle, as a function of frequency for the case when $R = 1\,\text{k}\Omega$ and $C = 1\,\mu\text{F}$. At what frequency (in Hz) is the output exactly in phase with the input?

2   Signals and Systems

"I have never before been engaged in any study that so totally consumed my attention and my time, as this has lately done."

Benjamin Franklin (1706–1790),
of his studies in electricity

2.1 Introduction

In this chapter we begin the development of a quantitative framework for signals and systems. Although much of our initial effort must be spent on *analysis*, the eventual goal is equally the more exciting and challenging one of *synthesis*. Synthesis is the major task of a designer who, faced with a host of possible solutions to an engineering problem, chooses a particular one which is both technically sound and effective in its use of resources. However, synthesis depends upon analysis, and goes hand-in-hand with it. Without analytical skills, one can neither appreciate how existing systems work, nor evaluate tentative new designs in a critical way.

Before we get down to detail, let us set the scene with some further practical examples. These will underline the fact that, although the systems we are considering are invariably electronic, the signals may arise in a wide variety of situations.

Figure 2.1 shows several signals which arise within electronic engineering, and demonstrates the complicated structure of many practical waveforms. Part (a) of the figure shows a small portion of a voltage waveform produced by a microphone, here representing the single spoken word 'Shade'. This is a continuous signal although, as we have seen in chapter 1, it may be coded into a discrete PCM format for transmission or processing.

In section 1.2 we mentioned the processing of EEG, or 'brainwave' signals. Figure 2.1(b) shows another example of a biomedical signal, known as an electrocardiogram, or ECG. This represents the electrical activity of the heart, and may be detected by electrodes placed on the chest. Like the EEG, the ECG is often used in hospitals for diagnosis. Since an ECG waveform is produced every time the heart beats, the signal is repetitive in nature. Another important aspect of this particular ECG is that it is contaminated by sinusoidal interference at mains supply frequency (50 or 60 Hz). This is quite often a problem when recording low-amplitude signals,

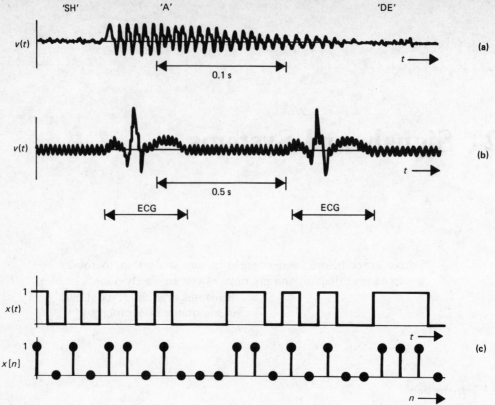

Figure 2.1 Electronic signals: (a) a speech waveform, (b) an ECG waveform, and (c) a PCM signal together with its sampled version.

because of mains pick-up in the electrode leads. An electronic filter may well be used to suppress the unwanted interference, while preserving the required signal.

Whereas the two signals described above are continuous, that shown in the upper part of figure 2.1(c) is a discrete sample-and-hold signal with only two possible levels, 0 or 1. Furthermore, transitions between these levels can occur only at particular instants of time. This is the typical form of a PCM signal, and might represent a coded version of an analog waveform such as speech or music. In fact, it could also represent virtually any other sort of data or information, and is of the type handled by digital computers and transmitted through digital communications and data networks. The simplicity of its structure, compared with (say) that of figure 2.1(a), is one of its most important technical attributes. Note that the instantaneously sampled version of the signal, shown below, contains exactly the same information and could therefore be used as a substitute for it.

A further good example of an electronic signal is that used by a television receiver to control the brightness of the 'flying spot' which generates the TV picture. Indeed, the whole field of the production, transmission and processing of pictures and images—including, for example, satellite weather maps and aerial photographs—provides important practical applications for signal and system concepts.

Figure 2.2 demonstrates that signals often arise in contexts not normally associated with electronic engineering. Figure 2.2(a) is a discrete signal, showing fluctuations in midday temperature at a certain place over a two-month period. Records of this type are of obvious

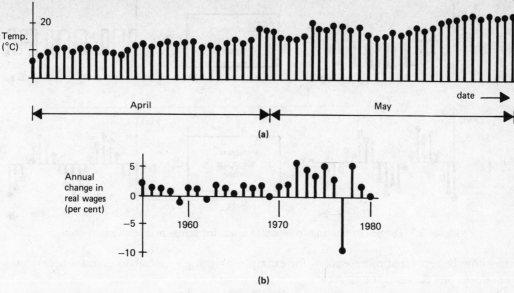

Figure 2.2

value to meteorological stations, and are often processed by digital computer—for example, to quantify trends or fluctuations, or to make predictions. The signal shown in part (b) of the figure is also discrete, showing annual fluctuations in real wages in the United Kingdom between 1955 and 1980. Economic trends and data are also widely stored in, and processed by, electronic computers.

We next consider some examples of systems. It is difficult to describe these in detail at this stage, because we have not covered the necessary groundwork. So we will restrict ourselves to indicating a few of the great variety of practical applications.

Several examples of systems have already been mentioned in chapter 1: cables for transmission of signals and messages, radio receivers, record players for reproducing music or speech from digital recordings, computers for processing biomedical signals, and low-pass filters for removing unwanted high-frequency noise or interference from a signal. Other electronic systems are used for recording or extracting information, for making decisions, for tracking targets, or for controlling machinery. The list is almost endless. Let us however add two further specific examples to it, taken from the field of *filtering* (we shall meet many types of filter in this book—especially in chapter 8).

It is helpful to emphasise that most practical signals, such as those in figures 2.1 and 2.2, contain a mixture of different frequencies. In many cases we need to extract or enhance some of these, and suppress others. A common situation is that of a signal contaminated by unwanted noise or interference—already referred to several times in this text. The signal and noise often occupy different frequency ranges, or *bands*, in which case a filter may be used to separate them. Figure 2.3 illustrates two examples. Part (a) shows an application of a *high-pass filter*, designed to transmit only the high-frequency components in a waveform. In this case the input $x(t)$ is a *sample-and-hold* binary waveform, corrupted by *baseline shifts*, which cause it to 'wander up and down' in a slow but unpredictable way. Such undesirable fluctuations make it more difficult to detect this character sequence correctly, and it is the task of the high-pass filter to remove them. As the figure shows, the filter transmits the sharp transitions of the waveform (which are rich in high frequencies), but largely suppresses the unwanted slow variations. The character sequence

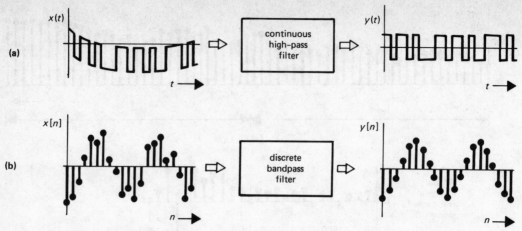

Figure 2.3 The use of filtering to separate a wanted signal from unwanted noise.

may now be recovered more easily—for example, by using a circuit to detect whenever the waveform $y(t)$ passes through zero.

Figure 2.3(b) illustrates the action of a discrete *bandpass filter*. In this case the sampled input $x[n]$ is predominantly at a particular sinusoidal frequency, but is contaminated by noise. This has the effect of superimposing random positive or negative errors on successive sample values. Luckily, the frequency components of such noise are widely distributed, so the selectivity of the bandpass filter is effective in suppressing most of the noise in the output $y[n]$.

It should be made clear that the term *filter* is used very often in electronic engineering, and includes many more devices than the low-pass, high-pass, and bandpass filters so far mentioned. We should also note, in passing, that practical filters introduce phase-shift (or time-delay) in the signals they process, as well as performing the desired filtering action. This effect has not been included in figure 2.3 (nor indeed in figure 1.6, which showed the action of a low-pass filter), for the sake of clarity.

Our brief survey of practical signals and systems is now completed. Its main aim will have been achieved if the reader has some appreciation of the diversity of practical signals, and of the electronic systems which are used to handle them.

2.2 Continuous and discrete signals

In this section we describe and discuss some basic types and properties of continuous and discrete signals, such as steps, impulses, and sinusoids. The reader may be tempted to question the value of such basic signals, with their rather simple waveforms and straightforward mathematical descriptions. After all, figures 2.1 and 2.2 have shown examples of practical signals which are very complicated in form and structure. Let us therefore outline straight away the main reasons why basic signals are so valuable to us.

Complicated practical signals may generally be considered as the *summation* of a number of simpler, basic, signals.

Many very useful practical systems are *linear*, or approximately linear. The response of a linear system to a number of signals applied simultaneously equals the summation of its responses to each signal applied separately. Thus if we can define the response of a linear system to basic signals, we can predict its response to more complicated ones.

For the above reasons, basic signals are also widely used as *test signals* for investigating the response of practical systems. They have the advantage of being relatively easy to generate.

2.2.1 *The independent variable: definitions and transformations*

The signals we shall consider in this book are almost invariably time functions. However, it is important to realise that time need not be the independent variable. For example, meteorologists may be interested in the variation of temperature or humidity with *altitude*, geologists with the density of strata as a function of *depth* below the Earth's surface, and electronic engineers with the variation of temperature with *distance* along, say, a cooling fin or heat sink. The analysis methods developed here would in principle be valid in all such cases.

We should also be clear that, while our discussion will be restricted to signals involving a single independent variable, there are plenty of examples of signals which are functions of two, or even more, such variables. A common one is the brightness of a two-dimensional picture or image, which varies with distance along *two* axes drawn at right angles.

In several figures already presented in this book, axes have been labelled to denote input and output signals, and time. Let us summarise the symbols we have used, and will use in the following chapters.

Input signals

$x(t)$ denotes a continuous input signal, which exists for all values of the independent continuous-time variable t.

$x[n]$ denotes a discrete, or sampled, input signal, which is defined *only* for integer values of the independent discrete-time variable n. Figure 2.4 shows, in detail, the symbols used for the various sample values, and the labelling of the time axis. (Note that in general n takes on integer values between $-\infty$ and $+\infty$, and that although $x[n]$ is defined only for a series of equally spaced instants in discrete-time, it often represents a sampled version of an underlying continuous-time variable.)

Output signals

$y(t)$ and $y[n]$ denote continuous and discrete-time output signals, respectively.

Electrical signals

When the signals referred to are specifically electrical, the symbols v and i are used to denote voltage and current respectively, with subscripts '1' and '2' for input and output. Upper-case symbols (V and I) denote either DC (steady) quantities, or frequency-domain variables (considered to be functions of frequency in hertz, or angular frequency in radians per second).

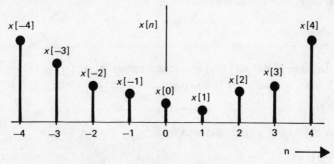

Figure 2.4 A discrete input signal.

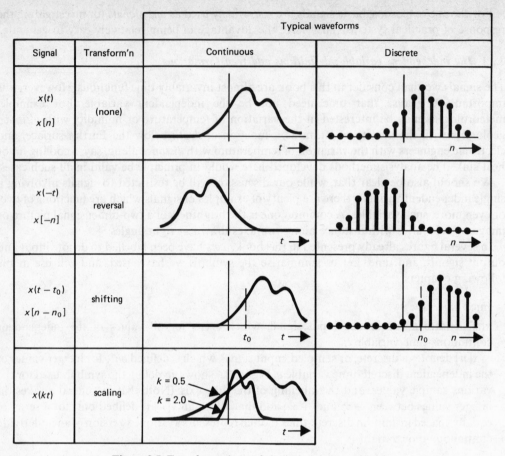

Figure 2.5 Transformations of the independent variable.

In many situations it is useful to be able to define mathematically the effect on a signal caused by a modification, or *transformation*, of the independent variable. The common transformations are time *reversal*, forward or backward *shifting*, and *scaling*. These are illustrated in figure 2.5, for arbitrary signal waveforms $x(t)$ and $x[n]$. The idea of scaling is not so easily applied to discrete signals, so is omitted from this discussion.

Example E2.1

A continuous-time signal $x(t)$ and a discrete-time signal $x[n]$ are shown in figure E2.1.1. Sketch and label carefully the following signals derived from $x(t)$

$$x(t - 2); \qquad x(1 - t); \qquad x(2t + 1)$$

and also the following signals derived from $x[n]$

$$x[n + 3]; \qquad x[2 - n]$$

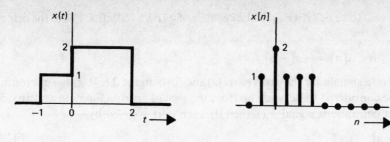

Figure E2.1.1

Solution

$x(t - 2)$ is the same as $x(t)$, but shifted *forward* by 2 seconds (it has the value of $x(0)$ when $(t - 2) = 0$, or $t = 2$). It is shown in figure E2.1.2(a).

$x(1 - t)$ is both shifted *and* reversed. The value $x(0)$ occurs when $(1 - t) = 0$, or $t = 1$. It is shown in figure E2.1.2(a).

$x(2t + 1)$ is shifted *and* scaled. The value $x(0)$ occurs when $(2t + 1) = 0$, or $t = -0.5$. The scaling is equivalent to a compression by a factor of 2. It is shown in figure E2.1.2(b).

$x[n + 3]$ is the same as $x[n]$, but shifted *backward* by 3 sampling intervals (it has the value $x[0]$ when $n = -3$). Hence it is as shown in figure E2.1.2(c).

$x[2 - n]$ is both shifted *and* reversed. It has the value $x[0]$ when $n = 2$, and is shown in figure E2.1.2(d).

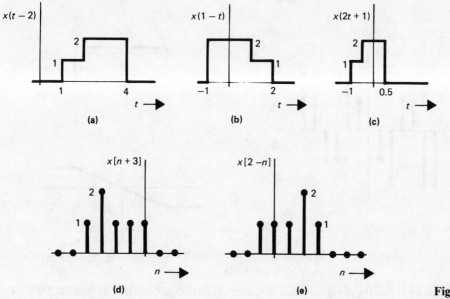

Figure E2.1.2

This is a convenient point to define the idea of *even* and *odd* signals. A signal is said to be even if it is identical with its own reflection about the origin. Thus even signals (either continuous or discrete) have the property that

$$x(t) = x(-t) \quad \text{or} \quad x[n] = x[-n]$$

Conversely, a signal is said to be *odd* if it equals the *negative* of its own reflection about the origin. Thus

$$x(t) = -x(-t) \quad \text{or} \quad x[n] = -x[-n]$$

Examples of even and odd signals are shown in parts (a) and (b) of figure 2.6. It is also interesting that *any* signal may be considered to be made up from the sum of an even function and an odd function. If we have a continuous signal $x(t)$, then its even part is given by

$$x_e(t) = \tfrac{1}{2}\{x(t) + x(-t)\} \tag{2.1}$$

and its odd part by

$$x_o(t) = \tfrac{1}{2}\{x(t) - x(-t)\} \tag{2.2}$$

An example of this is given in part (c) of the figure. An analogous pair of equations applies in the discrete case.

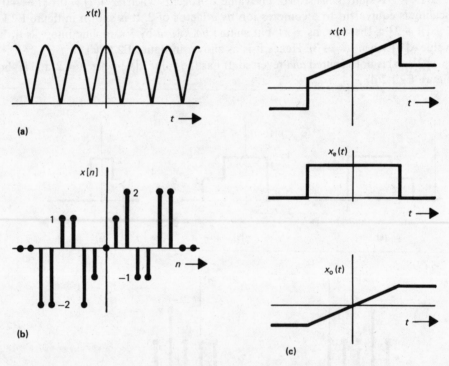

Figure 2.6 (a) An even signal, (b) an odd signal, and (c) the decomposition of a signal into its even and odd components.

Although such properties of signals may not seem of particular interest at present, they have important implications for the analysis of signals in terms of sine and cosine components. This is the topic of Fourier Analysis, to be covered in chapter 4.

2.2.2 *Steps, impulses, and ramps*

Step functions and impulse functions, in both their continuous and discrete forms, are among the most important of all basic signals. The ramp function is somewhat less so, but since it is closely related to the other two, it will also be covered in this section.

The continuous *unit step function* $u(t)$ is defined as follows

$$u(t) = 0 \qquad t < 0$$
$$u(t) = 1 \qquad t > 0$$

(2.3)

and is illustrated in figure 2.7(a). The discrete unit step function $u[n]$ is defined as

$$u[n] = 0 \qquad n < 0$$
$$u[n] = 1 \qquad n \geqslant 0$$

(2.4)

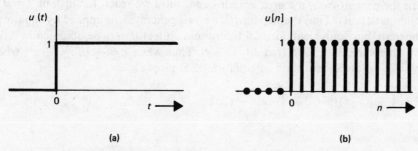

(a)   (b)

Figure 2.7 Continuous and discrete unit step functions.

It is shown in part (b) of the figure. Note that $u(t)$ has no definite value at $t = 0$: it changes abruptly from 0 to 1 at this instant, and is said to be *discontinuous*. However, $u[n]$ has the definite value of 1 when $n = 0$. Step functions arise widely in practice, and are commonly used as test signals for investigating system characteristics. The closing of a switch in a DC circuit often gives rise to a step function of voltage or current. This is illustrated in figure 2.8. If switch S_1 is closed at $t = 0$, a voltage step function is applied to circuit 1. If S_2 is opened at $t = 0$, a current step function is applied to circuit 2. We write these functions as $E u(t)$ and $I u(t)$ because they are not *unit* steps, but have amplitudes of E volts and I amps respectively.

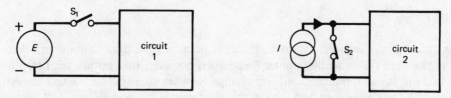

Figure 2.8 The production of step functions of voltage and current.

Another important example is that of a binary waveform such as the one already illustrated in the top part of figure 2.1(c). This may be regarded as a continuing sequence of positive and negative steps. It is easy to imagine that the response of a linear circuit or system to such a waveform must be very closely related to its response to a unit step.

Although it is hard at this stage to suggest such obvious practical applications for the discrete step function $u[n]$, we shall see later that it, too, has an important role in the analysis and testing of discrete-time signals and systems.

A further basic signal, which is probably even more important than the unit step, is the *unit impulse function*. Its continuous version, $\delta(t)$, may be thought of as an extremely narrow pulse, or 'spike', centred at the instant $t = 0$, and having *unit area*. Formally, its relationship with the unit step $u(t)$ may be defined as

$$u(t) = \int_{-\infty}^{t} \delta(\lambda)\,d\lambda \tag{2.5}$$

where λ is an auxiliary time variable which disappears when the limits of integration are inserted. $u(t)$ is said to be the *running integral* of $\delta(t)$. The meaning of this term is illustrated in figure 2.9 which shows a unit impulse function $\delta(\lambda)$ centred at $\lambda = 0$. When we integrate any function between $-\infty$ and t, we are effectively measuring the *area* under its curve over this interval. In the present case, the area remains zero until we reach the instant $\lambda = 0$. Then it suddenly jumps to unity. Thus the step function $u(t)$ is generated, as implied by equation (2.5). A slightly different, but equivalent, form of the running integral may be obtained in terms of an alternative time variable τ, such that $\lambda = (t - \tau)$. Thus when $\lambda = -\infty$, $\tau = +\infty$; when $\lambda = t$, $\tau = 0$; and $d\lambda = -d\tau$. Substitution in equation (2.5) gives

$$u(t) = \int_{\infty}^{0} \delta(t - \tau)(-d\tau) = \int_{0}^{\infty} \delta(t - \tau)\,d\tau \tag{2.6}$$

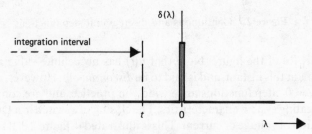

Figure 2.9 Illustration of the running integral.

A second possible definition of the impulse function $\delta(t)$ is as the *differential* of $u(t)$

$$\delta(t) = \frac{du(t)}{dt} \tag{2.7}$$

This equation gives rise to some formal difficulties, because $u(t)$ is discontinuous at $t = 0$, and its slope is therefore theoretically infinite. Remember, however, that no practical step function could ever display an infinitely rapid step change. So a sensible approach is to consider a step function with a finite *rise-time*, and then let this rise-time tend to zero. Figure 2.10 illustrates the argument by showing three step functions $u_1(t)$ to $u_3(t)$, with decreasing rise-times. Also shown is the differentiated function $\delta_1(t)$ to $\delta_3(t)$ in each case, which according to equation (2.7) should approximate the unit impulse function. Note that as the rise-time decreases, the slope of the step increases, but the area of the differentiated function remains unity. We may finally imagine that the 'true' impulse function $\delta(t)$ would be produced in the limit, as the rise-time of the step approached zero.

Although we have, for convenience, illustrated the argument with step functions rising *linearly* between 0 and 1 (producing flat-topped impulse functions), the basic idea does not depend on this assumption. The essential point is that the true unit impulse function $\delta(t)$ is of very short duration, very high amplitude, and *unit area*. Its detailed waveshape need not be specified.

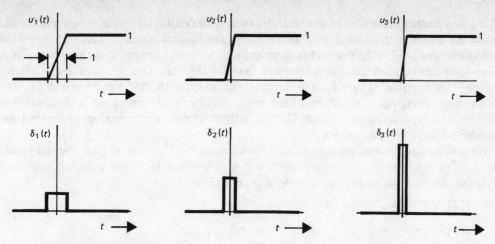

Figure 2.10 Approximations to the ideal continuous step and impulse functions.

Signals such as $\delta(t)$ and $u(t)$, although nominally continuous waveforms, display sudden discontinuities, or *singularities*. As we have seen, these can give rise to analytical difficulties. However, the mathematical complexities need not concern us unduly in this book, provided we bear in mind that some caution is required when dealing with *singularity functions*.

An impulse function is normally represented diagrammatically by an arrow, whose height denotes its *area*. Figure 2.11 shows three examples: a unit impulse $\delta(t)$, centred at $t = 0$; another unit impulse $\delta(t - t_0)$, shifted to the instant $t = t_0$; and a scaled, shifted, impulse of area k occurring at $t = t_1$.

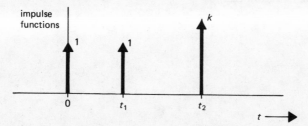

Figure 2.11 Shifted and scaled continuous impulse functions.

Let us now spend a little time on the practical meaning and significance of the unit impulse function. At first, the notion of an impulse with a duration tending to zero, and an amplitude tending to infinity, may seem rather artificial. Of course, any practical impulse—such as a voltage waveform generated by an electronic pulse generator—must have a finite duration and height. So the obvious question is: to what extent can it approximate the theoretical idea of an impulse? The answer is that it does so effectively, if its duration is very small *compared with the time scale of any other effects or phenomena we are considering.* For example, suppose we wish to test a system by applying an impulse, and we know that the system's response is likely to continue for (say) about 1 second after the impulse has been delivered. Then a pulse of duration (say) about 1 millisecond is likely to 'appear' extremely short to *that* system, and may be regarded as a good approximation to an ideal impulse. But a similar pulse might be quite inappropriate for impulse-testing another system which responded a great deal faster.

We may further illustrate the practical situation by a familiar example. When a golf ball is struck by a club, it receives a very short, sharp, mechanical impulse. This impulse, whose strength is measured as the product of force and time (or, more generally, as the *area* under the force–time curve), produces the subsequent flight of the ball. This may last many seconds. Clearly, the 'response' is very long in duration compared with the 'impulse' which causes it. Other things being equal, the flight is determined only by the strength (that is, the area) of the impulse—not its detailed waveshape. This is a fairly exact mechanical analogy of the electronic impulse we have been considering.

We now turn to the discrete version of the unit impulse, $\delta[n]$. Many of its properties parallel those of its continuous-time counterpart, but it is fortunately rather easier to define and visualise. Also known as the *unit sample*, it is defined as

$$\delta[n] = 1 \qquad n = 0$$
$$\delta[n] = 0 \qquad n \neq 0 \tag{2.8}$$

This is illustrated in figure 2.12. In effect it is just an isolated, unit-height, sample value at $n = 0$, surrounded on both sides by zeros. Just as the continuous-time unit step $u(t)$ is the *running integral* of the impulse function $\delta(t)$, so the discrete-time unit step $u[n]$ is the *running sum* of $\delta[n]$. This is quite simple to visualise. If we start at the left-hand side of figure 2.12, and move to the right adding up the sample values as we go, we generate the unit step function $u[n]$. This result may be written formally as

$$u[n] = \sum_{m=-\infty}^{n} \delta[m] \tag{2.9}$$

where m is a dummy integer variable. This equation is the discrete-time counterpart of the continuous integral, equation (2.5).

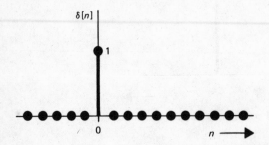

Figure 2.12 The discrete unit impulse function.

In similar fashion, just as $\delta(t)$ may be regarded as the *first derivative*, or *first-order differential*, of $u(t)$, so $\delta[n]$ is the *first-order difference* of $u[n]$. Thus the relationship

$$\delta[n] = u[n] - u[n-1] \tag{2.10}$$

holds good for all integer values of n. This is the first example in this text (and a very simple one!) of a *difference equation*, relating two discrete-time variables.

We shall see later that the discrete unit impulse $\delta[n]$ is of great value, not only as a test signal, but also for describing and analysing sampled signals and systems.

Ramp functions are not so important in practice as step or impulse functions, but are closely related to them and so deserve a mention here. A ramp waveform rises (or falls) linearly with time. Such waveforms are sometimes employed as test signals. Furthermore, triangular waveforms—which are quite widely used in electronic systems—may be regarded as a succession of positive and negative ramps. The continuous and discrete versions of the *unit ramp function* both have unit slope, and may be defined in terms of their respective unit step functions, as follows

$$r(t) = t\,u(t)$$

and

$$r[n] = n\,u[n] \tag{2.11}$$

Since $u(t)$ and $u[n]$ are zero for negative values of the independent variable, so are the ramp functions. They are illustrated in figure 2.13. Note also that $r(t)$ is the running integral of $u(t)$, and $r[n]$ is the running sum of $u[n]$. Also, $u(t)$ may be thought of as the first derivative of $r(t)$, and $u[n]$ as the first-order difference of $r[n]$. It is clear, therefore, that steps, impulses, and ramps are all very closely related.

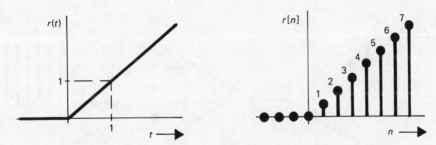

Figure 2.13 The continuous and discrete unit ramp functions.

Example E2.2

Write down mathematical expressions for the various step, impulse, and ramp functions shown in figure E2.2.

Solution

(a) This is a scaled, time-shifted, continuous step function, given by

$$x(t) = 3u(t - 2)$$

(b) This is similar to (a), but time-shifted backwards. Hence

$$x(t) = 2u(t + 2)$$

(c) This is a scaled discrete step function which is time-shifted and time-reversed. It is given by

$$x[n] = -2u[-4 - n]$$

(d) This discrete 'pulse' may be considered as the superposition of a discrete unit step function starting at $n = -3$, and an equal but *opposite* step function starting at $n = 5$. Hence

$$x[n] = u[n + 3] - u[n - 5]$$

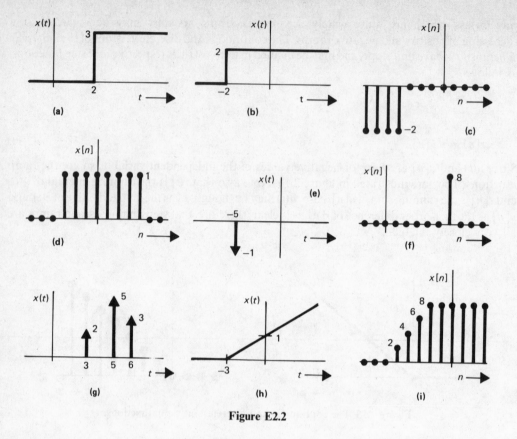

Figure E2.2

(e) This function is a continuous impulse of area -1, time-shifted to occur at $t = -5$. Hence

$$x(t) = -\delta(t + 5)$$

(f) This is a discrete impulse function of value 8, time-shifted to occur at $n = 6$. Hence

$$x[n] = 8\delta[n - 6]$$

(g) This function consists of 3 continuous impulses which may be considered superimposed, or added. Hence

$$x(t) = 2\delta(t - 3) + 5\delta(t - 5) + 3\delta(t - 6)$$

(h) This is a continuous ramp function, time-shifted to begin at $t = -3$, with a slope of $1/3$. Hence

$$x(t) = r(t + 3)/3$$

(i) This function may be considered as the superposition of two discrete ramps. One ramp starts at $n = -6$, with a slope of 2. Its upward trend may be stopped by adding a second ramp, starting at $n = -2$, with a slope of -2. Hence

$$x[n] = 2r[n + 6] - 2r[n + 2]$$

Note: There is more than one valid answer to several parts of this question.

We have now covered the basic ideas and mathematical definitions of steps, impulses, and ramps. We shall develop some further properties of these signals—particularly of impulse functions—in subsequent chapters.

2.2.3 *Exponentials, sines, and cosines*

It would be difficult to exaggerate the importance of exponential signals in electronic engineering, or indeed in many other branches of engineering and applied science. We shall see that such signals include, as particular cases, sine and cosine waveforms. The reader who has studied AC circuit theory will already be familiar with continuous sinusoidal functions of voltage and current. In our own review of continuous AC circuit concepts in section 1.4.2, we saw how the *j*-notation may be used to solve linear circuit problems when the excitation is sinusoidal. In this section we shall be considering sine and cosine waves in the more general context of exponential signals, and will extend the discussion to include discrete-time functions as well. Once again, the close parallels between continuous and discrete signals will become apparent.

The topic of exponential signals is conveniently introduced by considering the following analogous continuous and discrete functions

$$x(t) = A \exp(\alpha t) \tag{2.12}$$

and

$$x[n] = A \exp(\beta n) \tag{2.13}$$

where A, α, and β are constants. We shall restrict ourselves to real values of A, but will allow α and β to be real, imaginary, or complex. Let us start by considering the signals which are produced when α and β are real. Figure 2.14(a) shows two examples of real exponentials, one rising (α positive), the other falling (α negative). Part (b) shows a falling discrete real exponential (β negative). Note that if either α or β is zero, the corresponding signal has a constant value— representing, in electrical terminology, a *DC level*. In all cases, the function has the value A where it cuts the vertical axis. It is helpful to rewrite equation (2.13) as

$$x[n] = AB^n, \text{ where } B = \exp(\beta) \tag{2.14}$$

This shows that successive values of $x[n]$ form a geometric progression—an important property of a sampled real exponential.

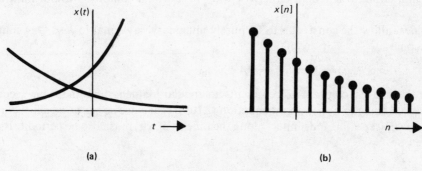

(a)   (b)

Figure 2.14 Real exponential signals.

A widely used parameter of a continuous real exponential is its *time constant*, τ, given by

$$\tau = \frac{1}{|\alpha|} \tag{2.15}$$

The smaller the time constant, the faster the exponential rises (or falls). In electrical or electronic circuits, time constants are simply related to values of resistance and capacitance, or resistance and inductance. There is a simple graphical method for measuring the time constant of an exponential curve, shown for a decaying exponential in figure 2.15. If a tangent to the curve is drawn at *any* point, and extended until it meets the *final value* (which the exponential approaches in the limit), then the time interval so defined equals the time constant τ. This is illustrated for two different tangents in the figure.

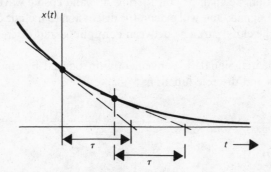

Figure 2.15 Measuring the time constant of a real exponential.

Real exponentials occur quite commonly. For example, decaying exponentials of voltage or current are characteristic of the transient response of circuits comprising resistors and capacitors, or resistors and inductors. They also arise in such phenomena as radioactive decay. Growing exponentials can occur in biological phenomena such as uninhibited cell division and growth, and in chemical reactions. In general, any process where the *rate of change* of a variable is proportional to the *value already reached* displays a real exponential characteristic. However, it is important to realise that no physical process can produce such a curve indefinitely (into the past for a decaying exponential, or into the future for a rising one). Some limiting mechanism, or *nonlinearity*, must eventually intervene. This might be the opening of a switch, the saturation of a transistor, or the burn-out of a component, in an electronic circuit; or the exhaustion of the reagents in a chemical reaction. Otherwise, the curve would continue without limit towards infinity.

Let us next allow the constant α to be purely imaginary, say equal to $j\omega_0$. Our continuous signal becomes

$$x(t) = A \exp(j\omega_0 t) = A \cos \omega_0 t + jA \sin \omega_0 t \tag{2.16}$$

It is clear that the real constant ω_0 represents an angular frequency in radians per second. The first important thing to notice about equation (2.16) is that since $\cos \omega_0 t$ and $\sin \omega_0 t$ are both strictly *periodic* (repeating indefinitely along the time axis), $x(t)$ must also be periodic. Its period T_0 is given by

$$T_0 = \frac{2\pi}{\omega_0} \tag{2.17}$$

Secondly, we see that $x(t)$ is now a *complex* signal with real and imaginary parts. Since in this book we will be restricting ourselves to *real* signals and waveforms, such an exponential may seem of little use as it stands. There are two ways round this difficulty. One is to consider just the real part, or just the imaginary part, of $x(t)$ as representing the actual signal—and to make it quite clear *which* part we have chosen. The second way, which is more elegant and useful from an analytical point of view, is to use the identities

$$A \cos \omega_0 t = \frac{A}{2} \exp(j\omega_0 t) + \frac{A}{2} \exp(-j\omega_0 t) \tag{2.18}$$

and

$$A \sin \omega_0 t = \frac{A}{2j} \exp(j\omega_0 t) - \frac{A}{2j} \exp(-j\omega_0 t) \tag{2.19}$$

These show that a real cosine wave may be considered as the sum, and a real sine wave as the difference, of a *pair* of imaginary exponentials. It is true that there is some conceptual difficulty with the terms involving $\exp(-j\omega_0 t)$, since their physical meaning is not obvious. In fact, since the term $\exp(j\omega_0 t)$ is associated with the positive frequency ω_0, we may think of $\exp(-j\omega_0 t)$ as implying a *negative frequency* $-\omega_0$. The notion of negative frequency may be regarded as a conceptual convenience to back up the mathematics, and its physical reality need not bother us unduly. It is better to focus on the idea that a real continuous sine or cosine may be built up from a pair of imaginary exponentials. In chapter 4 we shall meet the idea of negative frequency again, and expand on its value for signal and system analysis.

Rather than restrict ourselves to just sine or cosine functions, we may express *any* continuous wave of sinusoidal shape as

$$x(t) = A \sin(\omega_0 t + \phi) \tag{2.20}$$

$$x(t) = A \cos(\omega_0 t + \theta) \tag{2.21}$$

where ϕ and θ represent *phase angles* in radians. These allow for any shift of the signal along the time axis. A phase angle of 2π represents a shift of one complete period, or cycle.

This is also a good moment to emphasise that a sinusoidal waveform is regarded as a *single-frequency* signal. We have already noted several times that practical signals often contain a mixture of many frequencies. This means that they could be built up, or *synthesised*, by adding together many waves of sinusoidal shape having different frequencies. Other basic signals such as steps, impulses, or ramps, may also in principle be built up in this way. By the word 'frequency' we mean, in such a context, *sinusoidal* frequency. These are key ideas in Fourier Analysis, to be developed in chapter 4.

We now turn again to the discrete signal $x[n]$ already defined by equation (2.13), and allow the constant β to be purely imaginary. Suppose it equals $j\Omega_0$, where Ω_0 is a real constant. Then

$$x[n] = A \exp(\beta n) = A \exp(jn\Omega_0) = A \cos n\Omega_0 + jA \sin n\Omega_0 \tag{2.22}$$

This signal has many parallels with the continuous one just discussed. It is complex, although we may always consider just its real, or imaginary, part if we so wish. Alternatively, we may invoke the identities

$$A \cos n\Omega_0 = \frac{A}{2} \exp(jn\Omega_0) + \frac{A}{2} \exp(-jn\Omega_0) \tag{2.23}$$

and

$$A \sin n\Omega_0 = \frac{A}{2j} \exp(jn\Omega_0) - \frac{A}{2j} \exp(-jn\Omega_0) \qquad (2.24)$$

These show that a real, discrete-time, cosine or sine signal may, like its continuous counterpart, be considered as made up of a *pair* of imaginary exponentials. Once again, we may also express *any* discrete signal of sinusoidal form as a sine function with a phase angle, or as a cosine function with a phase angle, in a way analogous to that defined by equations (2.20) and (2.21). All these properties mirror those of the continuous sines and cosines already discussed, but we must also be aware of some important distinctions.

The first distinction we should consider concerns the question of *periodicity*. For whereas all continuous sines and cosines are strictly periodic functions, their discrete counterparts may not be so. Although successive samples of a discrete-time sinusoid lie on a sinusoidal *envelope*, their numerical values do not necessarily form a repetitive sequence. Intuitively, it is not hard to imagine that exact repetition will occur only if the spacing between samples bears some simple relationship to the period of the underlying continuous waveform. We may quantify this idea by returning to equation (2.22). Let us assume for the moment that $x[n]$ *is* truly periodic, and repeats every N sample values. This means that

$$x[n] = A \exp(jn\Omega_0) = A \exp(j\{n + N\}\Omega_0) = A \exp(jn\Omega_0) \exp(jN\Omega_0) \qquad (2.25)$$

and hence

$$\exp(jN\Omega_0) = 1 \qquad (2.26)$$

If this last equation is to hold, $N\Omega_0$ must be a multiple of 2π. In other words there must be an integer m such that

$$N\Omega_0 = 2\pi m, \text{ or } \frac{\Omega_0}{2\pi} = \frac{m}{N} \qquad (2.27)$$

We therefore conclude that $x[n]$ is only periodic if $\Omega_0/2\pi$ is a rational number (the ratio of two integers). Although we have derived this result for an imaginary exponential, it applies equally well to real sines and cosines.

Another difference between continuous and discrete sinusoidal signals concerns the question of frequency and time scales, and the nature of the discrete integer variable n. When we write a discrete signal as $x[n] = A \sin n\Omega_0$, we envisage n as a dimensionless variable which takes on only integer values. Hence the constant Ω_0 must be expressed in radians rather than radians per second, and we cannot think directly in terms of time and frequency. However, this formulation for $x[n]$ allows us to define instead the *number of samples in each cycle* of the sinusoid. Note that one complete cycle corresponds to

$$n\Omega_0 = 2\pi, \text{ or } n = \frac{2\pi}{\Omega_0} \qquad (2.28)$$

Hence there must be $2\pi/\Omega_0$ samples per cycle, regardless of the time or frequency scales of the signal. If, for example, we wish to generate a signal $x[n]$ having 8 samples per cycle, we must set Ω_0 equal to $2\pi/8$.

On many occasions, however, the above formulation is unhelpful. For example, in section 1.3 we introduced the Sampling Theorem, which states that an analog signal with frequency components up to some maximum frequency f_1 Hz may be represented by samples taken at a rate of at least $2f_1$ samples per second. Clearly, in such cases we *are* interested in frequency and time scales. A convenient way of introducing these is to define the time between successive samples, or *sampling interval*, as T. Hence the instants at which samples are taken are given by

$$t = nT, \qquad n = \ldots - 2, -1, 0, 1, 2, 3 \ldots \tag{2.29}$$

Note also that the sampling frequency f_s is

$$f_s = \frac{1}{T}$$

Let us now write our discrete signal as

$$x[n] = \sin\{(nT)\Omega_2\} \tag{2.30}$$

Since nT represents time in seconds, Ω_2 must be an angular frequency in radians per second. If f_2 is the sinusoidal frequency in hertz, then $\Omega_2 = 2\pi f_2$, and we may write $x[n]$ in the form

$$x[n] = \sin\left(\frac{n}{f_s} 2\pi f_2\right) = \sin\left(2\pi n \frac{f_2}{f_s}\right) \tag{2.31}$$

This alternative form clearly allows us to generate the sample series $x[n]$ if we know the frequency f_2 of the underlying continuous sinusoid, and the sampling frequency f_s. We have therefore recast the definition of a discrete sinusoid in terms of frequency in hertz, and time in seconds.

Figure 2.16 shows a number of sine and cosine signals, both continuous and discrete. Part (a) shows a portion of a continuous sinewave of period T_1 and amplitude C_1. Part (b) shows a cosine with the same period, but a greater amplitude C_2, and part (c) another sinusoid, with a

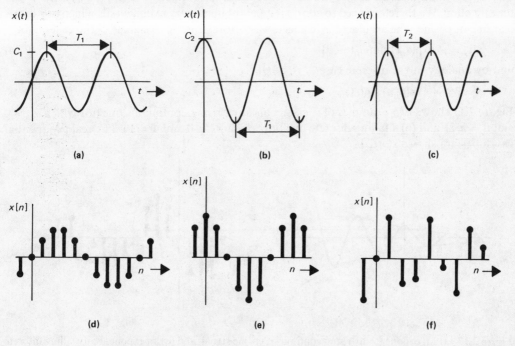

Figure 2.16 Continuous and discrete sine and cosine signals.

smaller period T_2. The discrete counterparts of the three signals are shown below. Note that (d) has exactly 10 samples per cycle of the underlying sinusoid, and is strictly periodic. Part (e) has 8 samples per cycle, and is likewise periodic. But in (f), equation (2.27) is not satisfied, so that although sample values lie along a sinusoidal envelope, their values do not repeat and the signal is not periodic.

Sinusoidal waveforms arise widely in engineering, and in the natural world: the mains electricity supply; signal generators, or oscillators, which are widely used in electronic laboratories; oscillations in circuits containing capacitance and inductance; the vibrations of a tuning fork; and many types of wave motion. But from our point of view, just as important as these direct manifestations of sinusoidal signals is the fact that *other*, completely different, signals may be considered as the summation of a number of sines and cosines of different amplitudes, phases, and frequencies. This explains why sinusoidal waveforms play such a key role in electronic engineering.

To complete our survey of exponential signals, we need to let the constants α and β (defined at the start of this section) become complex. It is not hard to imagine what will happen. We have seen that *real* values of α and β produce signals which rise or fall exponentially. *Imaginary* values produce sines and cosines. Therefore *complex* values may be expected to produce oscillatory signals having rising or falling amplitudes. Consider the continuous case

$$x(t) = A \exp(\{\alpha_0 + j\omega_0\}t) \tag{2.32}$$

where α_0 is now considered to be the real part, and $j\omega_0$ the imaginary part, of α. This may be rewritten as

$$x(t) = A \exp(\alpha_0 t) \exp(j\omega_0 t) \tag{2.33}$$

$A \exp(\alpha_0 t)$ represents a rising or falling exponential envelope, by which the frequency term $\exp(j\omega_0 t)$ is multiplied. Of course, we have once again the difficulty that $\exp(j\omega_0 t)$ is not a real time function. We therefore need to consider a pair of imaginary exponentials which produce a real sine or cosine. The argument is just as it was before, leading to signals of the general form

$$x(t) = A \exp(\alpha_0 t) \sin(\omega_0 t + \theta) \tag{2.34}$$

and by analogy in the discrete case

$$x[n] = A \exp(\beta_0 n) \sin(n\Omega_0 + \Phi) \tag{2.35}$$

Figure 2.17 shows two examples of such signals: (a) a rising continuous one (for which $\alpha_0 > 0$ and $\theta = \pi/2$), and (b) a falling discrete one (for which $\beta_0 < 0$ and $\Phi = 0$). The real exponential envelopes are shown dotted.

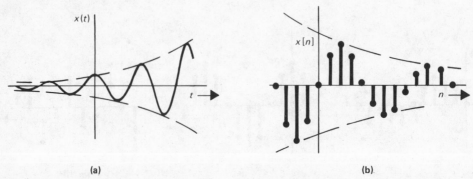

(a)   (b)

Figure 2.17 (a) An exponentially rising continuous cosine signal, and (b) an exponentially falling discrete sine signal.

Such waveforms are also important in practice. Sinusoidal oscillations with diminishing amplitudes are characteristic of electrical circuits containing resistance, capacitance, and inductance. They also arise in many types of vibrating mechanical system and structure. Exponentially increasing oscillations occur in various types of electronic circuit and system which are inherently *unstable* (sometimes by design, sometimes by accident!). These will be discussed at some length in chapter 7 (on feedback).

Example E2.3

Sketch carefully, and label, the following exponential and sinusoidal signals over suitable ranges of the independent variable

(a) $x(t) = 2 \exp(-t)$

(b) $x[n] = \exp(0.2n)$

(c) $x(t) = -0.5 \sin\left(\omega t + \dfrac{\pi}{6}\right)$

(d) $x[n] = \cos \dfrac{2\pi n}{8}$

(e) $x(t) = \exp(-t) \cos 4\pi t$

(f) $x[n] = \exp\left(\dfrac{n}{15}\right) \sin \dfrac{2\pi n}{12}$

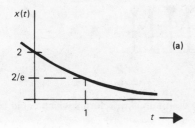

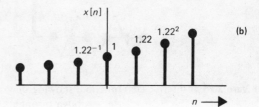

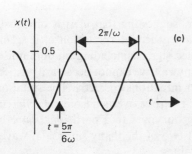

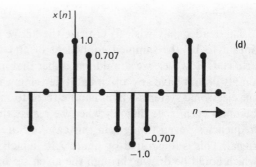

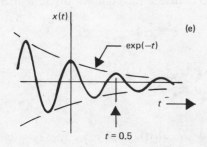

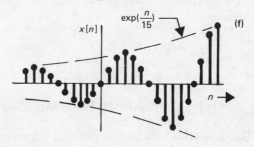

Figure E2.3

Solution

The various signals are shown in figure E2.3, which should be self-explanatory.

2.2.4 *Ambiguity in discrete signals*

A discrete signal $x[n]$, defined only at certain instants of time, generally represents some continuous underlying function. However, if we start with a given set of sample values, it is clear that a huge variety of continuous waveforms *could* be drawn through them. Take, for example, a 'straightforward' discrete signal such as the unit step function $u[n]$. Although we may think of this as being the sampled equivalent of the continuous unit step function $u(t)$, figure 2.18 illustrates another continuous waveform with the same sample values. It is clear that discrete signals are, in an important sense, ambiguous.

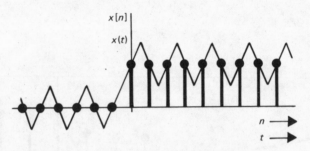

Figure 2.18 A discrete step function, showing one of the many continuous waveforms which could be drawn through its sample points.

The reader may wish to criticise the above example by suggesting that $u[n]$ is obviously 'meant to be' the sampled equivalent of $u(t)$, and that any other interpretation of it seems artificial. However, we should remember that many sampled signals (including random noise) simply do not have any 'obvious' underlying waveform. Anyway, we cannot necessarily expect the electronic systems which handle them to interpret our intentions correctly. The situation becomes even more difficult when we realise that ambiguity arises over sinusoids of different frequencies—even though, in this case, we are restricting ourselves to a particular *shape* of signal. This is illustrated by figure 2.19, which shows just two of the many sinusoidal waves which could be drawn through the given set of sample values.

Perhaps the best way of clarifying the situation is to consider the complex discrete-time exponential

$$x[n] = \exp(j\{\Omega_0 + 2\pi\}n) \tag{2.36}$$

where n may be any integer (positive or negative). We may write this as

$$x[n] = \exp(j\Omega_0 n)\exp(j2\pi n) = \exp(j\Omega_0 n) \tag{2.37}$$

This shows that a discrete exponential of frequency Ω_0 is *identical* to those of frequency $\Omega_0 \pm 2\pi$, $\Omega_0 \pm 4\pi$, and so on. The same is true for sines and cosines. As we increase the frequency from

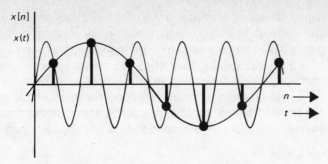

Figure 2.19 Ambiguity in sampled sinusoids.

zero, the rate of oscillation of a discrete-time sinusoid initially *increases*. Beyond $\Omega_0 = \pi$ it *decreases* again until $\Omega_0 = 2\pi$, where it is the same as at $\Omega_0 = 0$. As Ω_0 is further increased, the pattern repeats indefinitely at multiples of 2π. So the discrete-time version of a sinusoidal signal is not unique to a particular underlying frequency, but can represent any one of a repeating set of frequencies. Herein lies the ambiguity.

Let us now reconsider the Sampling Theorem, which we first introduced in section 1.3. This theorem tells us that any continuous signal containing frequencies up to some maximum f_1 Hz may be completely represented by samples taken at a frequency (or sampling rate) f_s such that $f_s \geq 2f_1$. Clearly, if 'complete representation' is to mean what it says, there must not be any ambiguity or confusion over which underlying signal is intended. This is possible because the minimum sampling rate demanded by the Sampling Theorem produces *at least two samples per cycle* of every frequency component present in the continuous waveform. Two samples per cycle corresponds to $\Omega_0 = \pi$ in our previous paragraph (see also equation (2.28) in the previous section). We have already argued that there is no ambiguity over which frequency is intended within the range $\Omega_0 = 0$ to $\Omega_0 = \pi$. It is only when we go outside this range that we get into difficulties. Therefore we may summarise by saying that the Sampling Theorem resolves the ambiguity problem in discrete-time sinusoidal signals by restricting the allowable frequency range of the underlying signal.

We may illustrate this last point by reconsidering figure 2.19. Although both the continuous sinusoids illustrated pass through the sample points, only the *lower* frequency one has at least two samples per cycle. Assuming that the Sampling Theorem has been obeyed, we therefore discard the higher-frequency signal as being 'not allowed'.

Although the Sampling Theorem provides the key to resolving the ambiguity problem in discrete-time exponentials and sinusoids, it does not help nearly so obviously with other types of signal—such as the unit step function $u[n]$ already shown in figure 2.18. Although this is not the moment to go into detail, we might just note that the continuous waveform drawn through the sample points of $u[n]$ involves sudden transitions and fast rates of change, implying the presence of high frequencies; and it is not difficult to imagine that these frequencies have been inadequately sampled, according to the Sampling Theorem. The corollary is that we should always try to construct a continuous waveform through a given set of sample points, using the lowest possible rates of change, and hence frequencies. In the case of the sample points of $u[n]$, it would not be surprising if this guideline resulted in a continuous waveform similar to $u(t)$. Although this discussion is very intuitive, it does suggest that the Samping Theorem holds important clues for resolving the ambiguity problem in discrete-time signals other than exponentials and sinusoids. These ideas will be more fully explored in chapter 8.

In section 1.3 we covered the processes of analog-to-digital and digital-to-analog conversion in some detail. The digital-to-analog converter (DAC) has the task of producing a continuous signal from a set of sample values. In fact, as we saw, it often produces a waveform of the sample-and-hold type, which may be further smoothed by a low-pass filter to remove its sudden jumps and transients. In the present context it is interesting to note that this process results in the lowest-frequency continuous waveform possible. In other words, of all the possible continuous signals which the DAC might produce, it actually produces the one with the smallest rates of change, and hence the lowest frequencies. In this sense it, too, assumes that the Sampling Theorem has been obeyed, and uses the assumption to resolve the ambiguity problem.

2.3 Continuous and discrete systems

In sections 1.1 and 1.2 we have already discussed, in general terms, what is meant by an electronic system. We have also described some additional practical engineering examples in section 2.1. We must now start to explore the technical properties of systems in more detail, and lay some solid groundwork. Some of this material may seem a little obscure at first. If it does, the reader is encouraged to return briefly to the above-mentioned sections for a reminder of the type of practical system we are considering, and to accept that the ideas contained in the rest of this chapter are essential to our purpose.

2.3.1 *Linearity and the Principle of Superposition*

The idea of system linearity and the Principle of Superposition have already been mentioned several times in this book—for example, in our discussion of the DAC network in section 1.3, and in our review of continuous circuit principles in section 1.4. A linear system may be defined as one which obeys the Principle of Superposition. The latter may be stated as follows.

> If an input consisting of the sum of a number of signals is applied to a linear system, the output is the sum, or *superposition*, of the system's responses to each of those signals considered separately.

Suppose that an input $x_1(t)$, applied to a continuous linear system, produces the output $y_1(t)$, and that input $x_2(t)$ produces output $y_2(t)$. Then the system is linear if its response to $\{x_1(t) + x_2(t)\}$ is $\{y_1(t) + y_2(t)\}$. A corollary is that its response to an input $ax_1(t)$ must be $ay_1(t)$, where a is a constant multiplier denoting scaling, or *weighting*. To generalise, the weighted sum of inputs

$$ax_1(t) + bx_2(t) + cx_3(t) + \ldots \tag{2.38}$$

must give rise to a corresponding weighted sum of outputs

$$ay_1(t) + by_2(t) + cy_3(t) + \ldots \tag{2.39}$$

where $a, b, c \ldots$ are constants. A precisely analogous result may be stated for a linear discrete-time system, so that a composite input

$$ax_1[n] + bx_2[n] + cx_3[n] + \ldots$$

must produce a composite output

$$ay_1[n] + by_2[n] + cy_3[n] + \ldots$$

In case the property of linearity appears trivial, or obvious, let us point out straight away that many quite simple systems are *not* linear. For example, consider a continuous system designed to square the instantaneous value of the signal applied to its input. Thus for two different input and output signals we may write

$$y_1(t) = \{x_1(t)\}^2$$

and

$$y_2(t) = \{x_2(t)\}^2$$

When these two inputs are applied simultaneously, the output is

$$y_3(t) = \{x_1(t) + x_2(t)\}^2 = \{x_1(t)\}^2 + \{x_2(t)\}^2 + 2x_1(t)x_2(t) \qquad (2.40)$$

which is clearly *not* the sum of its responses to $x_1(t)$ and $x_2(t)$ applied separately. If we think in terms of electronics, then circuits containing devices such as diodes and transistors are generally nonlinear. It is true that in many cases—amplifiers for example—we may treat them as approximately linear for the purposes for which they are designed. However, in other cases such circuits are *essentially* nonlinear, and must be viewed as such. On the other hand, a great many practical circuits and systems *are* linear, and we concentrate on these in this book.

An extremely important property of linear systems, which is closely related to the Principle of Superposition, is that of *frequency preservation*. That is to say, if we apply an input signal containing certain frequencies to a linear system, its output can contain only those same frequencies, and no others. Although no formal proof is offered here, it is not difficult to see how this property arises. In our brief review of continuous AC circuits in section 1.4, we noted that when a sinusoidal excitation is applied to a linear circuit, all currents, voltages, and signals arising in that circuit are also sinusoidal in form, at the *same frequency* as the excitation. The same is true of any linear system. If we now apply a complicated signal containing many sinusoidal frequencies, the Principle of Superposition tells us that the output must be the sum of the outputs due to each input frequency component, considered separately. It therefore follows that the output can only contain those sinusoidal frequencies present in the input.

It is easy to demonstrate that a nonlinear system, such as the 'squaring device' mentioned above, does not possess the frequency preservation property. Suppose a signal $\sin \omega_1 t$ is applied to its input. The output is therefore

$$y(t) = x^2(t) = \sin^2 \omega_1 t = \tfrac{1}{2}(1 + \cos 2\omega_1 t) = \tfrac{1}{2} + \tfrac{1}{2}\cos 2\omega_1 t \qquad (2.41)$$

There are two *additive* frequency components in the output: a constant value of $1/2$, representing a *zero-frequency* term (equivalent to a DC level), and another component of amplitude $1/2$, at the frequency $2\omega_1$. There is no component in the output at the frequency ω_1.

We should also mention two further aspects of linear systems at this stage, namely their *associative* and *commutative* properties. We can illustrate these in a qualitative and practical way. Suppose we have an *overall* linear system composed of a linear amplifier followed by a linear filter, as shown in figure 2.20. In essence, the associative property means that we may describe the performance of the overall system by appropriately combining, or *associating*, the individual properties of the amplifier and filter, considered separately. Although, once again, this may seem a rather obvious property, it is not one which is generally shared by nonlinear systems. It offers us great advantages in both analysis and synthesis. We may analyse a complicated linear system by breaking it down into a number of simpler *subsystems*. Alternatively we may synthesise an overall system—again, perhaps one of great complexity—by designing a number of independent subsystems, knowing that, when we put them all together,

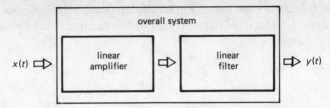

Figure 2.20 An overall system composed of two linear subsystems in cascade.

the overall performance will be as predicted by quite straightforward rules of association. The detailed nature of these rules will become clear in subsequent chapters.

The commutative property of linear systems means that if the subsystems of an overall system are arranged in series, or *cascade*, then those subsystems may be rearranged *in any order* without affecting overall performance. Thus in figure 2.20, we could place the filter before the amplifier, rather than after it, without affecting the output signal (even though there may be additional practical reasons for choosing one order rather than the other). Once again, this property is not generally shared by nonlinear systems.

2.3.2 *Other properties of systems*

In this short section, we summarise some further important properties of systems. These are: time-invariance, causality, stability, invertibility, and memory.

A *time-invariant* system is one whose properties, or characteristics, do not vary as a function of time. This implies that the only effect of a time-shift in a given input signal to the system is a corresponding time-shift in its output signal. The majority of engineering systems are time-invariant. However, as examples from electronics of systems whose characteristics change with time we might mention: the *automatic gain control* (AGC) circuits used in radio and communication receivers, which compensate for chance fluctuations in strength of the incoming signal, and the *sensitivity time control* (STC), or *swept gain*, circuits employed in many radar receivers, which allow for the fact that echos received from close objects or targets are much stronger than those from distant ones. Readers unfamiliar with these applications have no need to worry—they are mentioned only to indicate that not all practical electronic systems are time-invariant! One might add that the ageing of electronic equipment, which often produces performance changes, constitutes a type of time-variability. However, such ageing normally takes place over a long time scale—typically years—and is not usually considered in these terms.

In a *causal* system, the present output signal depends only upon present and previous values of the input. One might, therefore, assume that all practical engineering systems are necessarily causal, because they can hardly be expected to anticipate future inputs. There are various situations, however, where causality is not strictly necessary. For example, if we record a signal or data, and subsequently filter or process it on a digital computer, the computer program need not be causal. Of course, it might reasonably be objected that the *total* system, comprising the recording device as well as the computer, *is* causal, but at this point we run the danger of becoming entangled in semantics!

A *stable* system is one which produces a *bounded* output in response to a bounded input. This means that if the system is disturbed from its resting state by some input signal which does not grow without limit, or *diverge*, its output or response must likewise not diverge. In section 2.2.3 we considered examples of exponential signals (see figures 2.14 and 2.17) which grow without limit. If a system produced such a signal in response to a bounded input (such as an impulse or a step), it would be unstable. Of course, as we pointed out in section 2.2.3, no practical signal could ever grow indefinitely. There must always be some limiting mechanism to halt its growth. Similarly, the output of an unstable system must sooner or later cease to diverge, as a result of some nonlinear, or limiting, effect. Unstable engineering systems are quite common, and we shall see later (especially in chapter 7) that instability is intimately associated with the ideas of feedback. A good example of deliberately unstable electronic systems is provided by the variable-frequency signal generators, or oscillators, which are used in virtually every electronic laboratory. These produce an output signal *on their own*, without the need for any input (they need a power supply, or battery—but this is not an input *signal*).

We next define the term *invertibility*. If, for example, we have a continuous system fed with an input signal $x(t)$ and producing an output $y(t)$, then its *inverse* system would produce $x(t)$ if fed with $y(t)$. Thus, if we create an overall system by connecting a system and its inverse together in cascade, the overall system's output must be identical to its input. Practical systems are generally invertible since every possible input signal value gives rise to a distinct, unambiguous, output value. However, a simple example of a noninvertible system is the 'squaring device' mentioned in the previous section, for which

$$y(t) = \{x(t)\}^2$$

In this case knowledge of an output value $y(t)$ does not allow us to determine $x(t)$ unambiguously, since it could be positive or negative.

A system possesses *memory* if its present output depends upon previous input values. In electrical and electronic circuits and systems, memory implies the presence of energy storage elements such as capacitors or inductors. A purely resistive circuit is memoryless. The majority of useful electronic systems do possess memory. However, there are at least two important exceptions: amplifiers and attenuators, which are designed to increase or decrease the amplitude of a signal respectively. Ideally (although not always in practice) they are supposed to provide a pure scaling of the present input signal value, without regard to its past history. True memoryless systems have a performance which is independent of the frequency of the input signal. However, practical amplifiers, and to a lesser extent practical attenuators, never quite meet this criterion.

This brief discussion of system properties, plus the comments on system linearity in the previous section, will have shown the reader that the main interest of this book is in linear time-invariant (LTI) systems which are also causal, stable, and invertible. In addition, most of the systems we shall consider possess memory. Although this combination of properties by no means covers all practical electronic circuits and systems, it does encompass a wide range of very useful ones. A further important advantage of dealing with LTI systems is that their performance may be analysed in great detail with relative ease, using a set of ideas which form a coherent and satisfying body of theoretical knowledge.

Example E2.4

$x(t)$ and $y(t)$ denote the input and output signals of a continuous system, $x[n]$ and $y[n]$ the input and output signals of a discrete system. Determine which of the following properties are exhibited by each of the systems overleaf in (a) to (d)

     linearity
     time-invariance
     causality
     stability
     invertibility
     memory.

(a) $y[n] = 2x[n] + 3x[n - 1]$
(b) $y(t) = t\,x(t)$
(c) $y[n] = 2y[n - 1] + x[n + 1]$
(d) $y(t) = \cos\{2\pi\,x(t)\}$

Solution

(a) The output is a weighted sum of the present and previous inputs. It is bounded if the input sequence is bounded. A given input sequence is unambiguously related to the output sequence. Hence the system possesses all the properties listed above.

(b) The output depends only upon the present value of the input, so the system has no memory. It also depends upon the value of the independent variable, so the system is time-variant. But it possesses the properties of linearity, causality, stability, and invertibility.

(c) The present output depends upon a future input, so the system is not causal. Also, if the input signal ceases, the output goes on rising without limit since each output value is twice the previous one. So the system is unstable. However, it possesses the other four properties listed above: linearity, time-invariance, invertibility, and memory.

(d) Since a cosine function is periodic, many values of $x(t)$ would produce the same value of $y(t)$. Hence the system is not invertible. Neither is it linear, because if (for example) we double the value of $x(t)$ we do not double $y(t)$. Also, since $y(t)$ depends only upon the present input value $x(t)$, the system has no memory. However, it is time-invariant, causal, and stable.

2.3.3 *System block diagrams*

Since this book is primarily concerned with *electronic* signals and systems, we are naturally interested in circuits and their interconnections. Indeed, we have already illustrated some important ideas by referring to particular circuits—for example, in figures 1.9 and 1.14. However, the field of Signals and Systems is perhaps above all concerned with the recording, flow, and processing of *information*, regardless of the particular physical quantity—voltage, current, pressure, temperature, displacement, light intensity, and so on—used to represent it. So while it is true that most practical realisations of signals and systems employ electronic technology, and that most signals take the form of fluctuating *voltages*, this is not always, or necessarily, the case. We might note, for example, that recent developments in optical communications systems have resulted in a huge increase in the use of *light signals*. However, the concepts covered in this book apply in this case as well as in purely electronic systems.

The essential difference between a system block diagram and an electrical or electronic circuit diagram is that the former concentrates on the system's *function* rather than its detailed technological realisation, and indicates *information flow* within the system. Actually, three block diagrams—figures 1.6, 2.3, and 2.20—have already been introduced into this text without special comment or fuss! Figure 1.6, for example, shows several input and output signals, without specifying whether they are represented by voltages, currents, or any other physical variable. The thick arrows at the input and output of the various system 'blocks' are designed to indicate flow of information, rather than particular wires or connections (of course, any electrical signal needs *two* wires to connect it into or out of a system—very often an earth, or reference, and a 'live'). We now need to explain the use of block diagrams a little more carefully, and to introduce some new ideas.

A good way of clarifying the distinctions between a circuit diagram and a system block diagram is to take a simple practical example, such as the continuous circuit shown in figure 2.21(a). This combination of a resistor and a capacitor is widely used as an elementary form of low-pass filter. The input signal is the applied voltage $v_1(t)$, and the filtered output signal is the voltage $v_2(t)$ appearing across the capacitor. The output terminals are assumed to be open-circuit (in other words, negligible current is drawn from them). We do not need to analyse the filtering properties of the circuit in any detail here. However, we might just note that the two circuit elements form a simple potential-divider. At low enough frequencies the capacitor exhibits high impedance compared with the resistor, so most of $v_1(t)$ is developed across it and appears as output signal. But at high frequencies the capacitor behaves increasingly like a short-circuit, and $v_2(t)$ is very small. This simple argument is adequate to demonstrate the low-pass action of the circuit.

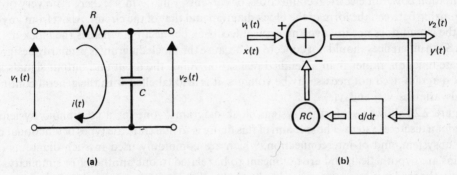

(a)   **(b)**

Figure 2.21 Equivalent circuit and system diagrams.

As our review of continuous AC circuits in section 1.4.2 has made clear, if we are thinking in terms of sinusoidal signals we may use the *j*-notation to analyse such a circuit. The more fundamental approach, however, which applies in principle to any input signal waveform, is to write down *differential equations* to describe the relationships between the various time-varying voltages and currents, and circuit elements. This approach is also valuable in allowing us to derive an equivalent system block diagram. In the present example, the appropriate equations are

$$v_1(t) = Ri(t) + v_2(t) \tag{2.42}$$

and

$$v_2(t) = \frac{1}{C} \int i(t)\, dt$$

or

$$C \frac{dv_2(t)}{dt} = i(t) \tag{2.43}$$

Hence the output signal is related to the input signal by

$$v_2(t) = v_1(t) - Ri(t) = v_1(t) - RC\frac{dv_2(t)}{dt} \tag{2.44}$$

Equation (2.44) may be represented by the block diagram in part (b) of figure 2.21. This shows that $v_2(t)$ equals $v_1(t)$, less the term $RC[dv_2(t)/dt]$ which is obtained by *feedback* of the output through a differentiator block. This is followed by a scaling, or multiplier, block of value RC. The subtraction specified in equation (2.44) is performed by the larger of the two circular blocks. Although widely referred to as an 'adder', it in fact performs addition *or* subtraction, as indicated by the small plus or minus sign next to each of its inputs. The reader should check that this simple block diagram does indeed represent the above differential equations, and therefore completely describes the signal processing action of the circuit.

Once again, we should emphasise that the system block diagram indicates the directions of information flow, not electrical connections or currents. Furthermore, there is no very obvious relationship between the form of the block diagram and that of the circuit. Apart from anything else, the circuit does not involve any explicit feedback connection, whereas the block diagram does. Such differences should not concern us, because the block diagram is primarily designed to indicate function, rather than a detailed realisation. Since the input and output signals in the block diagram need not necessarily be voltages, it is also labelled with the general continuous signal variables $x(t)$ and $y(t)$.

Figure 2.22 shows two further system block diagrams—one for a continuous system, the other for a discrete system. The sole aim of this figure is to illustrate the types of functional block and subsystem, and of interconnection, which are commonly used in such diagrams. Both systems are hypothetical, and are not meant to be related to one another. For simplicity—and because the reader is by now assumed to be able to distinguish between a block diagram and a circuit diagram—we have dispensed with the thick arrows and lines used in previous block diagrams.

The four types of block shown for the continuous system, in part (a) of the figure, are the

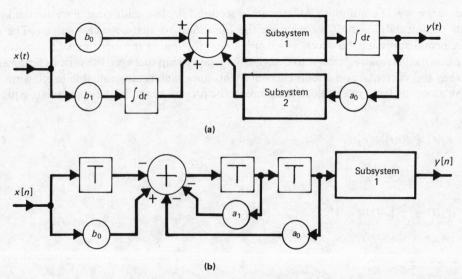

Figure 2.22 Further typical system block diagrams for (a) a continuous linear system, and (b) a discrete linear system.

adder/subtractor, the multiplier (or scaler), the integrator, and the 'subsystem' (subsystems may, in general, be broken down into combinations of the other, more basic, blocks—but it is not always necessary, or desirable, to do so). In our earlier example, shown in figure 2.21, we used a differentiator. This is acceptable in principle, but in practice integrators are generally preferred to differentiators because they are much easier to make. So the differential equations describing a system are normally recast to specify one or more integrations rather than differentiations. This may always be done, and underlines the important point that a given circuit or system has more than one possible block diagram representation. We should also note that both integration and differentiation are linear time-invariant operations, which obey the Principle of Superposition.

A preference for integrators over differentiators, on the basis that they are easier to make, may seem to contradict the earlier assertion that a system block diagram indicates function, rather than a detailed realisation. After all, if the block diagram is not meant to be a circuit diagram, it would not seem to matter whether we could *make* a given block easily or not! However, the truth probably lies somewhere in the middle, because continuous electronic systems *are* occasionally built up in the form of their block diagrams. The classic instance of this is the use of an analog computer to simulate an engineering system such as a vehicle suspension system, or the flight controls of an aircraft. The system under study is first described as a set of differential (or integral) equations. These are next used to create a system block diagram which is set up, block by block, on the analog computer using appropriate wiring connections. Analog computers incorporate devices such as adder/subtractors, multipliers, and integrators—but they generally avoid the use of differentiators. Although they are used a lot less nowadays than digital computers, they do still find occasional valuable application for the simulation and testing of the dynamic performance of systems.

In spite of the occasional use of analog computers for such purposes, we must be careful not to assume that they generally offer a sensible way of building up, or synthesising, a continuous electronic system. For example, the simple low-pass filter of figure 2.21(a) may be cheaply made from one resistor and one capacitor; it would hardly make sense to use an analog computer instead!

We now turn to part (b) of figure 2.22. This shows that the block diagram of a discrete linear system comprises adder/subtractors, multipliers (or scalers), subsystems, and time-delay elements. The latter type of block causes a discrete signal delivered to its input to be delayed by exactly one sampling interval (T). It takes the place of the differentiator (or integrator) in the continuous system block diagram. Just as the block diagram of a continuous system represents, in effect, the differential equations of the system, so the block diagram of a discrete system represents the corresponding *difference equations* of the system. Although the reader is probably unfamiliar with difference equations at present, we will have more to say about them in the next chapter.

Once again, the block diagram of figure 2.22(b) is primarily designed to show information flow rather than a detailed realisation of the discrete system. However, such systems, when made up using electronic hardware, do commonly involve digital circuits which are clearly identifiable as adder/subtractors, multipliers, and delay or memory elements. In this sense, therefore, the block diagram of a discrete system often bears a more obvious resemblance to its practical circuit realisation than is the case with most continuous, or analog, systems. An important exception is when the discrete system is implemented by programming a general-purpose digital computer or microprocessor. In this case it may be hard to discern the equivalence between the block diagram and the program software.

We should note a few additional features of the block diagrams shown in figure 2.22. Blocks are sometimes placed in series, or *cascade* (for example, the multiplier b_1 and the left-hand integrator in the upper diagram; two delay elements and subsystem 1 in the lower diagram). Sometimes they are placed in *parallel*, with a common input signal (for example, the two left-hand blocks in the lower diagram). Quite often there is *feedback* from output to input, or from a 'later' point in the system to an 'earlier' one (for example, the path including the multiplier a_0 and subsystem 2 in the upper diagram). In the case of parallel or feedback connections, an adder/subtractor block is normally required to combine two or more signals appropriately.

The reader who is clear about the ideas and terminology introduced in this section should have no difficulty in distinguishing between circuit and block diagrams, or in understanding the relationships between them. Although we have so far given only one simple case of a block diagram representing a practical circuit or system, there will be further examples in later chapters.

Problems to chapter 2

Section 2.2.1

Q2.1.   Figure Q2.1 shows a continuous signal $x(t)$. Sketch and label carefully the following signals

   (a) $x(t - 1)$
   (b) $x(3 - t)$
   (c) $x(2t)$
   (d) $x(t + 2) u(t)$
   (e) $x(t) u(2 - t)$.

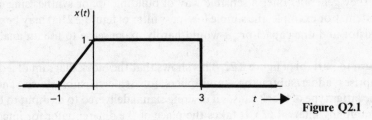

Figure Q2.1

Q2.2   Figure Q2.2 shows a discrete signal $x[n]$. Sketch and label carefully the following signals

   (a) $x[n - 3]$
   (b) $x[2 - n]$
   (c) $x[n - 1] u[n - 2]$
   (d) $x[1 - n] \delta[n - 2]$.

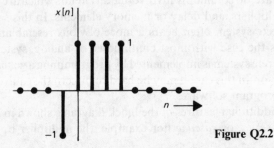

Figure Q2.2

Q2.3. Determine and sketch carefully the even and odd parts of the signals shown in figure Q2.3.

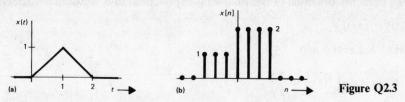

Figure Q2.3

Q2.4. If $x_1[n]$ is an even signal and $x_2[n]$ is an odd signal, show that

(a) $\{x_1[n]x_2[n]\}$ is an odd signal

(b) $\{x_2[n]\}^2$ is an even signal

(c) $\displaystyle\sum_{n=-\infty}^{\infty} x_2[n] = 0$.

Section 2.2.2

Q2.5. Under what circumstances, if any, would the continuous functions shown in figure Q2.5 be expected to behave like the unit impulse function $\delta(t)$?

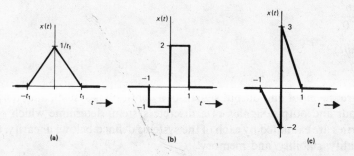

Figure Q2.5

Q2.6. Write down mathematical expressions for the various step, impulse, and ramp signals shown in figure Q2.6.

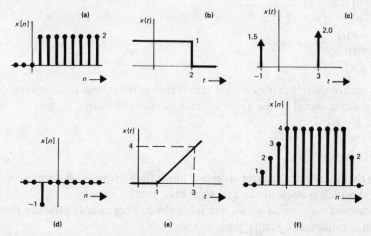

Figure Q2.6

Section 2.2.3

Q2.7.   Sketch carefully portions of the following exponential and sinusoidal signals

(a) $x(t) = \exp(t - 1)$

(b) $x[n] = 2 \exp(-n/2)$

(c) $x(t) = A \sin\left(100\pi t + \dfrac{\pi}{2}\right)$

(d) $x[n] = \cos \dfrac{\pi n}{6}$

(e) $x[n] = \exp(-n) \sin \dfrac{\pi n}{2}.$

Q2.8.   Determine whether or not each of the following signals is strictly periodic (that is, repetitive). If it is periodic, find its period.

(a) $x(t) = \sin\left(4t + \dfrac{\pi}{2}\right)$

(b) $x[n] = \sin \dfrac{\pi n}{7}$

(c) $x[n] = \cos \dfrac{\pi n^2}{10}$

(d) $x(t) = \cos(t)u(t).$

Sections 2.3.1 and 2.3.2

Q2.9.   If $x(t)$ and $y(t)$ are the input and output signals of a continuous system, and $x[n]$ and $y[n]$ are the input and output signals of a discrete system, determine which of the following properties are exhibited by each of the systems defined below: linearity, time-invariance, causality, stability, and memory.

(a) $y[n] = x[2 - n]$
(b) $y(t) = \cos(2\pi t)x(t)$
(c) $y[n] = x[n]x[n - 1]$
(d) $y[n] = x[n] + x[n - 1]$
(e) $y(t) = 3 - x(t)$
(f) $y(t) = \exp(t)x(t)$
(g) $y[n] = nx[n].$

Q2.10. Determine which of the following systems are invertible. If a system is not invertible, find two values of input signal to the system which produce the same output.
(a) $y[n] = x[2 - n]$
(b) $y(t) = \sin(x(t))$
(c) $y[n] = x[n]x[n - 1].$

Q2.11. (a) Why does the cascade connection of several linear time-invariant systems produce an overall system which is itself linear and time-invariant?
(b) Does the cascade connection of two nonlinear systems necessarily produce an overall system which is nonlinear? Justify your answer.

Section 2.3.3

Q2.12. Construct a system block diagram which is equivalent to the continuous circuit shown in figure Q2.12. If your diagram specifies differentiators, recast it in an equivalent form which uses integrators.

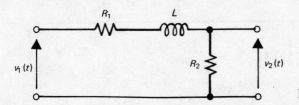

Figure Q2.12

Q2.13. Figure Q2.13 shows the block diagram of a discrete system. Assuming that $y[n] = 0$ for $n < 0$, sketch the output from the system when the input is (a) the discrete unit impulse function $\delta[n]$, and (b) the discrete unit step function $u[n]$.

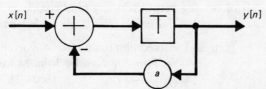

Figure Q2.13

3 Convolution

"**Convolution,** *n.* Coiling, twisting; fold, twist."
"**Convolvulus,** *n.* kinds of twining plant including bindweed."

The Concise Oxford Dictionary

"Then Satan first knew pain, and writhed him to and fro convolved."

in *Paradise Lost* by John Milton
(1608–1674)

3.1 Introduction

Convolution is a key operation in the analysis of signals and systems. Its technical meaning ties in well with normal English usage, defined by the first of our quotations: a kind of "coiling or twisting." In the present context, the main value of convolution is in allowing us to evaluate, or predict, the output signal from a linear time-invariant (LTI) system, given the form of its input signal. This is done by *convolving* the input signal function with a second function representing the system. As we shall see, this second function is the response of the system to a unit impulse, known as its *impulse response.*

When the output signal of an LTI system is derived by convolution, the operation takes place entirely in the *time-domain.* We represent both the input signal and the system by time functions, and convolve them to produce a third time function—the output signal. This is in contrast to so-called frequency-domain methods, in which the output signal is obtained by considering the system's response to the various *frequencies* present in the input (such methods provide the material for chapters 4 and 5). The convolution approach does not consider frequencies, but works in terms of time-domain impulses and impulse responses.

Convolution has traditionally been taught only in the later stages of degree courses in electronic and electrical engineering, because the "coiling or twisting" involved, when applied to continuous signals and systems, is neither mathematically simple nor particularly easy to visualise. In previous years many teachers and students of engineering, as well as practising engineers, would probably have echoed John Milton's assumption that convolution is associated with a certain amount of pain! Therefore frequency-domain methods, one of whose main advantages is that *convolution* is replaced by *multiplication*, have generally been tackled first. The situation has now been changed, however, by the increasingly widespread introduction of discrete signals and systems. Convolution in discrete-time is straightforward. Moreover, if one understands it well, one can go on to consider the continuous-time case with confidence.

As we shall see, time-domain convolution is really no more than a form of superposition. It makes use of the fact that *any* input signal may be considered as the summation of a number of weighted impulse functions. Since any LTI system obeys the Principle of Superposition, its output waveform must equal the summation of its responses to all such individual input impulses. This brief account of the convolution method shows that, before we can go into further detail, we need to develop two subsidiary themes. These are the characterisation of a signal by a set of impulses, and the manner in which an LTI system responds to an individual impulse.

3.2 Describing signals by impulse functions

The continuous unit impulse function $\delta(t)$, and its discrete-time counterpart $\delta[n]$, have already been described in section 2.2.2, together with the step and ramp functions which are closely related to them. Our main purpose in this section is to show how a summation of impulse functions may be used to build up *any* continuous or discrete signal.

We start with the discrete case because it is rather simpler. Suppose we have a general signal $x[n]$, a portion of which is shown in part (a) of figure 3.1. Clearly, this may be considered as the summation of the more basic signals shown below in parts (b) to (f) of the figure. Each of these is a unit impulse which has been *weighted* by the relevant value of $x[n]$, and *shifted* so as to occur at the appropriate instant. Its mathematical description is simple. For example, the signal shown in part (b) of the figure is $x[-2]\delta[n + 2]$. Hence we may write the complete signal $x[n]$ in the form

$$x[n] = \ldots + x[-2]\delta[n + 2] + x[-1]\delta[n + 1] + x[0]\delta[n]$$
$$+ x[1]\delta[n - 1] + x[2]\delta[n - 2] + \ldots \tag{3.1}$$

or

$$x[n] = \sum_{k = -\infty}^{+\infty} x[k]\delta[n - k] \tag{3.2}$$

Note that, for any value of n, only one of the terms on the right-hand side of equation (3.1) is nonzero. Also, since the integer k in equation (3.2) takes on a complete range of values between $\pm\infty$, $x[n]$ may be thought of as a completely general discrete-time signal (of course, if $x[n]$ is in fact zero for negative values of n, we may limit k to the range 0 to ∞, and so on).

This is a good moment to note that equation (3.2) demonstrates an important characteristic of the discrete unit impulse—its so-called *sifting property*. If we choose a particular value of n, such as $n = 5$, we obtain

$$x[5] = \sum_{k = -\infty}^{\infty} x[k]\delta[5 - k] \tag{3.3}$$

Now $\delta[5 - k]$ is nonzero only for $k = 5$, when it equals unity. So the product $x[k]\delta[5 - k]$ is likewise only nonzero for $k = 5$, when it has the value $x[5]$. We therefore see that equation (3.3)

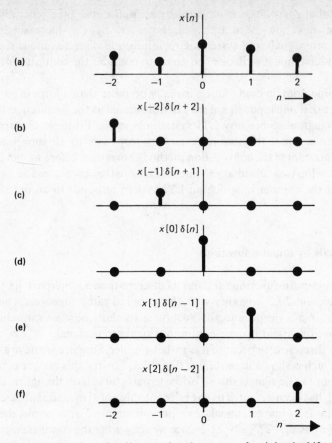

Figure 3.1 The representation of a discrete signal as a set of weighted, shifted, unit impulses.

represents the ability of the unit impulse function to select out, or *sift*, the particular value of $x[n]$ which coincides with it. This is a valuable property which we shall meet again later.

We now turn to the analogous problem in continuous time: how to represent any signal as the summation of a set of weighted, shifted, impulse functions. Figure 3.2 shows part of a continuous signal $x(t)$, plus an approximation to it formed by a contiguous set of narrow pulses. Each of these has width t_0 and a height equal to the value of the signal at the appropriate instant. In order to describe this approximation mathematically, let us define a standard pulse of width t_0,

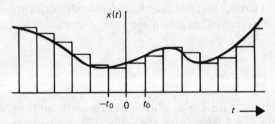

Figure 3.2 Approximating a continuous signal by a contiguous set of narrow pulses.

height $1/t_0$, and hence unit area

$$\delta_0(t) = \frac{1}{t_0}, \qquad 0 < t < t_0 \tag{3.4}$$

$$= 0, \qquad \text{elsewhere}$$

The approximation may be described as the summation of a large number of these standard pulses, each *weighted* according to the appropriate value of $x(t)$, and *shifted* to occur at the correct time. This summation is

$$\sum_{k=-\infty}^{\infty} \{t_0 x(kt_0)\} \delta_0(t - kt_0) \tag{3.5}$$

Note that each signal value $x(kt_0)$ must be multiplied by t_0 because the height of the standard pulse is $1/t_0$ rather than unity.

We next allow the width t_0 of the standard pulse to tend to zero. Let us write it as $d\tau$. As this happens, the pulse, still with an area of unity, tends to the true continuous unit impulse function. Furthermore, the discrete steps along the time axis (denoted by kt_0 in expression (3.5)) become vanishingly small. We may therefore write kt_0 as a continuous variable τ. In the limit we use an infinitely large number of impulse functions, and represent the signal $x(t)$ with perfect accuracy. The summation in expression (3.5) then becomes an integration, so that

$$x(t) = \int_{-\infty}^{\infty} \{d\tau x(\tau)\} \delta(t - \tau) = \int_{-\infty}^{\infty} x(\tau) \delta(t - \tau) \, d\tau \tag{3.6}$$

This equation is the continuous-time counterpart of equation (3.2) in discrete-time. Note that, just as k is a 'dummy' integer variable in equation (3.2), so τ is a 'dummy' continuous variable in equation (3.6), disappearing when the limits of integration are inserted. Equation (3.6) is certainly rather harder to derive and visualise than equation (3.2), but its interpretation is essentially the same. Any signal may be considered as a continuing sequence of weighted impulse functions. It is a very important result.

Equation (3.6) also represents the sifting property of the continuous unit impulse. For example, let us put $t = 0$, giving

$$x(0) = \int_{-\infty}^{\infty} x(\tau) \delta(\tau) \, d\tau \tag{3.7}$$

Now $\delta(\tau)$ represents an impulse of unit area concentrated at $\tau = 0$. So the product $\{x(\tau)\delta(\tau)\}$ represents a weighted impulse, also at $\tau = 0$, with an area equal to $x(0)$. Integration over all τ is equivalent to measuring the total area under the curve, which is just $x(0)$. So, once again, the unit impulse has selected out, or sifted, the value of $x(t)$ which is coincident with it.

The sifting property is a good illustration of the fact that the continuous unit impulse $\delta(t)$ is defined in terms of its properties, rather than its waveform. In section 2.2.2 we pointed out that $\delta(t)$—and other functions which display sudden discontinuities—are collectively known as singularity functions. Unlike most continuous signals, which have a particular value for each value of the independent variable, $\delta(t)$ has an undefined waveform. It is a narrow pulse, or 'spike', occurring at a known instant and possessing *unit area*. We now see that another of its properties is the ability to *sift* a particular value of another signal which is coincident with it.

Although we have included some comments on the sifting properties of unit impulses, the reader is asked to focus on the main results of this section. These are the description of discrete and continuous signals by sets of weighted impulses, as defined by equations (3.2) and (3.6).

3.3 **Impulse and step responses of linear systems**

Time-domain convolution involves the representation of an input signal by a series of weighted, shifted impulses. Each individual impulse gives rise to a response at the system output, and we find the total response—equal to the output signal—by superposition. Our next task is therefore to examine the nature of the response of an LTI system to an input impulse. We shall also consider its response to a unit step, since the impulse response and step response are very closely related.

Before getting down to detail, it is helpful to discuss some general aspects of the problem. Let us start by returning to the analogy of a golf club striking a golf ball, first mentioned in section 2.2.2. The blow delivered by the club is extremely short in duration, and approximates to an ideal mechanical impulse. This 'input signal' causes a rapid initial transfer of kinetic energy from the club to the ball, but thereafter the ball is *on its own*. Its flight, or 'response', is not further affected by the club, but only by the properties of the system. In this case, these would include the laws of motion and of gravity, air resistance, and so on. Therefore when once the initial energy transfer has taken place, the response is essentially *characteristic of the system* rather than of the input signal. In a similar way, if the blade of a kitchen knife is held firmly on a table with the handle overhanging the edge and the handle is given a sharp knock, the knife will vibrate rapidly up and down, displaying a decaying oscillation. This oscillation is effectively the response of the mechanical system to an input impulse. It is characteristic of the system rather than of the blow which causes it. The strength of the knock, or impulse, determines the overall amplitude, or scale, of the response, but not its detailed waveshape.

The mechanical examples described above are not strictly linear, because they include effects such as air resistance and friction. The insights they give into the nature of an impulse response are nevertheless valuable. When we consider an electronic or electrical system, very much the same ideas apply. An impulse, delivered as an input signal, excites a response which is determined by the system's properties. Furthermore, it may be shown that the impulse response of an LTI system—defined as its response to a *unit* impulse—is completely characteristic of the system. That is to say, the impulse response gives us *complete information* about the input–output properties of the system. We may use this to calculate its response to any input. Of course, since we have already shown that any input signal may be described as a set of weighted, shifted impulses, and since we know that any LTI system obeys the Principle of Superposition, this result is not particularly surprising.

The idea of an impulse response is further developed in figure 3.3. This figure indicates some general aspects of impulse response waveforms, and relates them to some of the properties of signals and systems we have already met in chapter 2. Part (a) of the figure summarises the generation of an impulse response by a continuous system. A unit impulse $\delta(t)$ occurring at $t = 0$ is delivered to its input, and produces an output signal $h(t)$. This is, by definition, the system's impulse response. In this example $h(t)$ is a decaying exponential waveform, and we shall see later that this is characteristic of a simple low-pass filter. Figure 3.3(b) shows the analogous situation in discrete-time, with a unit impulse $\delta[n]$ forming the input to the system and giving rise to an impulse response $h[n]$.

The remaining parts of figure 3.3 show more examples of impulse response waveforms. That in part (c) is itself an impulse at $t = 0$, so the continuous system it represents contains no memory or energy-storage elements. This is characteristic of a purely resistive system or circuit. The discrete impulse response in (d) is again a weighted impulse, but shifted to occur at $n = 3$. The system must therefore be a pure-delay network or element, which weights any input signal delivered to it and delays it by 3 sampling intervals.

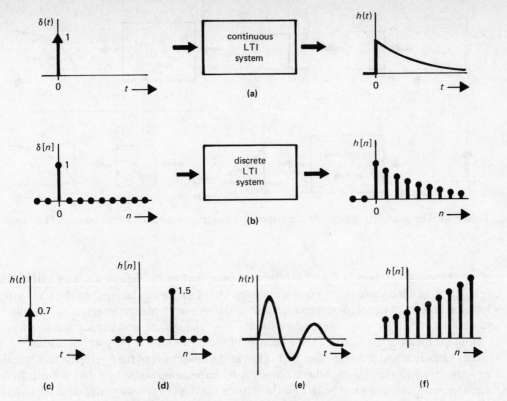

Figure 3.3 Impulse responses of LTI systems.

In practice, most useful electronic systems have rather more complicated impulse responses than these. For example, the one in part (e) takes the form of a decaying oscillation, and might well represent a tuned *RLC* circuit or a continuous bandpass filter. This may be explained by recalling that any impulse response reflects the *characteristic, or natural, behaviour of a system on its own*. If it contains a marked periodic oscillation at some frequency—say f_1 Hz—then it is clear that the system tends to exhibit this frequency if given the chance. Therefore it should cause no surprise if such a system, when receiving an input signal which contains many different sinusoidal frequencies, tends to transmit strongly only those in the region of f_1 Hz. In this intuitive way, we begin to see that there must be a connection between the impulse response of a system and its response to different sinusoidal frequencies. The precise nature of this connection is developed in the next chapter.

All the above impulse responses start at or after $t = 0$ (or $n = 0$), and therefore represent causal systems. Furthermore, the responses are all finite and bounded, so the systems are stable. For the sake of completeness, we illustrate the impulse response of a noncausal, unstable system in figure 3.3(f). The response begins before $n = 0$, and grows without limit as n increases. Such a system is unlikely to be encountered in practice!

We next consider the close relationship between a system's impulse response and its step response. The latter is, by definition, equal to its output signal when the input is a *unit* step. Since the continuous unit step $u(t)$ is the running integral of the unit impulse $\delta(t)$, and the discrete unit step $u[n]$ is the running sum of the unit impulse $\delta[n]$, it may come as no surprise that the responses of LTI systems to unit steps and impulses are similarly related. This is illustrated for a

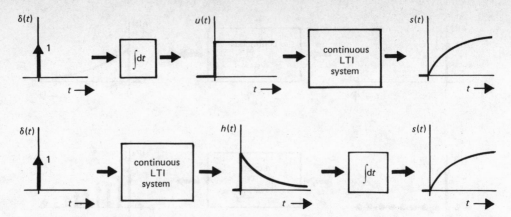

Figure 3.4 The relationship between the impulse and step responses of a continuous LTI system.

typical continuous system in figure 3.4. In the upper part of the figure, we start with a unit impulse $\delta(t)$, and integrate it to obtain a unit step $u(t)$. This forms the input to the LTI system which has an output equal to its step response $s(t)$. However, since the integrator is also linear and time-invariant, we may interchange the order of the system and the integrator without affecting the final output signal. This is because of the commutative property of cascaded LTI systems, already discussed in section 2.3.1. Thus in the lower part of the figure, the unit impulse forms the input to the system, whose output is its impulse response $h(t)$. $h(t)$ is fed into the integrator, whose output must be $s(t)$. So the step response is the running integral of the impulse response. As an alternative, we may view the impulse response as the differential of the step response

$$h(t) = \frac{\mathrm{d}}{\mathrm{d}t} s(t) \tag{3.8}$$

In an analogous way, the step response $s[n]$ of a discrete system is the running sum of its impulse response $h[n]$. Alternatively, the impulse response is the first-order difference of the step response

$$h[n] = s[n] - s[n-1] \tag{3.9}$$

Before ending this section, we should consider why step responses are important. There are several reasons. Firstly, although the process of time-domain convolution is normally defined in terms of a system's impulse response, there is an alternative approach based upon the step response. This method (referred to, in the continuous case, by the term *Duhamel integral*) considers the input signal as the superposition of a number of weighted, shifted *step* functions. Not surprisingly, it is closely related to the more common convolution based upon impulse functions, which we develop and use in this book. A second reason for the importance of step responses is that they are sometimes easier to visualise, or determine, than impulse responses. For example, it is often simpler to deduce the step response than the impulse response of a continuous RC circuit. The impulse response may then be found by differentiation. We shall meet an example of this a little later. Finally, step responses are important in their own right because step signals often arise in practice: for example, as test signals, when switches are closed in DC circuits, or in the form of pulses or pulse sequences.

3.4 Discrete-time convolution

The necessary groundwork has now been covered, and we may straightaway demonstrate discrete-time convolution by a simple example. Suppose we have an input signal $x[n]$ composed of just four nonzero sample values, as illustrated by figure 3.5(a). We also have a discrete LTI system with the impulse response $h[n]$ shown in figure 3.5(b). In part (c) of the figure, $x[n]$ is decomposed into a set of weighted, shifted impulses. Each of these generates its own version of the system's impulse response. Note carefully how each version is weighted in accordance with the value of $x[n]$ which causes it, and shifted so as to begin at the appropriate instant. The output signal $y[n]$ from the system is found by superposition of all these individual responses, and is shown at the bottom of the figure. Convolution of the input signal $x[n]$ and the impulse response $h[n]$ has been effected.

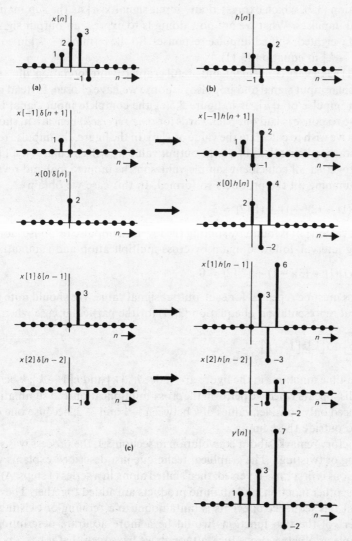

Figure 3.5 Discrete-time convolution.

In most practical cases there would be many more finite sample values in $x[n]$, and probably also more in $h[n]$, and we would therefore have to superpose many more individual responses to find the output signal. In the most general case, we may write

$$y[n] = \ldots + x[-2]h[n+2] + x[-1]h[n+1] + x[0]h[n]$$

$$+ x[1]h[n-1] + x[2]h[n-2] + \ldots \tag{3.10}$$

or

$$y[n] = \sum_{k=-\infty}^{\infty} x[k]h[n-k] \tag{3.11}$$

The last equation is very important, and is known as the *convolution sum*. Note its similarity with the earlier equation (3.2), which expressed any input signal $x[n]$ as the summation of a set of weighted, shifted impulses. What we are now doing is to express an output signal $y[n]$ as an equivalent set of weighted, shifted impulse responses. So the term $\delta[n-k]$ in equation (3.2) is replaced by $h[n-k]$ in equation (3.11).

Equation (3.11) has a very convenient and useful graphical interpretation, illustrated in figure 3.6 for the particular input signal and impulse response we have chosen. Instead of considering each constituent impulse of $x[n]$, as in figure 3.5(c), the complete input signal is now drawn. Next, the impulse response is laid out backwards (or *time-reversed*) beneath it, starting from the instant for which we wish to calculate the value of $y[n]$. In the figure, the impulse response is laid out backwards starting beneath $x[1]$, so the output value we will calculate is $y[1]$. This is done by multiplying together all coincident sample values in the input signal and reversed impulse response, and summing all the products so formed. In this case we obtain

$$y[1] = (3)(1) + (2)(-1) + (1)(2) = 3$$

The *next* output value $y[2]$ is found by shifting the reversed impulse response along to the right by one sampling interval, followed again by cross-multiplication and summation. Thus

$$y[2] = (-1)(1) + (3)(-1) + (2)(2) = 0$$

The same process must be repeated for each output signal value. We should note that figure 3.6 is just a graphical representation of equation (3.11) for the particular case when $n = 1$, that is

$$y[1] = \sum_{k=-\infty}^{\infty} x[k]h[1-k] \tag{3.12}$$

The two discrete-time functions in the figure are, indeed, $x[k]$ and $h[1-k]$, k being a 'dummy' variable which disappears when we perform the cross-multiplication and summation. Of course, in this case we need only consider values of k between -1 and $+2$, because one or both of the functions is zero outside these limits.

In the introductory remarks about convolution in section 3.1, the process was said to involve a kind of "coiling or twisting." The graphical technique just described explains why this is so. One of the functions is first time-reversed, then shifted along in a series of steps. At each step it is multiplied by the other function, and all finite products are added together. The reader may or may not feel that this sequence of events is tantamount to a "coiling or twisting"—perhaps a "rolling together" of the two functions would be a more accurate description. It is not a particularly simple or obvious procedure, although we have seen that it has a perfectly logical and straightforward explanation.

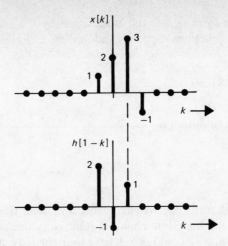

Figure 3.6 The graphical interpretation of the convolution sum.

This is also a good point to mention that the process of convolution is often denoted by an asterisk, and is commutative. Thus the convolution of $x[n]$ with $h[n]$ is written as $x[n]*h[n]$, and produces the same result as the convolution $h[n]*x[n]$. This may be quite easily demonstrated by reference to figure 3.7, which is identical to figure 3.6 except that the integer variable k is defined differently. It is now measured 'back into the past' from the instant for which we wish to calculate the output. Thus $k = 0$ coincides with the origin of the reversed impulse response, and k increases towards the *left-hand* side of the diagram. Therefore the reversed

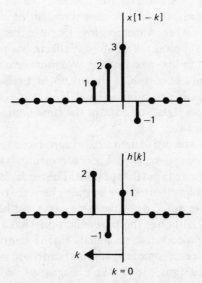

Figure 3.7 An alternative interpretation of the convolution sum, in which the integer variable k is measured 'back into the past' from the instant for which the output signal is to be calculated.

impulse response is now given by $h[k]$, and the input signal by $x[1 - k]$. The output $y[1]$ is found by multiplying the two functions together, and adding all finite products, as before

$$y[1] = \sum_{k=-\infty}^{\infty} h[k]x[1 - k] \qquad (3.13)$$

and in general we may write the output as

$$y[n] = \sum_{k=-\infty}^{\infty} h[k]x[n - k] \qquad (3.14)$$

The last result, equation (3.14), is the one we shall generally use in this text. It is identical to equation (3.11) except that x and h are interchanged. (One consequence is that the graphical procedure shown in figures 3.6 and 3.7 could as well have been carried out by reversing the input signal beneath the impulse response, rather than vice versa. The result would have been the same. However, to avoid confusion in this text, we will standardise by always reversing the impulse response.) Note also that, once again, the limits of k may generally be reduced in practice.

The graphical interpretation of convolution can provide some valuable insights into the behaviour of practical LTI systems. However, the simple forms of input signal and impulse response we have so far used to illustrate the basic idea of convolution are not really suitable for developing such insights. We need a more realistic input signal, and an impulse response which represents a more obviously useful system. We therefore next turn our attention to a very practical problem—that of *digital filtering* a discrete signal.

The particular problem we investigate is the low-pass filtering of the type of discrete signal previously shown in the top part of figure 2.2. This represents the variations in midday temperature at a certain place over a two-month period. Remember that such a signal will generally contain a mixture of sinusoidal frequencies—the lowest ones representing slow fluctuations or long-term trends, the higher ones representing day-to-day variations due to more rapid changes in the weather. A meteorologist or weather forecaster may well wish to *smooth* the signal, in order to suppress the day-to-day effects, but preserve the long-term trends. Such smoothing is equivalent to low-pass filtering. We must be careful not to get too involved here in a discussion of frequencies because, as already noted, time-domain convolution pays no direct attention to the frequencies present in a signal. However, these brief comments are made just to show that smoothing a signal or data in the time-domain is equivalent to low-pass filtering in the frequency-domain.

A portion of the temperature record of figure 2.2 is reproduced to a larger scale in figure 3.8(a). Its origin has been changed, for convenience. There are various ways in which such data might be smoothed to reduce their more rapid fluctuations. The reader is perhaps tempted to suggest that we use a pencil, and draw a smooth curve by eye! There are two main objections to such a method. Firstly, no two people would draw the same curve, neither could they explain exactly what they had done. Secondly, although this particular signal has a sampling period of 24 hours, we often need to smooth or process discrete signals having sampling periods of milliseconds, microseconds, or less. In such cases some fast, automatic method is clearly required. A common method of smoothing discrete signals is to take a *moving average*. Each sample value in the original signal $x[n]$ is replaced by a smoothed value $y[n]$, which is calculated by taking the *average* of $x[n]$ and a number of values to either side of it. In the present example, suppose we

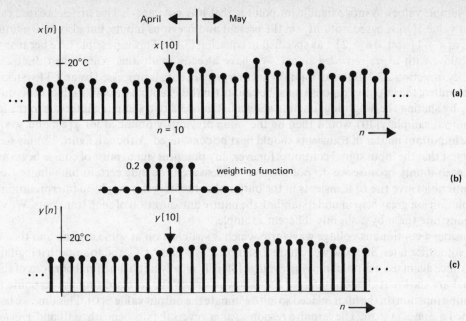

Figure 3.8 A moving-average filter applied to the smoothing of a discrete signal.

take a '5-point' moving average. In other words, each smoothed sample value $y[n]$ is found as the average of $x[n]$ and two values to either side of it

$$y[n] = \tfrac{1}{5}\{x[n+2] + x[n+1] + x[n] + x[n-1] + x[n-2]\} \qquad (3.15)$$

or

$$y[n] = 0.2x[n+2] + 0.2x[n+1] + 0.2x[n] + 0.2x[n-1] + 0.2x[n-2]\ldots \qquad (3.16)$$

Equation (3.16) shows that each output value $y[n]$ equals a weighted sum of 5 consecutive input values, the weights all being equal to 0.2 in this case.

The moving average process defined by equation (3.16) is illustrated graphically in part (b) of figure 3.8, for the particular case $n = 10$. The input signal must be multiplied by the *weighting function* shown, and all finite products added together to give the corresponding smoothed value $y[10]$. The weighting function shown in part (b) is then moved along step-by-step. At each step the multiplication and summation are repeated, generating the complete output signal $y[n]$ shown in part (c) of the figure.

It is not difficult to appreciate why $y[n]$ is a smoothed version of $x[n]$. Since any one input sample value contributes only 20 per cent of the value of any one output, rapid fluctuations between adjacent input values tend to be 'ironed out'. Clearly, this effect would be more pronounced if we were to average over more input samples. However, if we averaged over *too* many, we would 'iron out' the slower fluctuations, or trends, in the input signal as well.

The reader may have noticed that the process just described is identical to time-domain convolution. The weighting function used to calculate the moving average of $x[n]$ behaves just like an impulse response. This important conclusion means that we could smooth $x[n]$ automatically, by passing it into a discrete LTI system with an impulse response identical to a time-reversed version of the weighting function shown in figure 3.8(b). Actually in this particular case time-reversal makes no difference because the impulse response is symmetrical, with 5 equal sample values. A more significant point is that it is not causal. This arises because each output value $y[n]$ is based not only on the present and previous inputs, but also on the future inputs $x[n + 1]$ and $x[n + 2]$—as specified in equation (3.16). This is possible here because we are dealing with a *pre-recorded* signal. We have already made this point when discussing causality in section 2.3.2. But if an input signal or a piece of data is processed by an LTI system as it is generated, the impulse response must be causal. (In this example we could achieve this quite simply by shifting the weighting function shown in figure 3.8 two sampling intervals to the left. The output sample $y[10]$ would then be the value previously obtained for $y[8]$, and so on.)

The important matter of transients should next be considered. Although figure 3.8 may seem to suggest that the input signal continues for ever, any practical signal must of course begin and end—even if only because we do not observe or measure it outside certain time limits. Such discontinuities give rise to transients in the output. Fortunately the graphical interpretation of convolution is a great help in understanding the nature and duration of such transients. We will now illustrate these by a slightly different example.

Consider a continuous voltage waveform which is switched on at some instant, and then off again some time later. Suppose we require to sample it using an ADC, and to smooth it digitally. Let us once again use a 5-point moving average filter. Typically initial and final portions of such a signal are shown at the top of figure 3.9. Below is shown the reversed impulse response (or weighting function) of the filter, placed so as to estimate the output value $y[0]$. This time we have assumed a *causal* system. The impulse response, after reversal, falls beneath $x[0]$ and *previous* values of x only. Now since the input signal has been zero before $n = 0$, it is clear that the first few values of y (specifically, $y[0]$ to $y[4]$ inclusive) represent a start-up transient as the impulse response 'moves into' the input data. The transient is labelled (A) at the bottom of the figure and lasts for 5 sampling intervals. This is the duration of the impulse response. When once the impulse response has 'moved fully into' the input signal, the output $y[n]$ settles to what might be

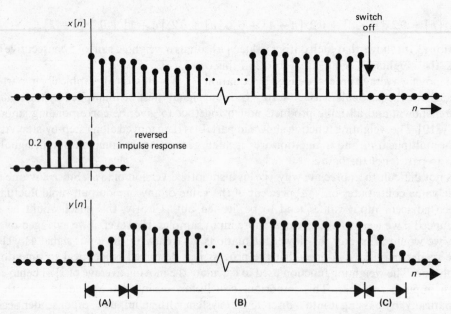

Figure 3.9 The generation of transients at the output of a LTI system, as a result of discontinuities in its input signal.

termed its true response, reflecting the slow trends in $x[n]$. This occurs during phase (B) of the waveform. Later, the input signal is switched off again, and its sample values suddenly drop to zero. This gives rise to a further output transient, labelled (C), as the impulse response 'moves out of' the input data. Once again, it has the same duration as the impulse response.

Essentially, such transients arise because the system possesses memory. When the input is first switched on, the system 'remembers' that it was recently zero. When the input is switched off again, the system 'remembers' that it was recently finite. We must therefore view such transients as an entirely necessary consequence of processing a *time-limited signal* with an LTI system *possessing memory*. They last for as long as the system memory lasts. This is an important insight which is neatly illustrated by the graphical interpretation of convolution. Of course, the shapes of such transients depend upon the particular form of the system's impulse response, and on the initial and final portions of the input signal. They are not necessarily ramp-like, as in this example.

Having covered some of the most important basic aspects of the convolution sum, it is time to consider how we might actually implement it using a discrete-time system. Once again, we may conveniently use the moving-average filter as an example. Returning to figure 3.9, it is clear that each output value of this *causal* version of the filter is given by

$$y[n] = \tfrac{1}{5}\{x[n] + x[n-1] + x[n-2] + x[n-3] + x[n-4]\} \tag{3.17}$$

A block diagram for implementing this system in electronic hardware is shown in figure 3.10. Four delay units are needed, each providing a delay of one sampling interval (T). The various outputs are added together, and scaled by a multiplier unit, to produce $y[n]$. It is quite simple to see that if a discrete unit impulse $\delta[n]$ is input on the left-hand side, the output signal is the required impulse response. Such a system is normally controlled by a master clock. Each time a new input value $x[n]$ is delivered on the input side—perhaps by an analog-to-digital converter (ADC)—previous inputs are moved one stage along the 'delay line'. The sample value $x[n-4]$ is lost. Remember that all samples are normally represented by a binary code between, say, 6 and 16 bits long, and that all the system blocks shown in figure 3.10 must handle these multibit codes. The processed signal $y[n]$ may be delivered to a digital-to-analog converter (DAC), if the digital processing is complete and a continuous output is required.

As an alternative to implementing the system with electronic hardware, a general-purpose digital computer or microprocessor could be programmed to execute equation (3.17). In principle, the computer could either work with a *pre-recorded* input signal, or it could work *on-line*. The term on-line implies that the input signal is provided directly via an ADC, and that the

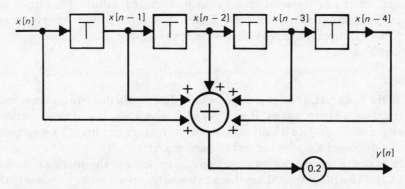

Figure 3.10 System block diagram for a 5-term discrete moving-average filter.

computer generates a new output sample every time an input sample is delivered. Clearly, this requires a computer fast enough to perform the set of arithmetic operations defined by equation (3.17) in less than one sampling interval, *T*. Cheap general-purpose computers are generally *serial* machines, which can perform only one operation at a time. They are therefore rather slow. If sampling rates above, say, a few tens of kilohertz are required, it is normally necessary to use special-purpose electronic hardware, as illustrated in figure 3.10.

Assuming for the moment that operating speed is not a problem, let us consider how a general-purpose computer may be programmed in BASIC to act as the required moving-average filter. In program no. 1, 250 input signal values are loaded into array X, and the filtered output is stored in array Y. For demonstration purposes it is convenient to use a set of random numbers for the input signal. This allows the smoothing action of the filter to be clearly seen. The BASIC instruction RND is therefore used in line 150 of the program. The random numbers lie in the range 0 to 1. The essential program feature is an iterative loop, which implements equation (3.17) over and over again for different values of N (program lines 180 to 200). We start with $N = 5$, to avoid over-running the input array when the term $X(N - 4)$ is used.

```
100 REM ***   PROGRAM NO.1       MOVING-AVERAGE LOW-PASS FILTER   **
110 REM
120 DIM X(250),Y(250)
130 REM
140 REM **  LOAD INPUT ARRAY WITH RANDOM NUMBERS IN RANGE 0-1   **
150 FOR J=1 TO 250:X(J)=RND:NEXT J
160 REM
170 REM *************  FIND OUTPUT BY CONVOLUTION  *************
180 FOR N=5 TO 250
190 Y(N)=0.2*(X(N)+X(N-1)+X(N-2)+X(N-3)+X(N-4))
200 NEXT N
210 REM
220 REM *****  PLOT OPTION          (INPUT ABOVE,OUTPUT BELOW) ****
230 CLS:FOR K=5 TO 250:PLOT 2*K,200:DRAW 2*K,200+X(K)*150
240 PLOT 2*K,1:DRAW 2*K,1+Y(K)*150:NEXT K
250 REM
260 REM ***  PRINT OPTION      (PAIRS OF INPUT/OUTPUT VALUES)  ***
270 FOR K=5 TO 250:PRINT X(K),Y(K):NEXT K
280 REM *********************************************************
```

We therefore see that a discrete LTI system may in principle be realised in either hardware or software. The two approaches are theoretically equivalent. The values of $y[n]$ will be the same in both cases—including any transients due to the time-limited nature of the input signal. Of course, there will generally be a number of practical reasons for choosing one or other approach. These include not only operating speed, but also relative cost, size, availability of equipment and components, and so on.

Example E3.1

(*Note:* In the main text, and figure 3.10, we have described a discrete system whose output depends only upon input values. It involves no feedback and is said to be *nonrecursive*. In this example, we introduce a simple feedback, or *recursive*, system. Such systems will be more fully discussed towards the end of section 3.6.)

Find and sketch the impulse response and step response of the discrete system shown in figure E3.1(a). Use the graphical approach to convolution to find its response to the 'pulse' input signal shown in part (b) of the figure, and comment on its form.

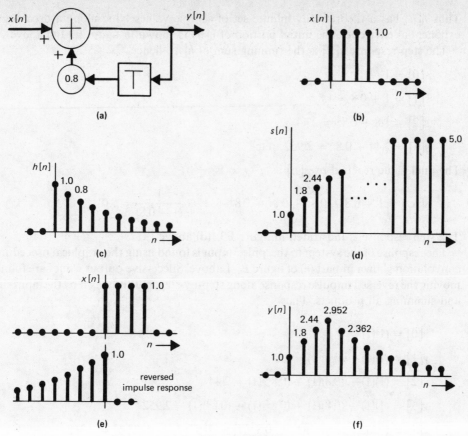

Figure E3.1

Solution

By inspection, we see that each output sample $y[n]$ of the system equals the coincident input $x[n]$, plus a feedback term equal to the output delayed by one sampling interval, and scaled by a weighting factor 0.8. Hence we may write

$$y[n] = x[n] + 0.8y[n-1]$$

If the input signal is a unit impulse $\delta[n]$ then the output must, by definition, be the impulse response $h[n]$. Therefore

$$h[n] = \delta[n] + 0.8h[n-1]$$

Now $\delta[n] = 1$ when $n = 0$, but is zero otherwise. Therefore when $n > 0$, only the feedback term contributes to $h[n]$. We may readily evaluate $h[n]$ term by term

$$h[0] = \delta[0] + 0.8h[-1] = 1$$
$$h[1] = \delta[1] + 0.8h[0] = 0.8$$
$$h[2] = \delta[2] + 0.8h[1] = 0.8^2$$
$$h[3] = \delta[3] + 0.8h[2] = 0.8^3 \quad \text{etc.}$$

Thus $h[n]$ has a theoretically infinite set of sample values lying along a decaying real exponential envelope. The initial portion of $h[n]$ is shown in figure E3.1(c) above.

The step response $s[n]$ is the running sum of $h[n]$, hence

$$s[0] = 1$$

$$s[1] = 1 + 0.8 = 1.8$$

$$s[2] = 1.8 + 0.8^2 = 2.44$$

$$s[3] = 2.44 + 0.8^3 = 2.952 \quad \text{etc.}$$

The final value reached by $s[n]$ as $n \to \infty$ is

$$s[\infty] = 1 + 0.8 + 0.8^2 + 0.8^3 + 0.8^4 + \ldots = \frac{1}{(1 - 0.8)} = 5.0$$

The step response is illustrated in figure E3.1(d) above.

The response of the system to the 'pulse' input is found using the graphical procedure for convolution shown in part (e) of figure E3.1 above. Successive output values are found by moving the reversed impulse response along step-by-step, multiplying it by the input signal, and summing all products. Thus

$$y[0] = (1)(1) = 1$$

$$y[1] = (1)(1) + (0.8)(1) = 1.8$$

$$y[2] = (1)(1) + (0.8)(1) + (0.8^2)(1) = 2.44$$

$$y[3] = (1)(1) + (0.8)(1) + (0.8^2)(1) + (0.8^3)(1) = 2.952$$

$$y[4] = (0.8)(1) + (0.8^2)(1) + (0.8^3)(1) + (0.8^4)(1) = 0.8y[3] = 2.362$$

$$y[5] = (0.8^2)(1) + (0.8^3)(1) + (0.8^4)(1) + (0.8^5)(1) = 0.8y[3] = 2.362$$

Clearly, $y[6] = 0.8y[5] = 1.511$, and so on. The output signal is drawn in part (f) of figure E3.1 above.

The form of the output signal $y[n]$ demonstrates several interesting points. The input signal $x[n]$ starts off by being like the unit step function $u[n]$. So the output is initially the same as the system's step response $s[n]$. However, after only 4 finite sample values the input returns to zero; so the output stops rising, and displays a falling exponential transient having the same form as the system's impulse response (each value of this transient being 0.8 times the previous value). We therefore see that the output 'pulse' is essentially in the form of two successive transients. The first, rising, one is not completed before the second, falling, one starts. This is because of the very limited duration of the input pulse. More generally, this example illustrates the 'spreading' of a pulse waveform along the time axis when it is processed by an LTI system containing memory. Equivalent effects in the case of a continuous-time voltage pulse are explored in the following section.

Now that we have covered discrete-time convolution with some care, we present a general-purpose computer program for demonstrating it. Program no. 2 accepts any form of input signal and causal impulse response, loaded using DATA statements. The particular input signal given in lines 200 and 210 is arbitrary; the impulse response in line 240 corresponds to a 10-point moving-average filter. The input signal is loaded into array X, starting at location X(20). This

```
100 REM ******  PROGRAM NO.2      DISCRETE-TIME CONVOLUTION *****
110 REM
120 REM ************** DEFINE AND CLEAR ARRAYS  **************
130 DIM X(75),Y(75),H(20)
140 FOR J=1 TO 75:X(J)=0:Y(J)=0:NEXT J
150 FOR J=1 TO 20:H(J)=0:NEXT J
160 REM
170 REM ****  READ DATA FOR INPUT SIGNAL AND IMPULSE RESPONSE ***
180 PRINT "NO. OF SAMPLES IN INPUT SIGNAL (MAXIMUM=55) ?"
190 INPUT NX:FOR J=1 TO NX:READ X(19+J):NEXT J
200 DATA 9,-2,7,-3,5,2,0,-2,6,3,-4,-5,-2,-3,-6,-3,5,2,7
210 DATA 2,2,3,3,-3,-4
220 PRINT "NO. OF SAMPLES IN IMPULSE RESPONSE (MAXIMUM=20) ?"
230 INPUT NH:FOR J=1 TO NH:READ H(J):NEXT J
240 DATA .1,.1,.1,.1,.1,.1,.1,.1,.1,.1
250 REM
260 REM ************ FIND OUTPUT BY CONVOLUTION  *************
270 FOR N=20 TO 75:FOR K=1 TO 20
280 Y(N)=Y(N)+H(K)*X(N-K+1):NEXT K:NEXT N
290 REM
300 REM ******************** PLOT OPTION  ********************
310 REM ** INPUT ABOVE,OUTPUT BELOW,SCALED TO SAME PEAK VALUE  **
320 XMAX=0:FOR J=1 TO 75:X1=ABS(X(J)):IF X1>XMAX THEN XMAX=X1
330 NEXT J
340 YMAX=0:FOR K=1 TO 75:Y1=ABS(Y(K)):IF Y1>YMAX THEN YMAX=Y1
350 NEXT K
360 CLS:FOR J=1 TO 75:PLOT 8*J,300:DRAW 8*J,300+X(J)*100/XMAX
370 PLOT 8*J,100:DRAW 8*J,100+Y(J)*100/YMAX:NEXT J
380 REM
390 REM ***  PRINT OPTION      (PAIRS OF INPUT/OUTPUT VALUES)  ***
400 FOR J=1 TO 75:PRINT X(J),Y(J):NEXT J
410 REM  **********************************************************
```

allows generation of the start-up transient. If (as in this case) the input signal finishes well before the end of array X, the complete stop-transient is also produced.

In this section we have introduced some important ideas about convolution and its implementation. Although we have concentrated on just one type of practical system—the discrete (or digital) moving-average filter—the reader is asked to remember that these ideas apply to a wide variety of LTI systems. We shall meet further aspects of convolution in later sections and chapters.

3.5 Continuous-time convolution

The mathematical description of convolution in continuous time is slightly more difficult than in discrete time, and the process is somewhat harder to visualise. Perhaps the main reason is that, whereas sampled signals are quite naturally represented by sets of weighted impulses, continuous signals are less so. However, the ideas underlying continuous-time convolution are in every respect analogous to those developed in the previous section. This makes our task a great deal easier.

In the previous section we saw how, just as a discrete input signal may be described as a set of weighted, time-shifted impulses, so the output signal from an LTI system may be described as a wet of weighted, shifted impulse responses. Exactly the same holds for continuous signals and systems. Although it would be quite possible to prove this rigorously, it seems adequate to infer it by analogy. Thus, since a continuous input signal $x(t)$ has been expressed in equation (3.6) as the superposition of an infinite set of shifted, weighted impulses

$$x(t) = \int_{-\infty}^{\infty} x(\tau)\delta(t - \tau)\,d\tau$$

so the output signal $y(t)$ from a continuous LTI system may be represented as the superposition of an infinite set of shifted, weighted impulse responses

$$y(t) = \int_{-\infty}^{\infty} x(\tau)h(t - \tau)\,d\tau \tag{3.18}$$

τ is an auxiliary, or 'dummy', time variable. In the discrete-time case we have also seen how x and h may be interchanged, because convolution is commutative. The same applies in continuous time, so that we may also write

$$y(t) = \int_{-\infty}^{\infty} h(\tau)x(t - \tau)\,d\tau \tag{3.19}$$

Equations (3.18) and (3.19) are alternative forms of the extremely important *convolution integral*. In equation (3.19), the variable τ may be interpreted as time measured 'back into the past' from the instant t for which we wish to calculate the system output $y(t)$. This is the form we shall generally adopt here.

Equation (3.19) has a useful graphical interpretation, equivalent to that previously illustrated for discrete time in figure 3.7. We show it for an arbitrary continuous signal $x(t)$, and impulse response $h(t)$, in figure 3.11. Suppose we wish to find the output signal at a particular instant $t = t_1$. A reversed version of the impulse response is placed below the input signal, starting from $t = t_1$. The two functions are then multiplied together, and their product integrated over all time—or, in practice, over the interval for which it is nonzero. Note that if we measure the auxiliary time variable τ back into the past from t_1, then the input signal is given by $x(t_1 - \tau)$, and the reversed impulse response by $h(\tau)$. Multiplication and integration then yields

$$y(t_1) = \int_{-\infty}^{\infty} h(\tau)x(t_1 - \tau)\,d\tau \tag{3.20}$$

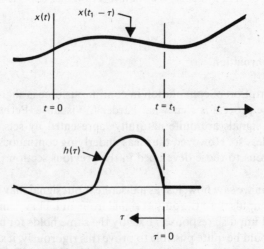

Figure 3.11 The graphical interpretation of continuous-time convolution.

which is equation (3.19) evaluated for the particular instant $t = t_1$. This is the counterpart of the earlier equation (3.13) in discrete time. To calculate the complete output signal $y(t)$ it would be necessary to move the reversed impulse response along in a series of infinitesimal steps, repeating the above procedure each time. Fortunately, however, $y(t)$ may often be derived *analytically*, using equation (3.19). The graphical interpretation is nevertheless valuable for determining the limits of integration, and for giving insight into the process of continuous-time convolution.

We next consider an example with important practical implications, using it to illustrate both the graphical approach and the question of integration limits. Suppose we wish to transmit a rectangular voltage pulse $v_1(t)$ along a cable, as shown in figure 3.12(a). This is a very common situation. It arises, for example, in many communications and measurement systems, or in the transmission of pulses within a digital computer. Generally speaking, the electrical constants of

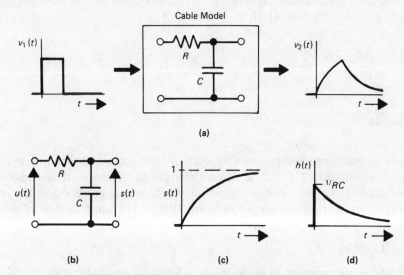

Figure 3.12 Pulse transmission along a cable.

a cable (its resistance, capacitance, and inductance) cause the pulse $v_2(t)$ reaching the far end to be somewhat distorted and spread out. If such effects are too severe, it may be impossible to detect or use the pulse. Very often, of course, we transmit not single isolated pulses, but a random-looking pulse stream representing a binary-coded signal or message (as in a PCM system). However, we may get a useful indication of what will happen by examining the distortion of a single pulse. In this illustration, we represent the cable by a simple lumped-component circuit model, comprising a single resistance and capacitance. It must be admitted straight away that this is not a very realistic model for most cables. It would be better to split the total resistance and capacitance up into a number of sections, to approximate the *distributed* nature of cable parameters (and we should maybe include inductance as well). However, the aim here is to illustrate some important ideas, rather than to give an accurate account of the behaviour of transmission cables.

The reader may have noticed that the simple RC circuit model of figure 3.12(a) is like the low-pass filter already discussed in section 2.3.3, and shown in figure 2.21. In addition, low-pass filtering has been mentioned at a number of other points in this book, including the previous section. Although we are in some danger of overemphasising this type of process, it is in fact very common in electronic engineering applications. Furthermore, it has the advantage of being relatively easy to understand and discuss in these early chapters. Later on, we will have ample opportunity to consider other types of filter and system. In the present context, we might just add that many cables do indeed have transmission properties which are broadly of the low-pass type.

If we are to solve this problem using the convolution integral, it is clearly necessary to know the impulse response of the cable model. This is an area where continuous-time convolution can be rather more awkward than its discrete-time counterpart. It is not generally quite so straightforward to determine the impulse response of a continuous system as of a discrete one (as we have seen in example E3.1 at the end of the previous section, the latter may sometimes be obtained more or less by inspection). The most common approach is by the Fourier or Laplace Transform, but since we have not yet met these, we will have to work from the differential equation describing the relationship between the circuit's input and output voltages. This has already been given by equation (2.44) in section 2.3.3

$$v_2(t) = v_1(t) - RC\frac{dv_2(t)}{dt}$$

or, rearranging

$$v_2(t) + RC\frac{dv_2(t)}{dt} = v_1(t) \tag{3.21}$$

In this case it is simpler to find the step response of the circuit, and then obtain the impulse response by differentiation. This technique has already been mentioned at the end of section 3.3. We therefore make the input a unit step function of voltage $u(t)$, and consider the voltage step response $s(t)$ on open circuit, as shown in figure 3.12(b). The usual method of solution is to assume a response of exponential form, together with a constant

$$s(t) = A\exp(\alpha t) + B \tag{3.22}$$

where A, α, and B are constants to be determined. Substituting $s(t)$ for $v_2(t)$ in equation (3.21), and putting $v_1(t)$ equal to a unit step of voltage, we obtain

$$\{A\exp(\alpha t) + B\} + RC\{A\alpha\exp(\alpha t)\} = 1, \qquad t > 0$$

Hence

$$A\exp(\alpha t)\{1 + RC\alpha\} + B = 1, \qquad t > 0 \tag{3.23}$$

To solve this equation, we may consider what happens as $t \to \infty$ and as $t \to 0$. The term $\exp(\alpha t)$ represents a transient which must decay to zero as $t \to \infty$, since we are clearly dealing with a stable system. Hence as $t \to \infty$, we have

$$0 + B = 1, \quad \text{hence } B = 1$$

Substituting for B in equation (3.23)

$$A\exp(\alpha t)\{1 + RC\alpha\} = 0 \tag{3.24}$$

Therefore, assuming $A \neq 0$

$$1 + RC\alpha = 0, \quad \text{so that } \alpha = -\frac{1}{RC} \tag{3.25}$$

Hence equation (3.22) becomes

$$s(t) = A \exp(-t/RC) + 1 \tag{3.26}$$

The form of the circuit model shows that $s(t)$ can only change with a finite slope immediately following the application of the input voltage step at $t = 0$, because the capacitor can only charge at a finite rate through the resistor. Hence $s(t) \to 0$ as $t \to 0$, giving

$$0 = A \exp(0) + 1, \quad \text{thus } A = -1$$

Finally, the step response must equal

$$s(t) = 1 - \exp(-t/RC) \tag{3.27}$$

As discussed in section 3.3, and summarised by equation (3.8), the impulse response $h(t)$ of a continuous LTI system is the derivative of its step response, so that

$$h(t) = \frac{d}{dt}\{1 - \exp(-t/RC)\} = \frac{1}{RC}\exp(-t/RC), \quad t > 0 \tag{3.28}$$

The step response and impulse response are therefore as shown in parts (c) and (d) of figure 3.12. These are similar waveforms to the ones used in figure 3.4 to illustrate the relationship between the impulse and step responses of an LTI system—although we did not, at that stage, mention *which* type of circuit or system they applied to.

The output signal from the cable model may now be evaluated, for the input voltage pulse shown in figure 3.12(a). Let us assume a pulse duration of 1 microsecond (μs), and a product RC in equation (3.28) of 0.5 μs. This product is the *time constant* of the real exponential signals $s(t)$ and $h(t)$, as previously illustrated by figure 2.15. If we work in units of microseconds for convenience, then equation (3.28) becomes

$$h(t) = 2\exp(-2t), \quad t > 0$$

Figure 3.13 gives the graphical interpretation of the convolution integral for two typical instants t_1 and t_2. Part (a) of the figure shows the input signal, and parts (b) and (c) the impulse response reversed from the instants t_1 and t_2 respectively. Note that t_1 is chosen 'within' the duration of the input pulse, whereas t_2 is 'beyond' it (there is, of course, no need to consider instants before $t = 0$, since the system is causal, and there would be no output). In each case, the variable τ is labelled 'back into the past' from the instant chosen. Careful examination of the figure shows that, since the input signal is only nonzero in the range $0 < t < 1$, the limits of integration are

$$\tau = 0 \text{ to } \tau = t_1 \qquad \text{in case (b)}$$

and

$$\tau = (t_2 - 1) \text{ to } \tau = t_2 \quad \text{in case (c)}$$

The general form of the convolution integral given by equation (3.19) may be rewritten in terms of input and output voltage signals as follows

$$v_2(t) = \int_{-\infty}^{\infty} h(\tau)v_1(t - \tau)\,d\tau \tag{3.29}$$

Inserting the relevant functions and integration limits, we obtain

$$v_2(t_1) = \int_0^{t_1} 2\exp(-2\tau)\,d\tau, \qquad 0 < t_1 < 1 \tag{3.30}$$

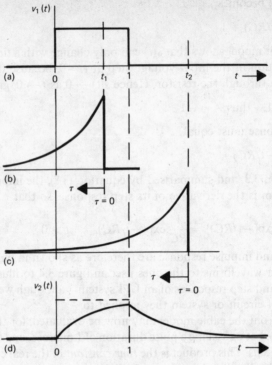

Figure 3.13

and

$$v_2(t_2) = \int_{t_2-1}^{t_2} 2 \exp(-2\tau)\, d\tau, \qquad 1 < t_2 < \infty \tag{3.31}$$

It is simplest to evaluate the indefinite integral first, and then apply the different limits for the two cases afterwards. Note also that although we have chosen *particular* instants t_1 and t_2 for the purposes of illustration, in fact we need to consider a full set of instants within the above ranges. In terms of a *general* instant t, therefore, the indefinite integral is

$$v_2(t) = \int 2 \exp(-2\tau)\, d\tau = -\exp(-2\tau) \tag{3.32}$$

Inserting the limits

$$v_2(t) = [-\exp(-2\tau)]_0^t = 1 - \exp(-2t), \qquad 0 < t < 1 \tag{3.33}$$

and

$$v_2(t) = [-\exp(-2\tau)]_{t-1}^t = -\exp(-2t) + \exp(-2t+2)$$

$$= \{\exp(2) - 1\}\exp(-2t), \qquad 1 < t < \infty$$

Hence

$$v_2(t) = 6.389 \exp(-2t), \qquad 1 < t < \infty \tag{3.34}$$

These two output functions represent different portions of the output signal. They arise because the input signal is discontinuous at $t = 1$. The complete output signal is drawn in part (d) of figure 3.13, and the input waveform is shown dotted, for comparison.

The reader may feel that the above problem is rather lengthy; however, it is essentially straightforward. The process may be summarised as follows

Find the impulse response of the LTI system.

For the given input signal, use the graphical interpretation of convolution to determine the limits of integration for the variable τ. If discontinuities in the input signal mean that there is more than one set of limits, note carefully the time interval over which each set applies.

Evaluate the indefinite integral, then insert the limits.

A number of interesting points are illustrated by the form of the output pulse from the cable model. As anticipated, the signal has been distorted from its rectangular shape, and spread considerably in time. Secondly, although we cannot define an exact pulse centre, because it is no longer symmetrical, what might be termed its 'centre of gravity' has clearly shifted to the right. This represents a time-delay. These are typical effects of processing a signal with a causal LTI system possessing memory. If we look at the shape of the output pulse in more detail, we see that it initially takes the form of the system's step response—because the input signal has a positive step at $t = 0$. However, the step response is not completed before the input pulse ends. From this instant onwards, the cable model has stored energy (in the capacitor) but no input excitation, so it displays its own characteristic response—in this case, a decaying real exponential. In view of our discussion at the start of section 3.3 about impulse responses reflecting the characteristic behaviour of systems when 'left on their own', it is not surprising that this particular circuit's impulse response is also a decaying real exponential (see figure 3.12(d)).

There is, finally, one rather different way of looking at the form of the output signal. Since the input pulse may be thought of as a positive step at $t = 0$, followed by a negative step at $t = 1$, we could also derive the output by superposing two step responses. This would be a rather simpler and faster way of solving this particular problem than the one we have used, but of course our aim here has been to illustrate the use of the convolution integral. The reader is encouraged to compare the above comments and results with those of the discrete-time worked example E3.1 at the end of the previous section, because there are many close parallels between them.

Before leaving the topic of pulse shape and distortion, we should emphasise that the severity of distortion depends on the *relative* values of pulse duration and cable time constant. In our example, we have assumed values of 1 μs and 0.5 μs respectively. The same degree of distortion would be experienced by a 10 μs pulse passing through a system with 5 μs time constant, and so on.

We should now consider some further general aspects of continuous-time convolution. In the previous section, we saw how a discrete-time impulse response behaves as a weighting function, in the sense that it weights present and previous values of the input signal to produce the current output. The same is true in continuous time. Indeed, a continuous impulse response is also sometimes referred to as a weighting function. Another name for it is *memory function*, denoting a system's ability to 'remember' the past history of its input signal. Of course, these terms are relevant only when describing an LTI system possessing memory.

In the previous description of the transients which occur at the output of a discrete LTI system when an input signal is switched on and off (see figure 3.9), we noted the value of the graphical interpretation of discrete-time convolution for exploring their nature and duration. In continuous time, too, such transients are an inevitable consequence of using an LTI system with memory. This may be illustrated by an example based, once again, on the simple *RC* circuit

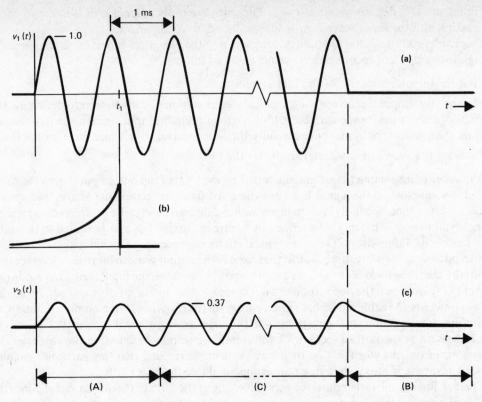

Figure 3.14 The graphical interpretation of convolution used to explore transients in the output signal of a continuous LTI system.

already shown in figure 3.12. However, rather than thinking of it necessarily as a model for a cable, let us just view it as a simple but widely used type of low-pass filter. Imagine that a sinusoidal voltage signal of frequency 1 kHz, obtained from a signal generator, is switched on and applied to this circuit, and later switched off again. Initial and final portions of such an input signal are shown in figure 3.14(a), with a break in the middle of the time axis for convenience. Let us assume a circuit time constant of 0.4 millisecond (ms) and that we need to find the form of the output signal. We are, admittedly, using this example primarily as a way of illustrating some important ideas. But in case this type of signal seems to have little practical significance, remember that switching transients do very often occur in electronic circuits and systems, and we may need to assess their form. In particular, switched sinusoidal signals are quite widely used as 'tone bursts' in signalling and telephone systems, for example to indicate that a line is ringing, engaged, or out of order.

It would be quite possible to evaluate the output signal analytically, using the convolution integral. (This is in fact given as problem Q3.14 at the end of the chapter.) Here we merely present the result graphically, and use it as a basis for discussion. Part (b) of figure 3.14 shows a reversed version of the impulse response, with a time constant of 0.4 ms, placed so as to estimate the output signal at an instant t_1. Since this impulse response has not quite 'moved fully into' the input signal, we must expect the output signal to be displaying a start-up transient. Similarly when the 1 kHz input is switched off again, there will be another transient as the reversed impulse response 'moves out of' the input signal. The basic argument is identical to that already developed for discrete-time in the previous section. In this case, the output signal is as shown in part (c) of the figure. Three portions of this signal may be identified. The first, labelled (A), includes the start-up transient which we expect to take the form of a real decaying exponential. It is hard to see this, because the circuit is also responding to the sinusoidal variations of the input signal, and the two are mixed together. Also, the transient does not end abruptly, but 'fades out' exponentially. Theoretically, it goes on forever. However, since a real decaying exponential falls to exp(-5) or less than 1 per cent of its initial value after 5 time constants have elapsed, this amount of time is often taken as the approximate duration of such a transient for practical purposes. In this case, 5 time constants equal 2 ms, which is marked as portion (A) of the output waveform. In fact one can see the effects of the transient only during the first half millisecond or so. The initial rise of the output waveform is not truly sinusoidal, and the first peak is slightly higher than subsequent ones.

The second output transient occurs when the input is switched off. It is much more obvious, since the circuit is 'on its own' and displays the expected decaying real exponential. This is marked as portion (B) on the figure.

The middle portion of the output waveform, labelled (C), is also very interesting. Firstly, it is strictly sinusoidal in form, and at the same frequency as the input. This is to be expected, since an LTI system responding to steady sinusoidal excitation can only modify the amplitude and phase of the input signal. It cannot generate any new frequencies. Notice that in this case the ratio of output to input amplitudes is considerably less than unity (in fact, 0.37), and that there is a substantial phase lag in the output (in fact, 68°). These values are much easier to derive using a frequency-domain approach based upon the *j*-notation (covered in section 1.4.2) than by time-domain convolution, but the graphical interpretation of convolution offers some valuable *qualitative* insight into why amplitude reduction and phase shift occur. As the reversed impulse response 'moves through' portion (C) of the input signal, and the two functions are multiplied together and integrated, the weighting action of the impulse response tends to *smooth out* the fluctuations in the input signal somewhat. This gives a reduced output amplitude. The effect is similar in principle to the smoothing action of the discrete moving-average filter discussed in the previous section—even though we now have an exponential rather than a 'rectangular' weighting function. If the input signal frequency were increased, this smoothing effect would be more severe. This explains the low-pass filtering action of the present circuit. As far as phase-shift is concerned, it is not difficult to appreciate that the reversed impulse response has to move somewhat *beyond* each input signal peak, in order to develop a peak value in the output. Such qualitative explanations for amplitude and phase changes, although by no means obvious, can be a great help in understanding the nature of an LTI system's response to sinusoidal excitation.

A number of important ideas underlying continuous-time convolution have now been covered: its mathematical basis and graphical interpretation, an application showing pulse distortion and delay caused by transmission through a cable, the problem of integration limits, the concept of an impulse response as a weighting or memory function, and the distinction between the transient and steady-state response of an LTI system with sinusoidal excitation. All these topics are very closely linked to the work we have done in the previous section on discrete-time convolution.

However, a few words of caution are in order. As already noted, all illustrations of practical applications have been based on simple low-pass, or smoothing, filters. This is a very restricted 'menu'! Furthermore, the simple cable model used in this section is not very realistic. Our aim, of course, has been to develop and demonstrate the basis of convolution by practical example, and we will find many opportunities for discussing more varied and complex systems later in this book. With these reservations in mind, we end the section with a rather different practical example based, once again, on a simple low-pass filter. This is designed to confirm the value of the convolution method, and to underline the relationships between the impulse, step, and ramp responses of an LTI system.

Example E3.2

The temperature of an oven is measured with a thermocouple, its output voltage being fed via a DC amplifier to a recorder. However, the recorded signal contains unwanted high-frequency noise, so it is decided to insert a low-pass filter between the amplifier and the recorder. Figure E3.2(a) shows the overall scheme, together with the relevant circuit components. Resistors R_1 and R_2 are chosen so that the output voltage from the amplifier changes by 10 mV for every 1°C change in oven temperature. The output impedance of the amplifier may be assumed negligible, and the input impedance of the recorder infinite. (Note that the scheme illustrated is very basic. A practical design would almost certainly need additional features and components—for example, to compensate for the voltage offset produced by the 'cold junction' of the thermocouple.)

After the oven has been off for a long time and its temperature is stable, it is switched on and heats up at a constant rate of 1°C per second. Find the steady error in recorded temperature due to use of the filter, when once any initial switching transient has died away. Also sketch the form of the output from the filter.

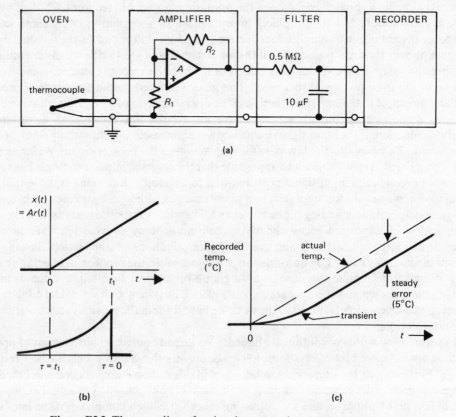

Figure E3.2 The recording of a signal representing oven temperature.

Solution

Let us firstly make some general comments about the measurement system. The amplifier is a standard noninverting operational amplifier which works right down to zero frequency (DC), as discussed in section 1.4.3. We need not concern ourselves with its details, because we are told that R_1 and R_2 have been chosen to give a 10 mV change in its output voltage for every 1°C change in oven temperature. The time constant of the filter, equal to RC, is here $(0.5\ \mathrm{M\Omega})(10\ \mu\mathrm{F}) = 5$ s. We may assume that connection of the filter does not affect the amplifier's output signal, since the latter's output impedance is negligible. Furthermore, since the recorder's input impedance is extremely large, the filter's output terminals are effectively open circuit. The filter's impulse response will therefore be of the form we have already derived, and shown in figure 3.12(d)—although the time constant is of course much greater here.

We may find the solution to this problem using two separate approaches: firstly, by convolution, and secondly, by evaluating the filter's response to a ramp input signal. Although we could work in terms of the numerical values given, it is more instructive to use algebraic symbols, inserting numerical values at the end.

Let us start with the convolution approach. When the oven is switched on, its temperature rises at a constant rate. The input signal to the filter is therefore a ramp of voltage, which we may denote by $Ar(t)$, where A is a constant. This is shown in part (b) of the figure. Note that we take the instant when the oven is switched on as $t = 0$, for convenience. Also, we do not need to concern ourselves with the starting temperature of the oven, since we are told that it has been steady for a long time—and we are interested here only in the *changes* which occur after $t = 0$. So again for convenience, we may take the initial level of the input signal as zero.

A reversed version of the filter's impulse response is drawn beneath the input signal in part (b) of the figure, positioned so as to estimate the filter output signal at an instant t_1. It is clear that the limits of integration in this case must be $\tau = 0$ to $\tau = t_1$. In general, the convolution integral is

$$y(t) = \int_{-\infty}^{\infty} h(\tau)x(t - \tau)\,\mathrm{d}\tau$$

Now

$$h(t) = \frac{1}{RC}\exp(-t/RC)$$

and

$$x(t) = Ar(t) = At \quad \text{for } t > 0$$

thus the output signal for a general instant t is

$$y(t) = \int_0^t \frac{1}{RC}\exp(-\tau/RC)A(t - \tau)\,\mathrm{d}\tau \quad \text{for } t > 0$$

$$= \frac{At}{RC}\int_0^t \exp(-\tau/RC)\,\mathrm{d}\tau - \frac{A}{RC}\int_0^t \tau\exp(-\tau/RC)\,\mathrm{d}\tau$$

The first of these integrals is straightforward. The second may be integrated by parts. Thus

$$y(t) = \left[\frac{At}{RC} \exp(-\tau/RC)(-RC) \right]_0^t$$

$$- \frac{A}{RC} \left\{ [\tau \exp(-\tau/RC)(-RC)]_0^t - \int_0^t \exp(-\tau/RC)(-RC)\, d\tau \right\}$$

$$\therefore \; y(t) = [-At \exp(-\tau/RC)]_0^t$$

$$- \frac{A}{RC} \left\{ [-RC\tau \exp(-\tau/RC)]_0^t - [R^2C^2 \exp(-\tau/RC)]_0^t \right\}$$

$$\therefore \; y(t) = -At \exp(-t/RC) + At$$

$$- \frac{A}{RC} \left\{ -RCt \exp(-t/RC) + 0 - R^2C^2 \exp(-t/RC) + R^2C^2 \right\}$$

$$\therefore \; y(t) = At + ARC \exp(-t/RC) - ARC \quad \text{for } t > 0 \tag{3.35}$$

The solution for $y(t)$ therefore consists of three parts. The first, equal to At, is the *desired* output from the filter, since this is the same as its input signal from the amplifier. The second, equal to $ARC \exp(-t/RC)$, is a filter *transient* due to the sudden switching-on of the oven at $t = 0$. The third, equal to $-ARC$, is an *error* which does not vary with time t. Hence when the transient has died away, we are left with this steady error at the filter output, which represents a constant error in the temperature reading. In this particular problem

$$A = 10 \, \text{mV per second}$$

corresponding to a change in oven temperature of 1°C per second, and

$$RC = 5 \text{ seconds}$$

The steady error introduced by the filter is therefore

$$-ARC = -50 \, \text{mV}$$

This represents a steady error of $-5°C$ in the recorded oven temperature. The form of the output signal is illustrated in figure E3.2(c), expressed in terms of oven temperature *versus* time.

Since the input signal to the filter in this case takes the form of a ramp function, an alternative method of solution is to find the ramp response of the filter. In section 2.2.2 we have seen that a unit step function is the running integral of a unit impulse, and that a unit ramp function is the running integral of a unit step. In section 3.3 we have explained why similar relationships hold between the responses of an LTI system to these various signals. Hence, in this problem, if we start with the filter's impulse response, we may derive its response to a unit ramp by performing *two* running integrations.

A running integral is found by summing the total area under a curve as time progresses. Thus in general the step response of a continuous LTI system may be derived from its impulse response as follows

$$s(t) = \int_0^\infty h(t - \tau)\, d\tau \tag{3.36}$$

where τ is the usual auxiliary time variable. However, when the impulse response is causal and therefore zero for $t < 0$, the integration limits are reduced and become 0 to t (this may be inferred by reference back to figure 2.9 and equations (2.5) and (2.6)). So in this example

$$s(t) = \int_0^t \frac{1}{RC} \exp(-\{t - \tau\}/RC)\,d\tau = [\exp(-\{t - \tau\}/RC)]_0^t$$

$$= \exp(0) - \exp(-t/RC) = 1 - \exp(-t/RC) \tag{3.37}$$

Similarly, the response to a unit ramp $r(t)$ is given by

$$q(t) = \int_0^t s(t - \tau)\,d\tau = \int_0^t \{1 - \exp(-\{t - \tau\}/RC)\}\,d\tau$$

$$= [\tau - RC \exp(-\{t - \tau\}/RC)]_0^t$$

$$= t + RC \exp(-t/RC) - RC \tag{3.38}$$

However, our input signal is a weighted ramp $Ar(t)$, so the filter output must be

$$At + ARC \exp(-t/RC) - ARC$$

which is the result we obtained by convolution.

The second method of solution may seem rather simpler than the first. However, it must be remembered that not many problems involve basic input signals such as steps or ramps—so we could not, in general, use the approach based on running integrals. The convolution method, of course, applies in principle to *any* form of input signal. We might also mention an interesting practical point. Since the filter introduces an undesirable steady error proportional to RC, it might appear sensible to choose a smaller value of this time constant. However, the filter would then be less effective at reducing the high-frequency noise which contaminates the wanted signal. So there is a trade-off between these two effects. Incidentally, part (c) of the figure does not show any residual high-frequency noise which may remain after filtering, for the sake of clarity.

3.6 Differential equations and difference equations

Most readers of this book will have taken a basic course in electrical circuit theory, and will know that the voltages, currents, and component values of a continuous linear circuit may be related to each other by a differential equation. Such an equation, known as a *linear differential equation with constant coefficients*, gives a fundamental description of the circuit's behaviour. It holds good, in principle, for any form of input signal or excitation. In an analogous way, the operation of a discrete linear circuit or system may be described by a *linear difference equation with constant coefficients*. The system block diagrams we developed in section 2.3.3 were, in effect, pictorial representations of these two types of equation. In this section, we aim to summarise the main features of such equations, to explain their value for an understanding of electronic LTI systems, and to introduce a certain amount of new terminology.

It may be helpful to emphasise at once that electronic and electrical engineers use a number of analytical methods which allow them to bypass the differential equations describing continuous LTI systems. This is because such equations are quite hard to deal with and solve. Various alternative techniques have been evolved over many years. These include the *j*-notation for use with steady-state sinusoidal excitation, the convolution integral, and the Fourier and Laplace

Transforms described in subsequent chapters. They make it unnecessary to give differential equations a great deal of attention here. The situation is, however, rather different in the case of difference equations. As we shall see, these are quite easy to manipulate and offer a rapid and direct way of solving certain problems. Even so, we should be aware at this point that other problems involving discrete LTI systems are best tackled using the discrete Fourier Transform or the z-transform, which we shall also meet later.

We start by recalling one example of a differential equation, and two examples of difference equations, which have already been discussed. In section 2.3.3, and again in the previous section, we used the following differential equation to describe the operation of a simple continuous low-pass filter comprising a resistor R and a capacitor C

$$v_2(t) + \frac{RC\,dv_2(t)}{dt} = v_1(t) \tag{3.39}$$

where v_1 and v_2 represent the input and output voltage signals respectively. Note that v_1 equals a linear combination of v_2 and its first derivative, and that the coefficient or multiplier RC is a constant determined by the values of the circuit elements. This explains the general name for such an equation: a linear differential equation with constant coefficients. Although it is derived in terms of input and output voltages, corresponding equations could be found to relate currents or charges in the circuit. Also, as pointed out in section 2.3.3, such an equation may be recast in terms of integrations rather than differentiations. However, the above formulation serves present purposes well.

Turning now to difference equations, we have already met the following examples, among others

$$y[n] = \tfrac{1}{5}\{x[n] + x[n-1] + x[n-2] + x[n-3] + x[n-4]\} \tag{3.40}$$

and

$$y[n] = 0.8y[n-1] + x[n], \quad \text{or } y[n] - 0.8y[n-1] = x[n] \tag{3.41}$$

The first of these specified a causal version of the discrete moving-average filter described in section 3.4. The second described the discrete LTI system used in worked example E3.1. In the first case, each output value $y[n]$ equals a linear combination of $x[n]$ and previous input values, and the multipliers are once again constant coefficients (they happen to be all equal to 1/5 in this example). In the second equation, $x[n]$ equals a linear combination of two outputs, $y[n]$ and $y[n-1]$.

The majority of practical electronic LTI systems have more complicated defining equations than the ones given above. For example, we might have a high-performance continuous filter made from R, L, and C components, and maybe operational amplifiers as well, or else a discrete system with feedback paths, and many multipliers, adders, and delay elements. However, in all cases it would be possible to describe their operation in terms of linear equations with constant coefficients. In general, such equations take the following forms. In the continuous case, we have

$$a_0 y(t) + a_1 \frac{dy(t)}{dt} + a_2 \frac{d^2 y(t)}{dt^2} + \ldots = b_0 x(t) + b_1 \frac{dx(t)}{dt} + b_2 \frac{d^2 x(t)}{dt^2} + \ldots \tag{3.42}$$

$x(t)$ represents the input signal or excitation, and $y(t)$ the output signal or response of interest. This equation may be written compactly as

$$\sum_{k=0}^{N} a_k \frac{d^k y(t)}{dt^k} = \sum_{k=0}^{M} b_k \frac{d^k x(t)}{dt^k} \tag{3.43}$$

For a discrete LTI system, the general form of difference equation is

$$a_0 y[n] + a_1 y[n-1] + a_2 y[n-2] + \ldots = b_0 x[n] + b_1 x[n-1] + b_2 x[n-2] + \ldots \qquad (3.44)$$

or

$$\sum_{k=0}^{N} a_k y[n-k] = \sum_{k=0}^{M} b_k x[n-k] \qquad (3.45)$$

The structure and complexity of a circuit or system determines how many terms appear on each side of the equation. The value of N, which indicates the highest-order derivative, or difference, of the output variable, is generally referred to as the *order* of the system. For example, the simple continuous RC filter described above (assuming v_2 and v_1 are equivalent to y and x respectively) is a first-order system since $N = 1$ and $M = 0$.

Although such equations give a fundamental description of the systems they represent, certain additional information is needed in order to find a system's response to a specified input signal. This information is given by the *auxiliary conditions* (also called boundary conditions). In practical terms, the auxiliary conditions allow for the possibility that energy or information is already stored in the system at the moment when we apply an input signal. This could arise, for example, if the system had not fully 'come to rest' following some previous excitation.

In the continuous case, the auxiliary conditions comprise the value of $y(t)$, and the values of its various derivatives appearing in the differential equation, at a suitable instant, or instants. Since we very often consider input signals which are applied at $t = 0$, the auxiliary conditions are commonly specified for an instant immediately before $t = 0$ (often denoted by $t = 0_-$). They are then called the *initial conditions*.

Similar ideas apply in the discrete case. We need to know the values of $y[n]$, $y[n-1]$, and so on, specified in the difference equation, caused by any previous input or excitation. The need for auxiliary conditions is indeed quite simple to demonstrate in the discrete case. Take, for example, the system with the difference equation quoted earlier in equation (3.41)

$$y[n] = 0.8y[n-1] + x[n]$$

Suppose that our input signal is zero prior to $n = 0$, but takes on finite sample values for $n = 0, 1, 2, \ldots$. Then clearly we can determine $y[0]$ only if we have a value for $y[-1]$; moreover, $y[-1]$ *could* be nonzero if the system was still responding to some *previous* input signal. Fortunately, however, we are generally concerned with systems which have come to rest, or stabilised, before an input signal is applied. So the auxiliary conditions are very often zero. This simplifies the problem considerably (a good illustration of this is the previous worked example E3.2, which dealt with the recording of the temperature of an oven).

Given a system's differential or difference equation, the auxiliary conditions, and the input signal, how is the output signal obtained? The reader who has taken an introductory course in linear circuit theory will probably recall that, in the case of a continuous LTI circuit described by a differential equation, the solution is generally found in two parts. These are the *particular solution*, or integral, and the *homogeneous solution*, also known as the *complementary function*. These two parts of the solution have a very interesting physical interpretation, which ties in closely with our work on convolution in the previous two sections. Broadly speaking, the particular solution gives us the steady-state response, whereas the homogeneous solution accounts for any transients in the output caused by discontinuities in the input. The superposition of these two components gives us the complete output signal. It will not surprise the reader to learn that the homogeneous solution, which accounts for transients in the output, has a lot to do with the system's impulse response, and therefore with its behaviour when left 'on its own'.

Before exploring these ideas quantitatively, we should note that the convolution method, as developed in the previous two sections, makes no clear distinction between the transient and steady-state components of an output signal. Provided we take care over limits of integration (or summation), it computes the complete output signal 'all at once'. It would indeed be difficult to disentangle the particular and homogeneous components of the start-up transient shown earlier in figure 3.14. This is an important distinction between convolution and the usual method of solution of a differential equation.

For reasons explained earlier, we do not intend to take the present discussion of differential equations and their solution any further. However, a rather more detailed and quantitative look at the particular and homogeneous components of a discrete output signal will be very useful. It will give some valuable practice in the manipulation of difference equations, and an opportunity to introduce some new terminology.

Let us therefore consider a discrete LTI system defined by the following difference equation

$$y[n] - y[n - 1] + 0.5y[n - 2] = x[n] \tag{3.46}$$

Note that, for the first time, we are involved with a system of *second-order*. Apart from this, there is no special significance in this choice of equation—except that it gives rather simple numerical values in the calculations we make below! Let us next assume an input signal of sampled sinusoidal form, which begins at $n = 0$

$$x[n] = \left\{ \sin\left(\frac{n\pi}{3} + \frac{\pi}{6} \right) \right\} u[n] \tag{3.47}$$

This signal is shown in part (a) of figure 3.15. Our aim is firstly to evaluate the output signal using the system's difference equation. Next, we will infer the *particular* component of the output. Finally, we will show that a homogeneous component is also present, which allows the *auxiliary conditions* to be satisfied.

We may rearrange the above difference equation as

$$y[n] = y[n - 1] - 0.5y[n - 2] + x[n] \tag{3.48}$$

and use it to evaluate the output signal term-by-term. We will assume that the system has 'come to rest', and that $y[-2] = y[-1] = 0$. These are the auxiliary (or, in this case, the initial) conditions. The first few finite output values are found as follows

$$y[0] = y[-1] - 0.5y[-2] + x[0] = 0 - 0 + 0.5 = 0.5$$

$$y[1] = y[0] - 0.5y[-1] + x[1] = 0.5 - 0 + 1.0 = 1.5$$

$$y[2] = y[1] - 0.5y[0] + x[2] = 1.5 - 0.25 + 0.5 = 1.75$$

and so on. Although these calculations are rather tedious to perform 'by hand', a pocket calculator makes them much faster—and a simple program run on a digital computer is even better. The output signal is illustrated in part (b) of the figure, with the sample values accurate to 2 decimal figures. It is clear that, as expected, there is a start-up transient that arises from the sudden application of the input. However, towards the right-hand side of the figure, the output has just about settled to its *steady-state* response, with successive sample values

$$\ldots 1, 2, 1, -1, -2, -1, 1, 2, 1 \ldots \quad \text{etc.}$$

These values should represent the *particular* component of the solution which we will denote by

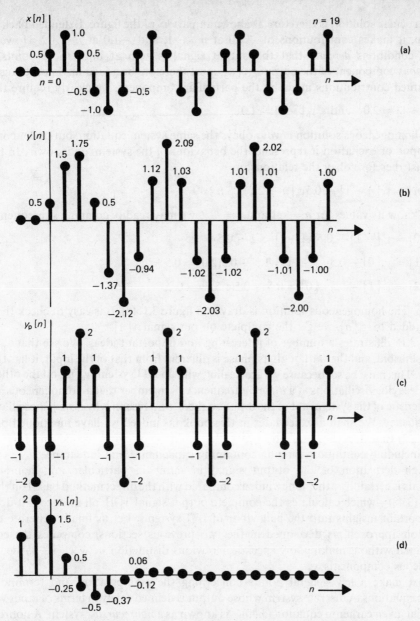

Figure 3.15 The output signal of a discrete second-order system in response to a switched sinusoidal input, together with the particular and homogeneous components of the solution.

$y_p[n]$. This assumption may be checked using the difference equation. For example, if we put $n = 19$ and refer to the figure for the required values, we obtain

$$y_p[19] = y_p[18] - 0.5y_p[17] + x[19] \qquad (3.49)$$

$$= -1.00 - 0.5(-2.00) + 1.00 = 1.00$$

which is correct.

The particular solution is therefore as shown in part (c) of the figure. Extended back beyond the origin, it makes contributions of -2.0 at $n = -1$, and -1.0 at $n = -2$. However, the auxiliary conditions *demand* that the output signal is zero at both these points, and a *homogeneous* component of the output, $y_h[n]$, must therefore be added in. Since it must cancel the unwanted contributions made by the particular component, we clearly require that

$$y_h[-1] = 2.0 \quad \text{and} \quad y_h[-2] = 1.0$$

Now the homogeneous solution *always* obeys the same system equation, but under conditions of zero input, or excitation it represents the behaviour of the system 'on its own'. In this case $y_h[n]$ must therefore obey the relationship

$$y_h[n] = y_h[n-1] - 0.5y_h[n-2], \qquad n \geqslant 0 \tag{3.50}$$

Since we know its values for $n = -1$ and $n = -2$, we may readily compute subsequent values

$$y_h[0] = y_h[-1] - 0.5y_h[-2] = 2 - 0.5 = 1.5$$

$$y_h[1] = y_h[0] - 0.5y_h[-1] = 1.5 - 0.5(2.0) = 0.5$$

$$y_h[2] = y_h[1] - 0.5y_h[0] = 0.5 - 0.5(1.5) = -0.25$$

and so on. The homogeneous solution is drawn in figure 3.15(d). It is easy to check that when $y_h[n]$ is added to $y_p[n]$, we get the complete output signal $y[n]$.

Figure 3.15 illustrates a number of interesting and important ideas. We see that $y_p[n]$ is a sampled sinusoid, and that although its phase is different from that of the input, it has the same frequency. This must be so, because we are dealing with an LTI system. $y_h[n]$, on the other hand, displays decaying oscillations at a *different* frequency. Remember that a homogeneous solution is characteristic of the system, not of the input, so there is no reason why it *should* oscillate at the input frequency. We shall also see later in this book (as indeed we have mentioned briefly in section 2.2.3) that decaying oscillations are characteristic of many second and higher-order systems, including continuous circuits containing capacitance and inductance.

Although derivation of the output signal in terms of particular and homogeneous components is certainly rather longwinded compared with the direct method based on the use of equation (3.48)—which calculates the complete output signal $y[n]$ 'all at once'—it does offer some important insights into the behaviour of LTI systems. Let us finally reiterate that the convolution approach, as developed in the two previous sections, computes the complete output signal without making any special or obvious distinction between its particular and homogeneous components.

We next make a few general points concerning the manipulation and terminology of difference equations. A discrete system whose output is defined solely in terms of input values— such as that given earlier in equation (3.40)—is known as a *nonrecursive* system. A nonrecursive difference equation is just an expression of the convolution sum, equation (3.14), for that particular system. The coefficients by which the various input signal values are multipied are those of the system's impulse response $h[n]$. Other difference equations, of which equation (3.48) is a good example, estimate $y[n]$ in terms of one or more previous *outputs*, as well as inputs. The systems they describe are known as *recursive* systems, and imply feedback. When we used equation (3.48) to compute the output signal for a given input signal, we in effect performed a convolution. However, this convolution was not obvious, because at no stage did we derive and use the system's impulse response. We *could* have derived $h[n]$ had we so wished, and convolved it with the input signal in the normal way. However, it would have been a much more lengthy process, because the impulse response of a recursive system generally involves a large number—

theoretically an infinite number—of terms (even though we may in practice ignore the very small ones in the 'tail' of the response). So the *implicit* convolution defined by a recursive equation is much more convenient than the *explicit* one based upon the system's impulse response.

Lastly, we should note that when a difference equation is rearranged to make $y[n]$ the subject, it is widely referred to as a *recurrence* formula. As we have seen, this formula may be used iteratively to calculate successive values of an output signal. This offers a ready method of solution for many problems involving discrete-time signals and LTI systems.

Example E3.3

(*Note:* This worked example is closely connected with the previous one, E3.2, and is designed to emphasise the parallels between analog and digital solutions to a practical engineering problem.)

A microcomputer system is being installed in the paintshop of a sheet metalwork factory, for monitoring and control of various automatic processes. One of its tasks is to measure and record the temperature at various parts of an oven, using thermocouples. One 'channel' of this system is shown in the functional block diagram of figure E3.3(a). The output signal from the DC amplifier is sampled every 10 seconds, by issuing a 'convert command' pulse to the ADC. The scaling of the input signal is so arranged that the numbers entering the microcomputer represent the oven temperature in °C, divided by 10. Thus a temperature of 200°C is represented by the decimal number 20, and so on. A storage array X is first cleared (that is, all its values are set to zero) and the temperature data are then entered as they are generated. The signal is processed by a first-order, low-pass digital filter, to reduce unwanted high-frequency noise, and the filtered output is stored in an array Y. (The first location in Y is set to zero, the output signal being loaded from the second location onwards.) On command from an operator, the contents of array Y may be output via a DAC to a visual display.

The filter's difference equation is

$$y[n] - 0.5y[n-1] = 0.5x[n]$$

In a particular instance, the oven temperature is 40°C when sampling begins, and is rising at a constant rate of 1°C per second.
(a) Find the impulse response of the filter, and use it to estimate the first 5 values of the output signal $y[n]$ which are loaded into storage array Y.
(b) Using the above difference equation as a recurrence formula, find the form of the complete output signal $y[n]$, and check that its first 5 values agree with those already calculated.
(c) Infer the particular component $y_p[n]$ of the output, and hence find the homogeneous component $y_h[n]$.
(d) Find which *initial* oven temperature (if any) would cause $y_h[n]$ to be zero for all n, assuming that the temperature still rises at 1°C per second.

Solution

(a) The impulse response $h[n]$ may be found by making $x[n]$ equal to a unit impulse function $\delta[n]$, and evaluating the output term-by-term. Thus

$$y[n] = 0.5y[n-1] + 0.5x[n]$$

becomes

$$h[n] = 0.5h[n-1] + 0.5\delta[n]$$

Hence

$$h[0] = 0.5(0) + 0.5(1) = 0.5$$

$$h[1] = 0.5(0.5) + 0.5(0) = 0.25$$

$$h[2] = 0.5(0.25) + 0.5(0) = 0.125 \quad \text{etc.}$$

The first few values of $h[n]$ are shown in part (b) of the figure. The oven temperature starts at 40°C, rises at 1°C per second, and is sampled every 10 seconds. Taking the scaling factor of 10 into account, the input signal $x[n]$ to the filter is therefore as shown in part (c) of the figure. Convolution of $x[n]$ with $h[n]$ yields the following first 5 filter output values

$$y[0] = 0.5(4) = 2.0$$

$$y[1] = 0.5(5) + 0.25(4) = 3.5$$

$$y[2] = 0.5(6) + 0.25(5) + 0.125(4) = 4.75$$

$$y[3] = 0.5(7) + 0.25(6) + 0.125(5) + 0.0625(4) = 5.875$$

$$y[4] = 0.5(8) + 0.25(7) + 0.125(6) + 0.0625(5) + 0.03125(4) = 6.9375$$

(b) The recursive recurrence formula of the filter is

$$y[n] = 0.5y[n-1] + 0.5x[n]$$

We may use it to compute successive values of $y[n]$, assuming that the first value in storage array Y is $y[-1]$ and equals zero. Thus

$$y[0] = 0.5(0) + 0.5(4) = 2.0$$

$$y[1] = 0.5(2.0) + 0.5(5) = 3.5$$

$$y[2] = 0.5(3.5) + 0.5(6) = 4.75$$

$$y[3] = 0.5(4.75) + 0.5(7) = 5.875$$

$$y[4] = 0.5(5.875) + 0.5(8) = 6.9375$$

$$y[5] = 0.5(6.9375) + 0.5(9) = 7.9688$$

$$y[6] = 0.5(7.9688) + 0.5(10) = 8.9844$$

$$y[7] = 0.5(8.9844) + 0.5(11) = 9.9922$$

$$y[8] = 0.5(9.9922) + 0.5(12) = 10.9961$$

$$y[9] = 0.5(10.9961) + 0.5(13) = 11.9981 \quad \text{etc.}$$

It is therefore clear that $y[n]$ is tending to follow $x[n]$, but with a steady-state error of -1.00, representing $-10°C$. Its first 5 values agree with those already estimated in (a) above. $y[n]$ is also shown in part (c) of the figure.

(c) The particular component of the solution, $y_p[n]$, represents the steady-state response of the filter, and the above results show that it must be given by

$$y_p[n] = x[n] - 1.00 \qquad n \geqslant -1$$

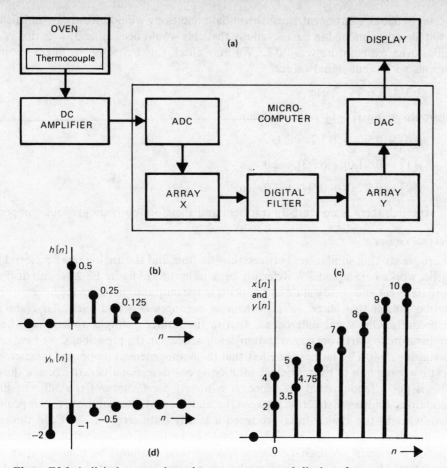

Figure E3.3 A digital approach to the measurement and display of oven temperature.

If extended back to $n = -1$, it would have the value

$$y_p[-1] = 2$$

However, $y[-1]$ must be zero to satisfy the initial conditions. So we require a homogeneous component of the solution $y_h[n]$ such that $y_h[-1] = -2$. Now $y_h[n]$ must obey the relationship

$$y_h[n] - 0.5y_h[n-1] = 0 \qquad n \geqslant 0$$

Hence

$$y_h[0] = 0.5(-2) = -1.00$$

$$y_h[1] = 0.5(-1.00) = -0.50$$

$$y_h[2] = 0.5(-0.50) = -0.25 \quad \text{etc.}$$

$y_h[n]$ is shown in part (d) of the figure. Clearly, the homogeneous component is a scaled and inverted version of the filter's impulse response $h[n]$.

(d) If the particular component $y_p[n]$ had *zero* value at $n = -1$, there would be no need for a homogeneous component since the initial conditions would already be satisfied. The result already obtained in part (c) shows that this would occur if $x[0] = 2$, that is, if the initial oven temperature was 20°C. We may check this by using the filter's recurrence formula with input signal values

2, 3, 4, 5, 6, 7 ... etc.

Again assuming $y[-1] = 0$, we obtain

$y[0] = 0.5(0) + 0.5(2) = 1.0$

$y[1] = 0.5(1.0) + 0.5(3) = 2.0$

$y[2] = 0.5(2.0) + 0.5(4) = 3.0$ etc.

As expected, there is no start-up transient and therefore no homogeneous component.

General comments

There are striking similarities between this solution, and the analog one developed in the earlier worked example E3.2. Referring back to part (c) of figure E3.2, we can distinguish both transient and steady-state components in the output signal from the filter—although we did not, at that stage, refer to them as homogeneous and particular components respectively. One slight difference is that in the former example we assumed the oven temperature to start from a zero 'datum' level, whereas in the present case we have taken it as starting at 40°C. This has the effect that the homogeneous component must provide a positive correction to the particular solution in one case, but a negative one in the other. This is not a fundamental difference. It is merely a reflection of the different starting conditions. Another distinction between the analog and digital solutions to this problem is that, whereas the analog filter produced a steady-state error of -5°C, in the present example it is -10°C. However, this should not be taken to mean that the digital filter method is inferior. Somewhat different effective time constants have been chosen for the two filters. The digital filter, although having a larger steady-state error, also produces a more pronounced low-pass, or smoothing, action. It would therefore give a better reduction of any high-frequency noise present. The analog and digital approaches are, in fact, strictly equivalent in this respect.

3.7 Other aspects of convolution

Convolution has so far been presented as a method of finding the output signal from an LTI system, given its impulse response and input signal. This time-domain operation is indeed one of the most valuable and commonly used in the whole field of signals and systems. However, convolution has rather wider uses and implications than this, and we use this short section to summarise some of them.

We have already referred several times to the fact that convolution is *commutative*. That is to say, given two discrete-time functions or signals $x_1[n]$ and $x_2[n]$, or two continuous-time ones $x_1(t)$ and $x_2(t)$, we may write

$$x_1[n]*x_2[n] = x_2[n]*x_1[n]; \quad \text{and} \quad x_1(t)*x_2(t) = x_2(t)*x_1(t) \tag{3.51}$$

Recalling that in the graphical interpretation of convolution one function is reversed beneath the other, followed by cross-multiplication and summation (or integration), the commutative property implies that it makes no difference which of the two functions is reversed. In terms of an input signal and an impulse response, it also means that the roles of the two functions are interchangeable. An input signal $x[n]$ applied to a discrete LTI system with impulse response $h[n]$ would produce exactly the same output signal as an input $h[n]$ applied to a system with impulse response $x[n]$.

There are two more basic aspects of convolution which should be discussed here. These are the *associative* property (already mentioned briefly in section 2.3.1), and the *distributive* property. The associative property may be summarised by the following expressions

$$x[n]*\{h_1[n]*h_2[n]\} = \{x[n]*h_1[n]*h_2[n]\}$$

and

$$x(t)*\{h_1(t)*h_2(t)\} = \{x(t)*h_1(t)*h_2(t)\} \qquad (3.52)$$

Its main practical implication is that a cascaded combination of two or more LTI systems may be condensed into a single LTI system. The overall impulse response is found by convolving the individual impulse responses. This may be demonstrated quite easily in the discrete case. Suppose, for example, we have two discrete systems in cascade as shown in figure 3.16, with impulse responses $h_1[n]$ and $h_2[n]$, and an input signal $x[n]$. We may find the overall output $y[n]$ in two ways: *either* by convolving $h_1[n]$ with $h_2[n]$ to produce the impulse response $h[n]$ of the overall system, and then convolving $h[n]$ with $x[n]$, *or* by convolving $h_1[n]$ with $x[n]$, and then convolving the result with $h_2[n]$. The reader is encouraged to check the equivalence of these two methods of finding $y[n]$, for the particular functions shown in the figure.

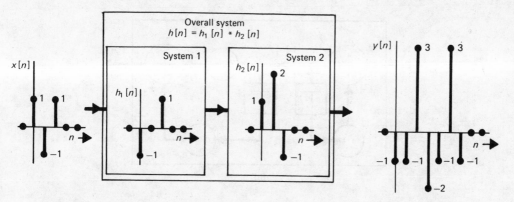

Figure 3.16 An application of the associative property of convolution and LTI systems.

Whereas the associative property of convolution has important implications for cascaded LTI systems, its *distributive* property has important implications for LTI systems in *parallel*. It may be summarised as follows

$$x[n]*\{h_1[n] + h_2[n]\} = \{x[n]*h_1[n]\} + \{x[n]*h_2[n]\}$$

or, in the continuous case

$$x(t)*\{h_1(t) + h_2(t)\} = \{x(t)*h_1(t)\} + \{x(t)*h_2(t)\} \qquad (3.53)$$

Thus if we have systems in parallel, they are equivalent to a single system whose impulse response equals the *sum* of the individual impulse responses. This is perhaps a rather more obvious result than that implied by the associative property, and there seems little need to demonstrate it by an example (although it is illustrated by problem Q3.20 at the end of this chapter).

The first-mentioned of these three major properties of convolution—commutativity—has a useful practical application in reducing the complexity of discrete recursive LTI systems. We may show this in the following way. Suppose we need to implement a filter in electronic hardware, and it has the following first-order difference equation

$$a_0 y[n] + a_1 y[n-1] = b_0 x[n] + b_1 x[n-1] \tag{3.54}$$

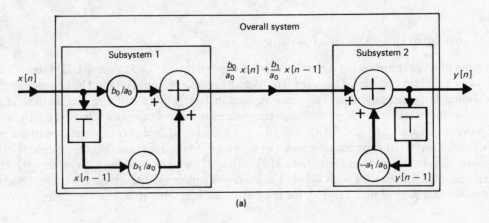

(a)

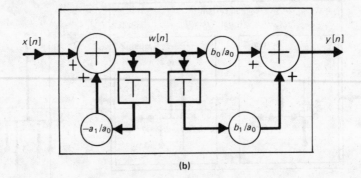

(b)

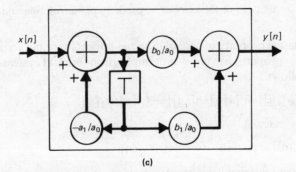

(c)

Figure 3.17 Using the commutative property of convolution and LTI systems to reduce the hardware complexity of a discrete recursive filter.

We may rewrite the equation, making $y[n]$ the subject

$$y[n] = -\frac{a_1}{a_0} y[n-1] + \frac{b_0}{a_0} x[n] + \frac{b_1}{a_0} x[n-1] \tag{3.55}$$

The two input (x) terms may be implemented by subsystem 1 in the block diagram of figure 3.17(a). These are combined with the feedback, or recursive, term $-(a_1/a_0)(y[n-1])$ in subsystem 2, producing the output $y[n]$. This particular arrangement would clearly need 2 delay units, 3 multipliers, and 2 adders, and is often referred to as the *direct form I realisation*. However, the commutative property of convolution for LTI systems means that the order of cascaded systems may be altered, without affecting the overall performance. Therefore we may interchange subsystems 1 and 2 to give the overall system shown in part (b) of the figure. Note that the signal $w[n]$ at the output of the first adder is passed into two parallel delay units. This is clearly unnecessary, and we can make a saving of one delay unit as shown in figure 3.17(c). This alternative scheme is often called a *direct form II realisation*. Another name is *canonic realisation*, which implies that it uses the smallest possible number of delay units, and hence the minimum amount of storage. Although the saving in this simple example may not seem very significant, it can be a great deal more worthwhile in complicated systems.

Everything we have said so far about convolution has implied that it is a time-domain procedure for use in the analysis of signals and linear systems. However, convolution may also be thought of as a mathematical operation to be carried out on two functions—regardless of what those functions represent. Taking this broader view, it need cause no surprise that the convolution integral is used, for example, in the theory of probability and random processes. In this case the functions convolved are certainly not time functions representing signals and systems! Even in the context of the present book, we shall see that convolution has wider uses and implications than those so far discussed. For example, some of the modulation techniques which are so important in electronic communications involve convolution of *frequency* functions. The reader is therefore asked to bear in mind that the story of convolution presented in this chapter, although reasonably comprehensive in the context of signals and LTI systems, is not complete.

Problems to chapter 3

Sections 3.2 and 3.3

Q3.1. Describe the various signals shown in figure Q3.1, using sets of weighted, shifted, unit impulse functions.

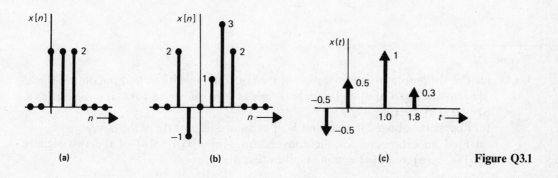

(a)   (b)   (c)   **Figure Q3.1**

Q3.2. Which of the following impulse responses describe causal, stable, LTI systems? Give reasons for your answers.

(a) $h[n] = 4\delta[n-1]$

(b) $h[n] = 2u[n-3] + 5u[n+2]$

(c) $h(t) = \delta(t) + u(t-2)$

(d) $h(t) = \{\sin t\}u(t)$

(e) $h[n] = \cos\dfrac{n\pi}{4}, \qquad -1 < n < 10$

$h[n] = 0, \quad$ elsewhere

(f) $h(t) = 2\exp(-2t)\sin\left(3t + \dfrac{\pi}{2}\right), \qquad t > 0$

$h(t) = 0, \qquad t < 0$

(g) $h(t) = \displaystyle\sum_{k=0}^{\infty} \delta(t-k).$

Q3.3. (a) Sketch carefully the step responses of the systems whose impulse responses are defined in parts (a), (c) and (g) of Q3.2.

(b) The combination of a capacitor and a resistor shown in figure Q3.3(a) is widely used as a simple high-pass filter (that is, one which transmits strongly sinusoidal signals above a certain frequency, but reduces signals of lower frequencies). If the output voltage $v_2(t)$ is measured on open-circuit, then the circuit's step response $s(t)$ may be shown to be as illustrated in part (b) of the figure. Find an expression for, and sketch, its impulse response $h(t)$.

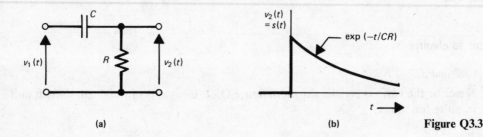

(a)   (b)   **Figure Q3.3**

Section 3.4

Q3.4. (a) Use the graphical interpretation of the convolution sum to find the output signal $y[n]$ for the input $x[n]$ and impulse response $h[n]$ shown in part (a) of figure Q3.4. Sketch $y[n]$ carefully.

(b) Repeat the above for $x[n]$ and $h[n]$ as shown in part (b) of the figure.

(c) Find an expression for the convolution $y[n] = x[n]*h[n]$ of the two signals: $x[n] = \alpha^n u[n]$ and $h[n] = \beta^n u[n]$, given that $\alpha \neq \beta$.

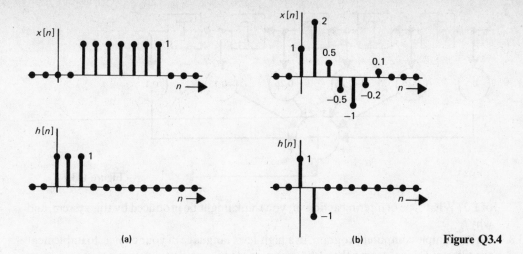

(a)   (b)   **Figure Q3.4**

Q3.5. If the solution to part (a) of Q3.4 is expressed in the form of a convolution sum

$$y[n] = \sum_{k=-\infty}^{\infty} h[k]x[n-k]$$

what actual ranges of the integer variable k are required, given the time-limited nature of $x[n]$ and $h[n]$?

Q3.6. A 5-term moving-average low-pass filter is defined by the following difference equation

$$y[n] = \frac{1}{5} \sum_{k=-2}^{2} x[n-k]$$

It is used to smooth the discrete signal shown in figure Q3.6, which represents a recording of mean daily wind speed through the month of January in Mallaig, Scotland. Estimate (at least) the first 10 finite output values from the filter, and the 4 values representing the transient which occurs at the end of the input data.

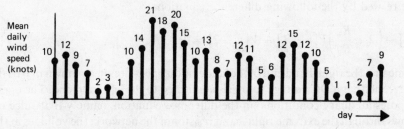

Figure Q3.6

Sketch $y[n]$ carefully, and make sure you can identify the transients. Can you think of any way of reducing the transients and, if so, do you think it would have much practical value?

Q3.7 Figure Q3.7 shows a block diagram representation of a nonrecursive digital filter. Find and sketch its impulse response $h[n]$ and its step response $s[n]$. Why does the step response settle to zero, even though a unit step function $u[n]$ continues forever at a level

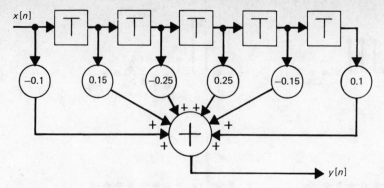

Figure Q3.7

of 1.0? What type of filtering action do you think might be produced by this system, and why?

Q3.8.   Write a simple computer program, in a high-level language of your choice, to implement the filter of Q3.7. Assume that 1000 pre-recorded input signal values are stored in an array X, and that the filtered output is to be loaded into an array Y.

Q3.9.   A discrete recursive filter is defined by the differnece equation

$$y[n] - 0.6y[n-1] + 0.4y[n-2] = x[n]$$

Calculate the first 10 terms of its impulse response $h[n]$ and of its step response $s[n]$, correct to at least 3 decimal figures. Sketch both functions. Approximately what sampled sinusoidal frequency do you think this filter would transmit most strongly, if the sampling interval of the system is 1 ms, and why?

Q3.10. (*Note:* This problem covers an interesting and useful application of difference equations to resistive 'ladder' networks, including the DAC network we have already met in chapter 1. The discrete 'signals' to be derived here do not represent time functions, but functions of *position* along the ladder.)

A few sections of a resistive ladder network are shown in figure Q3.10(a). The network should be imagined as continuing to both sides of the figure. Voltages and currents are as specified. It is convenient to consider the ladder section to the right of the nth section to be the $(n-1)$th section, and so on. Show that the voltages at successive nodes of the ladder are related by the following difference equation

$$V[n] - \left(2 + \frac{R_1}{R_2}\right)V[n-1] + V[n-2] = 0$$

Now assume that the right-hand end of the ladder is on open-circuit, as shown in part (b) of the figure, and that a DC voltage source is connected to the left-hand end. The open-circuit imposes auxiliary conditions on the difference equation, namely that since no current flows through the extreme right-hand resistor of the network, the voltages at the two right-hand nodes *must be the same*. Assume, for convenience, that this voltage is 1 volt, and that the extreme right-hand node is numbered $[-1]$. Then the auxiliary conditions are

$$V[-1] = V[0] = 1$$

(a) Let $R_2 = 2R_1$. Use the difference equation to find the voltage present at node $[8]$. If a DC voltage source of 5 volts is *actually* connected to node $[8]$, what voltage will *actually* appear at node $[-1]$?

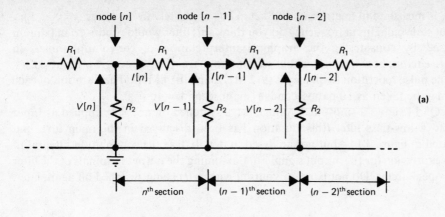

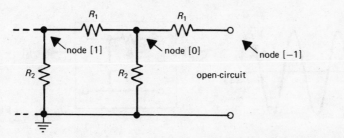

(b) Let $R_2 = 2R_1$, but now terminate the right-hand end of the network by connecting a resistor of value R_1 between node $[-1]$ and earth. Find the new auxiliary conditions. If the voltage at node $[-1]$ is 1 mV, what must be the voltage at node $[8]$? What is the relationship between this network and the R–$2R$ ladder network used as a DAC, and described in chapter 1? How difficult (or easy) would it be to obtain the above results using the basic rules of DC circuit analysis?

Section 3.5

Q3.11. Use the convolution integral to find and sketch the output signal $y(t)$ of a continuous LTI system, given the following input signals and impulse responses

(a) $x(t) = \exp(-t)u(t)$ and $h(t) = u(t - 2)$
(b) $x(t) = \exp(t)$, $t < 0$; $x(t) = \exp(-t)$, $t > 0$ and
     $h(t) = 1$, $0 < t < 1$; $h(t) = 0$ elsewhere
(c) $x(t) = \sin \pi t$, $0 < t < 2$; $x(t) = 0$ elsewhere, and $h(t)$ as in part (b) above.

Q3.12. In section 3.5 of the main text we have described the distortion of a rectangular pulse, as it passes through a cable modelled by a simple *low-pass RC* circuit. In problem Q3.3 above the step response of a simple *high pass RC* circuit is given. Use this information to estimate the response of such a high-pass circuit with a time constant $RC = 0.5 \ \mu s$ to a rectangular voltage pulse of magnitude 1 volt and duration 1 μs. Sketch carefully the output pulse, and compare it with part (d) of figure 3.13 in the main text. Can you account qualitatively for the differences between the two types of distortion?

Q3.13. The impulse response of an analog bandpass filter is given by

$$h(t) = \{\exp(-t) \sin 4\pi t\}u(t)$$

where t is measured in microseconds. Sketch $h(t)$ accurately in the range $0 < t < 3 \ \mu s$. To what sinusoidal input frequency do you think this filter would produce a maximum response? By considering the graphical interpretation of convolution, infer, in *qualitative terms*, how the filter would respond to a 'train' of very narrow input pulses, when the pulse repetition frequency is (a) 2 MHz, and (b) 4 MHz. The duration of each pulse may be taken as 50 nanoseconds (1 nanosecond $= 10^{-9}$ s).

Q3.14. Figure Q3.14 shows a sinusoidal voltage $v_1(t)$, switched on at $t = 0$, applied as input signal to a low-pass filter (this situation has been discussed in the main text, and illustrated in figure 3.14—but not analysed in detail). Use the convolution integral to find an expression for the output signal $v_2(t)$, assuming the output terminals of the filter are on open-circuit. Do not concern yourself with $v_1(t)$ being switched off again later.

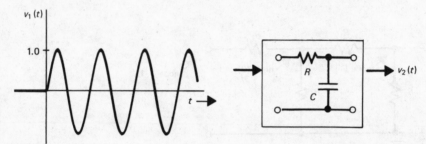

Figure Q3.14

Assume that $RC = 1$ ms, and that the signal frequency is 1000 radians/second. Sketch the form of $v_2(t)$ accurately in the interval $0 < t < 6$ ms. After the initial switching transient has died away, what is the amplitude of the output signal?

   Hint: The numerical values in your solution will be much simpler if you take 1 ms as a unit of time, and 1000 radians/second as a unit of frequency.

Q3.15. Worked example E3.2 in the main text concerned the measurement of oven temperature using a thermocouple, followed by amplification and filtering of the signal with a continuous filter. The oven temperature was assumed to rise at a steady rate of 1°C per second. Repeat the convolution for the case when the oven temperature $x(t)$ is initially steady at 20°C, and then rises exponentially towards a final value of 520°C according to the expression

$$x(t) = \{20 + 500[1 - \exp(-t/\tau_0)]\}°C, \qquad t > 0$$

where the thermal time constant of the oven, τ_0, is 250 seconds. The filter's time constant is 5 seconds.

   What error in temperature reading is caused by the filter at the following times: (a) $t = 100$ s, (b) $t = 250$ s, (c) $t = 500$ s, (d) $t \to \infty$? Why does the error reduce as time proceeds?

Q3.16. It is quite common to use electronic systems based on radar or optical techniques for the automatic tracking of airborne objects such as projectiles or weather balloons. In a particular case, a projectile is fired upwards from the ground with an initial vertical velocity of $100 \ m \ s^{-1}$. Taking the acceleration due to gravity (g) as $10 \ m \ s^{-2}$, and neglecting effects such as air resistance, its height above the ground after t seconds is given by

$$d(t) = 100t - 5t^2 \text{ metres}, \qquad 0 < t < 20$$

An automatic tracking system, used to follow the vertical trajectory, generates a voltage signal proportional to $d(t)$. However, the signal is subject to high-frequency noise, and is therefore low-pass filtered prior to recording. A first-order *RC* filter is used, having a time constant of 1 second. Use the convolution integral to estimate the height error introduced by use of the filter, at the instant when the projectile reaches its *highest point* above the ground.

Section 3.6

Q3.17. A discrete, recursive, LTI system is described by the following difference equation

$$y[n] - 1.6y[n - 1] + 0.8y[n - 2] = x[n]$$

Compute the first 20 values of its step response $s[n]$, assuming that the system has settled, or come to rest, prior to $n = 0$. What would be the steady-state value reached by $s[n]$ as $n \to \infty$? Change the initial conditions to $y[-2] = 1.25$, $y[-1] = 0$, and assess the effect this has on the step response of the system.

Q3.18. A digital filter with the recurrence formula

$$y[n] = -y[n - 1] - 0.5y[n - 2] + x[n]$$

has an input signal given by

$$x[n] = \frac{2}{\sqrt{3}} \sin\left(\frac{2n\pi}{3} + \frac{\pi}{3}\right) u[n]$$

Use the recurrence formula to compute the output signal values $y[0]$ to $y[12]$ inclusive, given the auxiliary conditions $y[-2] = y[-1] = 0$. Infer the form of the particular solution $y_p[n]$ and, by extending it back to $n = -1$ and $n = -2$, infer the homogeneous solution $y_h[n]$. Tabulate the values of $y[n]$, $y_p[n]$ and $y_h[n]$ to 2 decimal places over the range $-2 \leqslant n \leqslant 9$, and check that $y[n] = y_p[n] + y_h[n]$.

Section 3.7

Q3.19. Two identical first-order, low-pass, *RC* filters are cascaded as shown in figure Q3.19. A voltage follower (as described in section 1.4.3 of the main text) is inserted between them to act as a 'buffer'. This means that the first filter is not significantly loaded by the second one, and both filters may be assumed to have open-circuit outputs. Use the associative property of convolution and LTI systems to determine the impulse response of the overall system, and sketch its waveform.

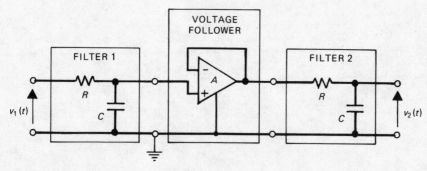

Figure Q3.19

Q3.20. Two discrete LTI subsystems, whose recurrence formula are given in figure Q3.20, are connected in parallel to form an overall system. Use the distributive property of convolution and LTI systems to find the impulse response $h[n]$ of the overall system for $0 \leqslant n \leqslant 8$, and sketch it carefully over this range.

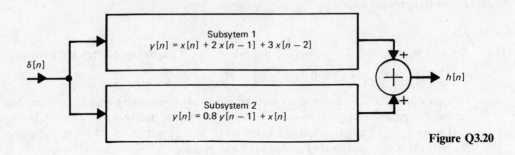

Figure Q3.20

4 Fourier Analysis: Continuous Signals and Systems

"Thus it appears that the lobster's tail is composed of a series of segments which are fundamentally similar, though each presents peculiar modifications of the plan common to all."

from an essay by T.H. Huxley
(1825–1895)

4.1 Introduction

Jean Baptiste Joseph, Baron de Fourier, was thirty years old when he accompanied Napoleon on the latter's Egyptian campaign in 1798. He became governor of Lower Egypt and contributed many scientific papers to the Egyptian Institute which Napoleon founded, but when the French army capitulated in 1801 he returned to France and was made Prefect of the Department of Grenoble.

In 1807 Fourier submitted his ideas on the solution of heat flow problems using trigonometric series to the Institut de France. The value of such series for describing the motion of vibrating strings had been strongly debated for over 50 years, and Fourier's ideas were considered too controversial to be accepted. It was therefore another 15 years before his monumental treatise, *Théorie analytique de la chaleur*, was published. In it, Fourier confirmed that periodic signals could be represented as weighted sums of harmonically related sinusoidal frequencies, and, very importantly, he went on to show that nonrepetitive, or *aperiodic*, signals could be considered as the infinite sum (or integral) of sinusoids which are *not* harmonically related. As we shall see, these two key ideas form the basis of the *Fourier Series* and the *Fourier Transform* respectively. Originally applied to heat flow, they have had a profound influence on many branches of engineering and applied science, and constitute one of the principal tools for the frequency-domain analysis of signals and LTI systems.

The whole structure of frequency-domain analysis so permeates modern electronic engineering that a number of related ideas have already received a mention in this book. For example, in section 1.2 the possibility of using a digital computer to perform a frequency analysis of a biomedical signal (the EEG) was outlined. Our review of the *j*-notation in section 1.4.2

emphasised that impedances are essentially frequency-domain functions, and made the point that a complex signal may be considered as the summation, or superposition, of a number of sines and cosines of suitable frequency, amplitude, and relative phase. Section 2.1 referred to the filtering of signals on the basis of their frequency ranges, or bands, and in section 2.2 we saw that exponential functions—which include sine and cosine waves—form an extremely important family of basic signals. These are just some examples of the invasion of earlier chapters of this text by ideas which stem from the work of Fourier.

In the previous chapter we saw how the input signal and impulse response of an LTI system may be convolved to produce the output signal. This raises an obvious question: if convolution in the time-domain offers such a satisfactory method of analysing signal flow through linear systems, why do we need an alternative frequency-domain approach at all? There are a number of reasons, of which the following are perhaps the most important:

Exponential and sinusoidal signals occur quite often in the natural world, and in the world of technology, and are generally best dealt with using a frequency-domain approach. For example, the j-notation offers a fast and convenient method for solving linear circuit problems under conditions of steady-state sinusoidal excitation.

Even when a signal is not exponential or sinusoidal in form, it may be analysed into component frequencies. As we have noted in section 1.4.2, the response of any LTI system to each such component is quite simple. All it can do is alter the amplitude and phase, *not* the frequency. The output signal may then be found by superposition.

If frequency-domain functions are used to describe both an input signal and an LTI system, then, as we shall see a little later, a third frequency-domain function representing the output signal may be found by *multiplication*. Multiplication is often simpler to perform, and visualise, than the equivalent time-domain *convolution*.

The practical design of systems such as those used in electronic communications often starts from a specification based upon frequencies and frequency bands. For example, certain frequency ranges are well known to be much more suitable for long-range radio communication than others, because of the effects of propagation through the earth's atmosphere. Clearly, the frequency content of any signals to be transmitted via such systems should be considered at an early stage of the design.

We must therefore regard Fourier analysis, and the other frequency-domain techniques to be covered in chapter 6, as essentially *complementary* to time-domain convolution. As we progress through these chapters, it should become clear which types of problem are most likely to be successfully, and economically, tackled by a frequency-domain approach.

In much of this book the applications of ideas to continuous and discrete signals and systems are developed side by side, to emphasise the close parallels between them. In the case of Fourier analysis, however, we deliberately cover continuous signals and systems before considering the discrete case. In part, this decision reflects the historical development of Fourier techniques, which was concerned exclusively with continuous-time phenomena; in part it follows the fairly common view that, although the concepts of Fourier analysis are certainly of great value in discrete time, their applications to electrical and electronic engineering are more *naturally* introduced by reference to analog signals, circuits, and systems.

4.2 Continuous signals

4.2.1 *Signals, vectors, and orthogonal functions*

A fundamental notion of Fourier analysis is that practical signals may be broken down into sets of sinusoidal (or exponential) functions of appropriate frequency, amplitude, and phase. Conversely, we may in principle build up, or *synthesise*, a practical signal waveform by adding together a number of such basic functions. In theory, it may be necessary to add an infinite number of them in order to synthesise the signal perfectly. In practice, of course, we must work with a finite number, producing a waveform which is an *approximation* to the actual shape. Before we get down to the details of Fourier analysis, it is worth considering the whole question of signal approximation by a set of basic sinusoidal functions from a rather general point of view. This will help put the rest of the chapter's material into a wider perspective.

If a signal is strictly repetitive, or *periodic*, then the sinusoidal waves needed to synthesise it are *harmonically related*. In other words, their frequencies bear a simple integer relationship to one another. Let us take an example. Suppose we wish to build up the periodic sawtooth signal shown in figure 4.1(a). Such signals are of considerable practical importance—for example, they are widely used as *timebase* waveforms in TV receivers and oscilloscopes to control the

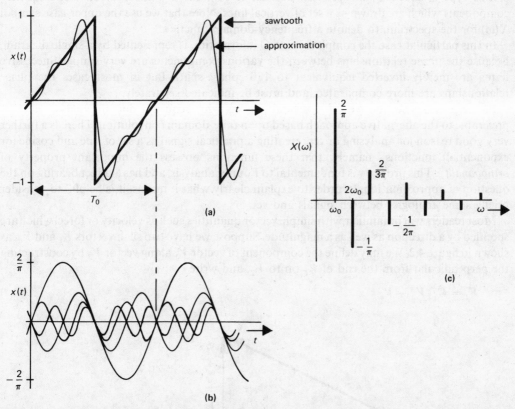

Figure 4.1 (a) A periodic sawtooth signal, (b) the first four terms of its Fourier Series, and (c) its frequency spectrum. Also shown in part (a) is an approximation of the signal formed by summing the four sinusoids in part (b).

horizontal deflection of the 'flying spot' on the tubeface. Using formulae which we develop in the next section, this may be represented by the following *Fourier Series*

$$x(t) = \frac{2}{\pi} \sin \omega_0 t - \frac{1}{\pi} \sin 2\omega_0 t + \frac{2}{3\pi} \sin 3\omega_0 t$$

$$- \frac{1}{2\pi} \sin 4\omega_0 t + \frac{2}{5\pi} \sin 5\omega_0 t - \ldots \tag{4.1}$$

The sawtooth therefore contains the angular frequencies ω_0 (known as the *fundamental* component), $2\omega_0$ (the *second harmonic*), $3\omega_0$ (the *third harmonic*), and so on, with amplitudes which diminish with frequency. Note that the fundamental component $(2/\pi) \sin \omega_0 t$ has the same period $(T_0 = 2\pi/\omega_0)$ as the sawtooth itself. Theoretically, the series contains an infinite number of terms. If we sum a limited number of them—say just the first four, which are drawn in figure 4.1(b)—we obtain an approximation to the true signal. This approximation is also shown in part (a) of the figure. The approximation is poorest in those regions where the sawtooth undergoes sharp changes or transitions. This is not surprising, because sudden changes are rich in the higher-order harmonics which we have omitted.

The Fourier Series for the sawtooth is summarised graphically by the *frequency spectrum* of figure 4.1(c), which indicates the amplitudes of the various components in the signal. A spectrum of this type is called a *line spectrum* because it contains a number of distinct frequency components which are drawn as a set of vertical lines. Note that we use the upper-case symbol $X(\omega)$ for the spectrum, to denote a frequency-domain function.

In this particular case the complete spectral information is represented by a single diagram, because the phase relationships between the various components are very simple. Successive terms are merely inverted (equivalent to 180° phase-shift). But in most cases the phase relationships are more complicated, and must be indicated separately.

In the previous section we listed several reasons why frequency-domain analysis may be preferable to the alternative approach based upon time-domain convolution. There is a further very good reason for analysing or representing a practical signal as a set of sine and cosine (or exponential) functions—namely, that these functions possess the important property of *orthogonality*. This property is fundamental to Fourier analysis, and has a direct bearing on the question of approximation. In order to explain clearly what it means, it is helpful to consider briefly some analogies between signals and vectors.

Most readers will be familiar with simple vector quantities such as velocity or force, which are specified by a direction as well as a magnitude. Suppose we have two such vectors V_1 and V_2, as shown in figure 4.2. We may define the component of vector V_1 along vector V_2 by constructing the perpendicular from the end of V_1 on to V_2, and write

$$V_1 = C_{12} V_2 + V_e \tag{4.2}$$

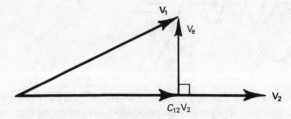

Figure 4.2 Vectors and orthogonality.

where C_{12} is a scalar multiplier, or coefficient. Thus if we are trying to approximate V_1 by a vector in the direction of V_2, the error in the approximation is the vector V_e. The *best* approximation is obtained when C_{12} is chosen to make the error vector as short as possible (as in the figure). We then say that the component of V_1 along V_2 equals $C_{12}V_2$. If C_{12} is zero, then one vector has no component along the other and the vectors are *orthogonal*. Conversely if $C_{12} = 1$ and V_e is zero, V_1 and V_2 must be identical in both magnitude and direction.

Similar ideas apply to signals. Suppose we wish to approximate a signal $x_1(t)$ over a certain interval $t_1 < t < t_2$ by another signal $x_2(t)$. In the context of the present chapter, we may think of $x_2(t)$ as a sinusoidal or exponential waveform. We therefore write

$$x_1(t) = C_{12}x_2(t) + x_e(t) \qquad t_1 < t < t_2 \tag{4.3}$$

where $x_e(t)$ is a third signal representing the approximation error. Now $x_e(t)$ will, in general, vary over the specified time interval, and we need to consider carefully how it may be 'minimised' by adjusting the value of C_{12}.

At first sight, it might appear sensible to minimise the *average* value of $x_e(t)$ over the interval $t_1 < t < t_2$. However, the disadvantages of such an *error criterion* is that positive and negative errors occurring at different instants would tend to cancel each other out. This difficulty is avoided if we adjust C_{12} to minimise the average, or mean, *squared* error (if we think of $x_e(t)$ as an electrial voltage or current this is equivalent to minimising the *error power*; it is also the same as minimising the *root mean square, or r.m.s., error*). The mean square error over the chosen time interval is given by

$$\overline{x_e^2(t)} = \frac{1}{(t_2 - t_1)} \int_{t_1}^{t_2} x_e^2(t)\, dt = \frac{1}{(t_2 - t_1)} \int_{t_1}^{t_2} \{x_1(t) - C_{12}x_2(t)\}^2 \, dt \tag{4.4}$$

The value of C_{12} which minimises this function may be found by differentiating with respect to C_{12} and equating to zero

$$\frac{d}{dC_{12}} \left[\frac{1}{(t_2 - t_1)} \int_{t_1}^{t_2} \{x_1(t) - C_{12}x_2(t)\}^2 \, dt \right] = 0 \tag{4.5}$$

Expanding the bracket and changing the order of integration and differentiation, we obtain

$$\frac{1}{(t_2 - t_1)} \left[\int_{t_1}^{t_2} \frac{d}{dC_{12}} x_1^2(t) \, dt - 2 \int_{t_1}^{t_2} \frac{d}{dC_{12}} x_1(t)C_{12}x_2(t) \, dt \right.$$
$$\left. + \int_{t_1}^{t_2} \frac{d}{dC_{12}} C_{12}^2 x_2^2(t) \, dt \right] = 0 \tag{4.6}$$

The first integral within the square brackets is zero, since $x_1(t)$ is not a function of C_{12}. Hence

$$\frac{1}{(t_2 - t_1)} \left[-2 \int_{t_1}^{t_2} x_1(t)x_2(t) \, dt + 2C_{12} \int_{t_1}^{t_2} x_2^2(t) \, dt \right] = 0$$

and therefore

$$C_{12} = \frac{\int_{t_1}^{t_2} x_1(t)x_2(t) \, dt}{\int_{t_1}^{t_2} x_2^2(t) \, dt} \tag{4.7}$$

By direct analogy with the vectors shown in figure 4.2, if C_{12} is zero we say that $x_1(t)$ contains no component of $x_2(t)$, and that the signals are orthogonal in the interval $t_1 < t < t_2$. In this case it is clear that

$$\int_{t_1}^{t_2} x_1(t)x_2(t) = 0 \tag{4.8}$$

Conversely if $x_1(t)$ and $x_2(t)$ are identical over the selected interval, C_{12} must equal unity.

We now relate this important result to the Fourier Series for the sawtooth waveform already quoted in equation (4.1). Suppose, for example, we try to approximate the sawtooth by a sinusoid at the fundamental frequency ω_0, without for the moment concerning ourselves with the second and higher-order harmonics. Since the sawtooth and the fundamental component are both strictly periodic with the same period T_0, it is clear that an approximation over one complete period must be equally valid for all *other* periods of the waveforms—and therefore for all time. Denoting the sawtooth signal in figure 4.1(a) by $x_1(t)$, one period is

$$x_1(t) = \frac{2t}{T_0}, \qquad 0 < t < \frac{T_0}{2}$$

$$= \frac{2t}{T_0} - 2, \qquad \frac{T_0}{2} < t < T_0$$

Alternatively, if we write $T_0 = 2\pi/\omega_0$, then

$$x_1(t) = \frac{\omega_0 t}{\pi}, \qquad 0 < t < \frac{\pi}{\omega_0}$$

$$= \frac{\omega_0 t}{\pi} - 2, \qquad \frac{\pi}{\omega_0} < t < \frac{2\pi}{\omega_0} \tag{4.9}$$

Let us now approximate it over the interval $0 < t < 2\pi/\omega_0$ by the sinusoid

$$x_2(t) = \sin \omega_0 t$$

Equation (4.7) becomes

$$C_{12} = \frac{\displaystyle\int_0^{\pi/\omega_0} \frac{\omega_0 t}{\pi} \sin(\omega_0 t)\,dt + \int_{\pi/\omega_0}^{2\pi/\omega_0} \left(\frac{\omega_0 t}{\pi} - 2\right) \sin(\omega_0 t)\,dt}{\displaystyle\int_0^{2\pi/\omega_0} \sin^2(\omega_0 t)\,dt} \tag{4.10}$$

Both integrals in the numerator of this expression may readily be integrated by parts; each has the value $1/\omega_0$. The denominator is found as follows

$$\int_0^{2\pi/\omega_0} \sin^2(\omega_0 t)\,dt = \int_0^{2\pi/\omega_0} (\tfrac{1}{2} - \tfrac{1}{2} \cos 2\omega_0 t)\,dt$$

However, the integral of a cosine over a complete number of periods is zero, so we obtain

$$\int_0^{2\pi/\omega_0} \tfrac{1}{2}\,dt = \left[\frac{t}{2}\right]_0^{2\pi/\omega_0} = \frac{\pi}{\omega_0}$$

and hence

$$C_{12} = \frac{\dfrac{1}{\omega_0} + \dfrac{1}{\omega_0}}{\dfrac{\pi}{\omega_0}} = \frac{2}{\pi} \tag{4.11}$$

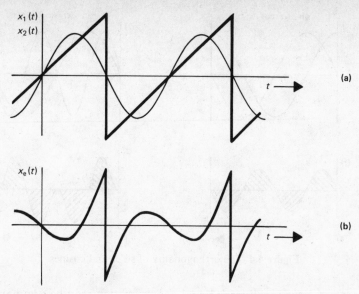

Figure 4.3 Approximation of a periodic sawtooth signal by a sinusoid at the fundamental frequency.

Therefore the 'amount' of the signal $x_2(t) = \sin \omega_0 t$ present in the sawtooth is $(2/\pi) \sin \omega_0 t$. Any other amount would give a larger mean-square error over a complete period. The sawtooth, its sinusoidal approximation, and the error signal $x_e(t)$ are all illustrated in figure 4.3.

Referring back to equation (4.1), it is interesting to see that the fundamental component of the sawtooth's Fourier Series is also $(2/\pi) \sin \omega_0 t$. This is because the Fourier method is also based upon a minimum mean-square (or 'least-square') error criterion. When we meet the formulae for calculating the amplitudes of the various harmonics in the next section, their similarity with equation (4.7) will be apparent.

There is another important point to be made. A little earlier we mentioned that an advantage of sine and cosine (or exponential) functions for signal representation is their mutual orthogonality. Thus the set of functions

and $\left. \begin{array}{l} \sin n\omega_0 t \\ \cos n\omega_0 t \end{array} \right\} \quad n = 0, 1, 2, 3, \ldots$

are orthogonal over any time interval equal to one complete period of the fundamental frequency ω_0. We do not prove this here, but instead illustrate it for two typical cases in figure 4.4. Part (a) of the figure shows one period of the waves $\sin \omega_0 t$ and $\cos \omega_0 t$, and, drawn beneath, their product. If we integrate this product the result is zero, because the shaded *positive* area above the axis equals the shaded *negative* area beneath it. Therefore equation (4.8) is satisfied and the functions $\sin \omega_0 t$ and $\cos \omega_0 t$ are orthogonal. In figure 4.4(b), the same is seen to be true for $\sin \omega_0 t$ and $\sin 2\omega_0 t$. Note that when $n = 0$, $\sin n\omega_0 t = 0$ and $\cos n\omega_0 t = 1$, so that the complete set of orthogonal functions is

$1, \sin \omega_0 t, \cos \omega_0 t, \sin 2\omega_0 t, \cos 2\omega_0 t, \ldots$

The first member of the set represents a steady level or DC component, also referred to as a zero-frequency component.

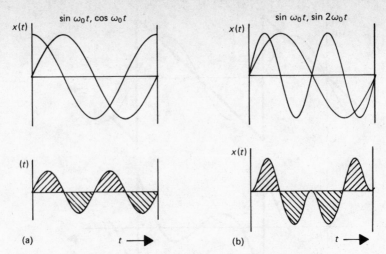

Figure 4.4 The orthogonality of sines and cosines.

The advantage of orthogonality for signal approximation may be summarised as follows. Suppose we have approximated a periodic signal—such as the sawtooth already discussed—by its fundamental component, and we now wish to improve the approximation by incorporating a second harmonic component. It is obviously a nuisance if, having found the second harmonic, we have to go back and recalculate the fundamental. In other words, it is unfortunate if the inclusion of the new term upsets the minimum mean-square error already achieved for the fundamental on its own. But it may be shown that, since the various harmonics are mutually orthogonal, such recalculation is unnecessary. (Again, no proof is offered here, although it is not a difficult one. It is included as problem Q4.1 at the end of the chapter.) The value of any one component is unaffected by incorporating further harmonics in the approximation; and the approximation is always the best (in the least-square error sense) that can be achieved with a given number of harmonic terms. This is a valuable feature of Fourier analysis.

It should not be assumed that sines and cosines (or exponentials) form the only set of orthogonal functions. There are several other such sets, including the *Legendre* and *Laguerre* polynomials, and the *Chebyshev* polynomials which we shall meet in chapter 8 in our treatment of electronic filters. However, the sine and cosine set is by far the most widely used in electrical and electronic engineering. The foregoing discussion of signal approximation and orthogonality in terms of this set leads naturally to the Fourier Series, which will now be presented in more detail.

4.2.2 *The Fourier Series*

4.2.2.1 *Analysis and synthesis of periodic signals*

The basis of the Fourier Series is that a complicated periodic waveform may be analysed into, or synthesised from, a number of harmonically related sine and cosine functions constituting an orthogonal set. If we have a continuous periodic signal $x(t)$ with a period T_0, then $x(t)$ may be represented by the series

$$x(t) = A_0 + \sum_{k=1}^{\infty} B_k \cos k\omega_0 t + \sum_{k=1}^{\infty} C_k \sin k\omega_0 t \qquad (4.12)$$

where $\omega_0 = 2\pi/T_0$. Certain restrictions, known as the *Dirichlet conditions*, must be placed on $x(t)$ for the series to be valid. The integral of the magnitude of $x(t)$ over a complete period must be finite, and the signal can have only a finite number of discontinuities in any finite interval. Fortunately, these conditions do not exclude signals of practical interest in electronic engineering.

Let us consider how the coefficients of the Fourier Series—A_0, B_k, and C_k—are determined. Recalling the minimum mean-square error criterion described in the previous section, and using equation (4.7), we obtain

$$A_0 = \frac{\int_0^{T_0} x(t)(1)\,dt}{\int_0^{T_0} (1)\,dt} = \frac{1}{T_0}\int_0^{T_0} x(t)\,dt = \frac{\omega_0}{2\pi}\int_0^{2\pi/\omega_0} x(t)\,dt \qquad (4.13)$$

A_0 is simply the average, or mean, value of the signal $x(t)$. It is also called its DC level, or zero-frequency component. The cosine coefficients B_k are given by

$$B_k = \frac{\int_0^{T_0} x(t)\cos(k\omega_0 t)\,dt}{\int_0^{T_0} \cos^2(k\omega_0 t)\,dt} \qquad (4.14)$$

Now the r.m.s. value of a cosine (or sine) wave is $1/\sqrt{2}$, and its mean-square value is $1/2$. The latter may be found by integrating the square of the waveform over one (or more) complete periods, and dividing by the baseline, giving

$$\frac{1}{T_0}\int_0^{T_0} \cos^2(k\omega_0 t)\,dt, \qquad k = 1, 2, 3$$

Since this equals $1/2$, the denominator of equation (4.14) must equal $T_0/2$ for any integer value of k. Thus

$$B_k = \frac{2}{T_0}\int_0^{T_0} x(t)\cos(k\omega_0 t)\,dt = \frac{\omega_0}{\pi}\int_0^{2\pi/\omega_0} x(t)\cos(k\omega_0 t)\,dt \qquad (4.15)$$

and similarly

$$C_k = \frac{2}{T_0}\int_0^{T_0} x(t)\sin(k\omega_0 t)\,dt = \frac{\omega_0}{\pi}\int_0^{2\pi/\omega_0} x(t)\sin(k\omega_0 t)\,dt \qquad (4.16)$$

In other words, we may find the 'amount' of any sine or cosine harmonic in a periodic signal $x(t)$ by multiplying the signal by that sine or cosine, and integrating over a complete period. Although the integration limits are given as $t = 0$ to $t = 2\pi/\omega_0$ in the above formulae, we may in fact integrate over *any* complete period. For example, it is often convenient to use the limits $t = -\pi/\omega_0$ to $+\pi/\omega_0$.

In section 2.2.1 we discussed even and odd signals, illustrating them in figure 2.6. It is intuitively fairly obvious that any even signal can only be built up using functions which are themselves even. Similarly, an odd signal can only be built up from other odd functions. Now all cosines are even, and all sines are odd. So if $x(t)$ is even, all its Fourier Series coefficients C_k must be zero, and if it is odd, all coefficients B_k must be zero. The sawtooth signal already discussed is a good example of this. Since it is an odd time function, its Fourier Series contains only sine components.

Example E4.1

Evaluate the Fourier Series coefficients for the sawtooth waveform illustrated in figure 4.1, and hence confirm the validity of equation (4.1) in the main text.

Solution

The signal is an odd function of time, hence all its cosine coefficients B_k must be zero. Furthermore, since the waveform clearly has equal areas above and below the axis, its average value, or DC component, is also zero. Thus $A_0 = 0$. In calculating the sine coefficients C_k it is convenient to integrate over the interval $t = \pm \pi/\omega_0$, since this avoids the discontinuity in the signal. Using equation (4.16) we obtain

$$C_k = \frac{\omega_0}{\pi} \int_{-\pi/\omega_0}^{\pi/\omega_0} x(t) \sin(k\omega_0 t)\, dt$$

$$= \frac{\omega_0}{\pi} \int_{-\pi/\omega_0}^{\pi/\omega_0} \frac{\omega_0 t}{\pi} \sin(k\omega_0 t)\, dt$$

$$= \left(\frac{\omega_0}{\pi}\right)^2 \int_{-\pi/\omega_0}^{\pi/\omega_0} t \sin(k\omega_0 t)\, dt$$

Integration by parts gives

$$C_k = \left(\frac{\omega_0}{\pi}\right)^2 \left\{ \left[\frac{-t}{k\omega_0} \cos(k\omega_0 t)\right]_{-\pi/\omega_0}^{\pi/\omega_0} + \int_{-\pi/\omega_0}^{\pi/\omega_0} \frac{\cos(k\omega_0 t)}{k\omega_0}\, dt \right\}$$

$$= \left(\frac{\omega_0}{\pi}\right)^2 \left\{ \frac{-\pi}{k\omega_0^2} \{\cos(k\pi) + \cos(-k\pi)\} + \left[\frac{\sin k\omega_0 t}{k^2 \omega_0^2}\right]_{-\pi/\omega_0}^{\pi/\omega_0} \right\}$$

Now $\cos k\pi = \cos(-k\pi)$, since a cosine function is even, and $\sin k\pi = 0 = \sin(-k\pi)$ for all values of the integer k. Hence

$$C_k = \left(\frac{\omega_0}{\pi}\right)^2 \left(\frac{-\pi}{k\omega_0^2}\right) 2 \cos k\pi = -\frac{2}{k\pi} \cos k\pi$$

If k is $1, 3, 5 \ldots$ then $\cos k\pi = -1$; whereas if k is $2, 4, 6 \ldots$ then $\cos k\pi = 1$. Successive coefficients C_k are therefore as follows

$$C_1 = -\frac{2}{\pi}(-1) = \frac{2}{\pi}; \qquad C_2 = -\frac{2}{2\pi}(1) = -\frac{1}{\pi}$$

$$C_3 = -\frac{2}{3\pi}(-1) = \frac{2}{3\pi}; \qquad C_4 = -\frac{2}{4\pi}(1) = -\frac{1}{2\pi}$$

and so on. These results confirm the Fourier Series for the sawtooth signal quoted in equation (4.1) of the main text.

We have already noted that the Fourier Series is simplified in the case of an even or odd function, by losing either its sine or its cosine terms. A different type of simplification occurs if a signal possesses what is known as *half-wave symmetry*. A number of periodic waveforms are illustrated in figure 4.5, and all but two of them exhibit such symmetry. In mathematical terms, half-wave symmetry exists when

$$x(t) = -x\{t + (T_0/2)\} = -x\{t + (\pi/\omega_0)\} \tag{4.17}$$

In other words, any two values of the signal separated by half a period are equal in magnitude

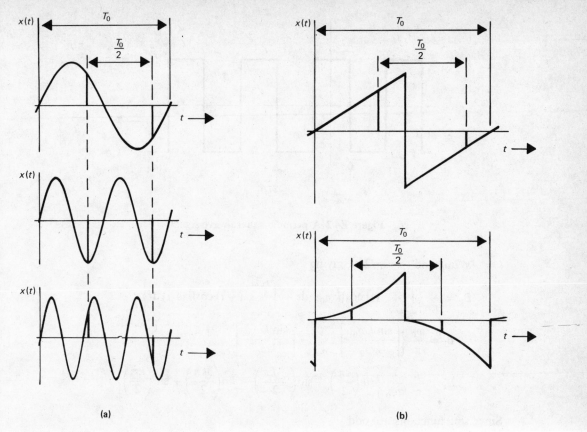

Figure 4.5 Illustrations of half-wave symmetry. All the signals shown exhibit this property, except the second-harmonic sinusoid in part (a) and the upper signal in part (b).

but opposite in sign. The figure shows that a sine wave of period T_0, and its third harmonic, both have this property, whereas the second harmonic does not. Generalising, only odd-order harmonics exhibit half-wave symmetry. Therefore any periodic signal $x(t)$ with half-wave symmetry cannot contain even-order harmonic components.

Example E4.2

Find the Fourier Series representation of the periodic square-wave signal illustrated in figure E4.2.

Solution

In this case $x(t)$ is an even time function with zero mean value. Hence all the sine coefficients C_k must be zero, and $A_0 = 0$. The signal also displays half-wave symmetry, and we must therefore expect the cosine coefficients B_k to be zero for $k = 2, 4, 6 \ldots$. Using equation (4.15), we have

$$B_k = \frac{\omega_0}{\pi} \int_0^{2\pi/\omega_0} x(t) \cos(k\omega_0 t)\, dt$$

However, in this case it is slightly more convenient to integrate over the period between

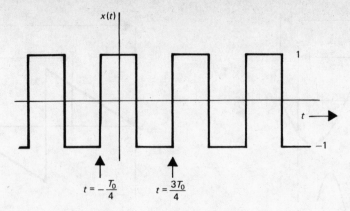

Figure E4.2 A periodic square-wave signal.

$t = -\pi/2\omega_0$ and $t = 3\pi/2\omega_0$, giving

$$B_k = \frac{\omega_0}{\pi}\left\{\int_{-\pi/2\omega_0}^{\pi/2\omega_0}(1)\cos(k\omega_0 t)\,dt + \int_{\pi/2\omega_0}^{3\pi/2\omega_0}(-1)\cos(k\omega_0 t)\,dt\right\}$$

$$\therefore B_k = \frac{\omega_0}{\pi}\left\{\left[\frac{\sin k\omega_0 t}{k\omega_0}\right]_{-\pi/2\omega_0}^{\pi/2\omega_0} - \left[\frac{\sin k\omega_0 t}{k\omega_0}\right]_{\pi/2\omega_0}^{3\pi/2\omega_0}\right\}$$

$$\therefore B_k = \frac{\omega_0}{\pi}\frac{1}{k\omega_0}\left\{\sin\left(\frac{k\pi}{2}\right) - \sin\left(\frac{-k\pi}{2}\right) - \sin\left(\frac{3k\pi}{2}\right) + \sin\left(\frac{k\pi}{2}\right)\right\}$$

Since sine functions are odd

$$\sin\frac{(-k\pi)}{2} = -\sin\frac{k\pi}{2}$$

hence

$$B_k = \frac{1}{\pi k}\left\{3\sin\left(\frac{k\pi}{2}\right) - \sin\left(\frac{3k\pi}{2}\right)\right\}$$

Now if k is an even number

$$\sin\left(\frac{k\pi}{2}\right) = 0 = \sin\left(\frac{3k\pi}{2}\right)$$

giving $B_k = 0$. This confirms that, as expected, the signal contains no even-order harmonics. If $k = 1, 5, 9\ldots$ then

$$3\sin\left(\frac{k\pi}{2}\right) - \sin\left(\frac{3k\pi}{2}\right) = 3 - (-1) = 4$$

and if $k = 3, 7, 11\ldots$ then

$$3\sin\left(\frac{k\pi}{2}\right) - \sin\left(\frac{3k\pi}{2}\right) = -3 - (1) = -4$$

Successive cosine coefficients are therefore as follows

$$B_1 = \frac{4}{\pi}; \quad B_2 = 0; \quad B_3 = -\frac{4}{3\pi}; \quad B_4 = 0; \quad B_5 = \frac{4}{5\pi}; \quad \text{and so on}$$

The Fourier Series representation of the signal is therefore

$$x(t) = \frac{4}{\pi}(\cos \omega_0 t - \tfrac{1}{3}\cos 3\omega_0 t + \tfrac{1}{5}\cos 5\omega_0 t - \tfrac{1}{7}\cos 7\omega_0 t + \ldots)$$

In the foregoing examples, we have always integrated over a complete period to derive the coefficients. However, in the case of an odd or even signal it is sufficient, and often simpler, to integrate over only one-half of a period and to multiply the result by 2. Furthermore, if the signal is not only even or odd, but also displays half-wave symmetry, it is adequate to integrate over a quarter of a period, and multiply by 4. Such closer limits are possible because the function being integrated repeats twice within one period when the signal is either even or odd, and four times within one period when it also exhibits half-wave symmetry. This is illustrated by figure 4.6. At the top of the figure is shown one period of an odd signal which also displays half-wave symmetry. When we multiply it by the sine function in part (b) of the figure, we obtain the waveform in part (c). It is clear that the total area under this waveform is four times its area between $t = 0$ and $t = \pi/2\omega_0$.

The amount of work involved in calculating the Fourier Series coefficients of a signal is therefore reduced if the waveform is either even or odd, and this may sometimes be arranged by a judicious choice of time origin. For example, figure 4.7 shows three versions of a periodic square wave which differ only in their time origin. Part (a) shows an even signal, symmetrical about $t = 0$, and as we have seen in worked example E4.2 its fundamental component is $(4/\pi)\cos \omega_0 t$. The square wave in part (b) is identical except that it is odd, and has a fundamental

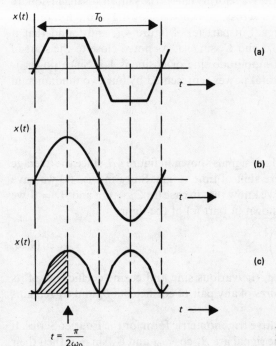

Figure 4.6 Reducing the integration limits of a Fourier Series.

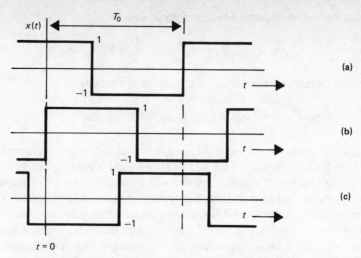

Figure 4.7 Three versions of a periodic square wave.

equal to $(4/\pi) \sin \omega_0 t$. The shift of time origin has therefore merely had the effect of converting a Fourier series containing only cosines (a *cosine series*) into one containing only sines (a *sine series*). But the amplitude of a component at any given frequency is, as we would expect, unaltered. The situation in part (c) of the figure is, however, rather more complicated because the square wave is neither even nor odd, and must be expected to include both sine and cosine terms in its Fourier Series.

The clue to the relationship between the values of the various coefficients in case (c) and those in cases (a) and (b) lies in the *average power* of the waveform. This is the same as its mean-square value if we regard the signal as a voltage applied across, or a current flowing through, a resistor of value 1 ohm. Suppose we analysed the signal in part (c) of figure 4.7, and found that it contained fundamental components $B_1 \cos \omega_0 t$ and $C_1 \sin \omega_0 t$. As noted close to the start of this section, the mean-square value of a unit-amplitude sine or cosine is $1/2$. Since power is proportional to the *square* of amplitude, the total power represented by our two fundamental components is given by

$$\frac{B_1^2}{2} + \frac{C_1^2}{2}$$

However, this value must be the same for all three signals shown in figure 4.7, since the average power of a signal cannot be altered by a mere shift of time origin. Since in case (a) we have already found that $B_1 = 4/\pi$ and $C_1 = 0$, and we know that in case (b) $C_1 = 4/\pi$ and $B_1 = 0$, we conclude that for a waveform such as that shown in part (c) of the figure

$$\frac{B_1^2}{2} + \frac{C_1^2}{2} = \frac{1}{2}\left(\frac{4}{\pi}\right)^2, \quad \text{or } B_1^2 + C_1^2 = \left(\frac{4}{\pi}\right)^2 \tag{4.18}$$

Hence as the time-origin of a signal is shifted, the various sine and cosine coefficients of its Fourier Series change, but the *sum of the squares* of any pair of coefficients B_k and C_k remains constant.

The above ideas lead naturally to an alternative trigonometric form for the Fourier Series. If the two fundamental components of a periodic signal are $B_1 \cos \omega_0 t$ and $C_1 \sin \omega_0 t$, then their sum may be expressed using standard trigonometric identities

$$B_1 \cos \omega_0 t + C_1 \sin \omega_0 t = (B_1^2 + C_1^2)^{1/2} \cos\left(\omega_0 t - \tan^{-1}\frac{C_1}{B_1}\right)$$

$$= (B_1^2 + C_1^2)^{1/2} \sin\left(\omega_0 t + \tan^{-1}\frac{B_1}{C_1}\right) \tag{4.19}$$

Thus the cosine and sine components at a particular frequency may be expressed as a single cosine, or sine, wave plus a phase-shift. If this procedure is applied to all the harmonic components of a Fourier Series, we get the following alternative forms for equation (4.12)

$$x(t) = A_0 + \sum_{k=1}^{\infty} (B_k^2 + C_k^2)^{1/2} \cos(k\omega_0 t - \phi_k) \tag{4.20}$$

or

$$x(t) = A_0 + \sum_{k=1}^{\infty} (B_k^2 + C_k^2)^{1/2} \sin(k\omega_0 t + \theta_k) \tag{4.21}$$

where

$$\theta_k = \tan^{-1}\frac{C_1}{B_1} \quad \text{and} \quad \theta_k = \tan^{-1}\frac{B_1}{C_1}$$

This is a good moment to consider briefly the *total power* in the signal. The average power represented by any one frequency component is, as argued above, given by

$$\tfrac{1}{2}(B_k^2 + C_k^2)$$

The power represented by the signal's average value A_0 is simply A_0^2. Therefore the total mean power is given by

$$A_0^2 + \frac{1}{2}\sum_{k=1}^{\infty} (B_k^2 + C_k^2)$$

However, the total mean power must also equal the average value of $\{x(t)\}^2$ taken over one complete period, so that

$$A_0^2 + \frac{1}{2}\sum_{k=1}^{\infty} (B_k^2 + C_k^2) = \frac{1}{T_0}\int_{-T_0/2}^{T_0/2} \{x(t)\}^2 \, dt \tag{4.22}$$

This is a version of *Parseval's Theorem*, and expresses an interesting tie-up between the frequency-domain and the time-domain. The total average power in any periodic signal may be found *either* by adding together the powers represented by the individual frequency components in its Fourier Series, *or* as the mean-square value of its time-domain waveform.

Now that we have covered some important basic aspects of the Fourier Series, it is time to consider some practical applications. We illustrate these by two rather different examples. First, suppose that a square-wave signal such as that already described in worked example E4.2 is to be sent along a cable, or via some other transmission system, which is *bandlimited*. To simplify the discussion, we will assume that the cable or system transmits frequencies up to some *cut-off* value f_1 Hz without reduction of amplitude, and that it rejects higher frequencies completely. Let us take the period of the square wave as 1 μs. It is clear that the number of signal harmonics reaching the receiving end will increase as f_1 is increased. As already shown in example 4.2, the

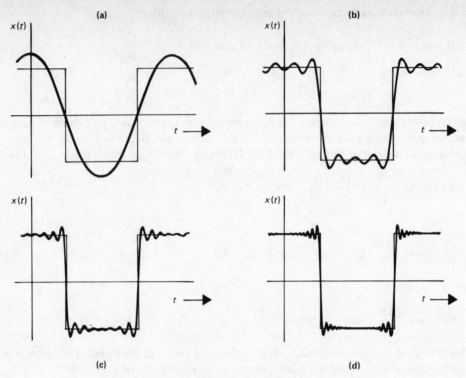

Figure 4.8 The effects of bandlimiting a square wave.

relevant Fourier Series is

$$x(t) = \frac{4}{\pi} (\cos \omega_0 t - \tfrac{1}{3} \cos 3\omega_0 t + \tfrac{1}{5} \cos 5\omega_0 t - \tfrac{1}{7} \cos 7\omega_0 t + \ldots) \qquad (4.23)$$

Since in this case the signal's period is $1 \, \mu s$, its fundamental frequency is $1 \, \text{MHz}$ ($\omega_0 = 2\pi \times 10^6$), its third harmonic frequency is $3 \, \text{MHz}$, and so on. Figure 4.8 illustrates the effects on the signal of four different system bandwidths. In part (a) $f_1 = 2 \, \text{MHz}$ and only the fundamental component is transmitted (the original square wave is also shown, for comparison). In part (b) $f_1 = 8 \, \text{MHz}$, so that harmonics up to and including the 7th are transmitted. Parts (c) and (d) of the figure assume bandwidths of 16 and 32 MHz, allowing through harmonics up to the 15th and 31st respectively. Notice how the received signal becomes more and more like the transmitted one as the bandwidth increases, although it would be theoretically necessary to have infinite bandwidth to achieve a perfect result. In practical engineering systems we normally wish to *restrict* the bandwidth occupied by a given type of signal or transmission, because bandwidth is related to cost (if there is bandwidth to spare, it may often be used to transmit more than one signal at a time, using *multiplexing techniques*).

The above example is very closely related to the work already done in section 4.2.1 on signal approximation. The received signals illustrated in figure 4.8 are all approximations to the transmitted square wave. For a given number of harmonics, they all fulfil the criterion of least mean-square error. Note, however, that although the approximation improves as more harmonics are included, the oscillations or 'ripples' nearest to the sudden discontinuities in the square wave remain more or less constant in size. The maximum *overshoot* is about 9 per cent of the amplitude of the discontinuity. This effect was investigated in detail by the mathematician Josiah Gibbs at the end of the 19th century, and is known as the *Gibbs phenomenon*.

Before leaving this discussion of the effect which a bandlimited system can have on the harmonic components of a signal, the reader should appreciate that we have made two simplifications. Firstly, we have asssumed a *sudden* cut-off frequency f_1, whereas most practical systems would give rise to a more *gradual* reduction in the amplitude of successive harmonics. Secondly, we have taken no account of alterations in the relative *phases* of the various harmonics at the output from the system. In other words we have assumed a cosine series at the output, just as there is a cosine series at the input. In fact, the majority of continuous LTI systems produce modifications to phase relationships which would distort the output signal waveshapes from those illustrated in figure 4.8. In spite of these simplifications, the above example gives some useful insights into the value of the Fourier Series representation of a periodic signal.

Our next illustration is quite different, and relates to the practical problem of deriving a DC power supply from the AC mains. A huge variety of electronic equipment and systems—from X-ray machines in hospitals to personal computers—is required to work from the sinusoidal mains supply (typically between 200 and 240 volts r.m.s. at either 50 or 60 Hz), but requires DC voltage and current for its internal operation. Figure 4.9 illustrates a simple way of achieving such a transformation from AC to DC. The AC mains voltage, a small portion of which is shown in part (a) of the figure, is *full-wave rectified* to produce the signal $v_1(t)$ shown in part (b). Whereas the original sinusoid has zero average, or DC, value, its rectified version has a substantial DC component (shown dotted in the figure). It is the task of the DC power supply to extract this component, while reducing all other frequencies in $v_1(t)$ as much as possible. The design specification for a DC power supply normally states, among other factors, the maximum output fluctuation (or *ripple*) which can be tolerated. Figure 4.9(c) shows a possible circuit for such a supply. We should be clear that most practical circuits are more elaborate than this, and

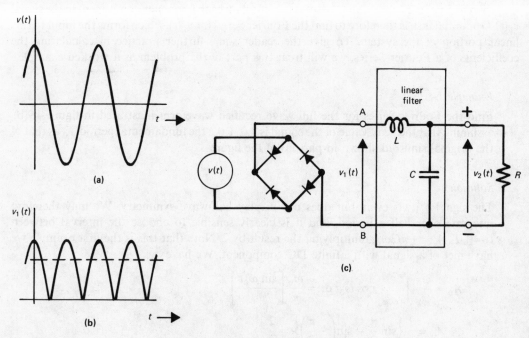

Figure 4.9 DC power supply.

that complex integrated circuits are widely used to achieve cheap and effective DC power supplies with low levels of ripple. Nevertheless, conventional power supplies of the type shown in figure 4.9(c)—or variations on it—are still used. Our purpose here is, of course, to illustrate a further application of Fourier analysis rather than become involved in a detailed discussion of power supplies!

The circuit shown in the figure first rectifies the input sinusoid $v(t)$ using a *diode bridge*, and then reduces the AC components in the rectified signal $v_1(t)$ with a simple *LC* filter. The latter must have low-pass characteristics, since it is required to pass the DC component of $v_1(t)$, but suppress all higher frequencies. It is quite easy to understand in qualitative terms how the filter works. At zero frequency the inductor is nominally a short-circuit, and the capacitor an open-circuit. The DC component of $v_1(t)$ is therefore passed straight through to the resistive load R. However, for frequencies above zero the inductive impedance rises and the capacitive impedance falls, both effects tending to reduce the AC voltage reaching the load.

The problem we will tackle using Fourier analysis is as follows. We have a power supply of the type shown in figure 4.9(c), fed from a 220 volt (r.m.s.), 50 Hz mains supply. $L = 5$ henries (5 H), $C = 10 \, \mu F$, and we need to predict the percentage ripple in the DC output if a 2 kΩ load is connected. As we shall see later, the DC output voltage is about 200 volts, implying a load current of about 0.1 amp and a substantial power output of around 20 watts.

The approach is to find the Fourier Series of the full-wave rectified sinusoid shown in figure 4.9(b), and then assess the effect of the *LC* filter on each of its frequency components in turn. By adding up, or superposing, the various output frequencies, we may estimate the magnitude of the output ripple. Before starting the analysis we must be clear on one very important point, namely that the diode-bridge is highly *nonlinear*. This *must* be so, since its job is to produce a zero-frequency component which is not present in its sinusoidal input. As we have already mentioned in sections 1.4.2 and 2.3.1, only a nonlinear system can produce new frequencies. However, all the circuit elements to the right of terminals AB in figure 4.9(c) are linear, and we may therefore use the *j*-notation to assess their effect on each frequency component in the signal $v_1(t)$. Our initial task is therefore to find the Fourier Series for $v_1(t)$, which forms the input to this linear portion of the system. To give the reader some further practice in calculating the coefficients of a Fourier Series, we will treat this part of the problem as a worked example.

Example E4.3

Find the Fourier Series for the full-wave rectified waveform illustrated in figure 4.9(b), assuming that the peak value of the signal is 1.0. Take the fundamental period T_0 as that of the original sinusoid shown in part (a) of the figure.

Solution

The signal $v_1(t)$ is even, but does not display half-wave symmetry. We may therefore integrate over half a period, and it is clearly sensible to choose the interval between $t = \pm T_0/4 = \pm \pi/2\omega_0$, multiplying the result by 2. Note that this is the first example we have met of a signal with a finite DC component. We have

$$A_0 = \frac{\omega_0}{\pi} \int_{-\pi/2\omega_0}^{\pi/2\omega_0} \cos \omega_0 t \, dt = \frac{\omega_0}{\pi} \left[\frac{\sin \omega_0 t}{\omega_0} \right]_{-\pi/2\omega_0}^{\pi/2\omega_0}$$

$$\therefore A_0 = \frac{1}{\pi} \left\{ \sin \frac{\pi}{2} - \sin \left(-\frac{\pi}{2} \right) \right\} = \frac{2}{\pi}$$

Since the signal is even, all coefficients C_k must be zero. The coefficients B_k are given by

$$B_k = \frac{2\omega_0}{\pi} \int_{-\pi/2\omega_0}^{\pi/2\omega_0} \cos(\omega_0 t) \cos(k\omega_0 t) \, dt$$

which may be evaluated using a double integration by parts. It is a little lengthy, but straightforward. To simplify the working, let us first evaluate the indefinite integral I, defined as

$$I = \int \cos(\omega_0 t) \cos(k\omega_0 t) \, dt$$

$$\therefore I = \cos(\omega_0 t) \frac{\sin(k\omega_0 t)}{k\omega_0} - \int (-\omega_0 \sin \omega_0 t) \frac{\sin(k\omega_0 t)}{k\omega_0} \, dt$$

$$\therefore I = \cos(\omega_0 t) \frac{\sin(k\omega_0 t)}{k\omega_0)} + \frac{1}{k} \int \sin(\omega_0 t) \sin(k\omega_0 t) \, dt$$

Now

$$\int \sin(\omega_0 t) \sin(k\omega_0 t) \, dt = \sin \omega_0 t \frac{(-\cos k\omega_0 t)}{k\omega_0} - \int \omega_0 \cos \omega_0 t \frac{(-\cos k\omega_0 t)}{k\omega_0} \, dt$$

$$= -\frac{\sin(\omega_0 t) \cos(k\omega_0 t)}{k\omega_0} + \frac{1}{k} \{I\}$$

Hence

$$I\left(1 - \frac{1}{k^2}\right) = \frac{\cos(\omega_0 t) \sin(k\omega_0 t)}{k\omega_0} - \frac{\sin(\omega_0 t) \cos(k\omega_0 t)}{k^2 \omega_0}$$

However, when we consider the limits of integration, we see that $\cos \omega_0 t = 0$ for both $t = \pi/2\omega_0$ and $t = -\pi/2\omega_0$. Therefore, the definite integral simplifies to

$$I\left(1 - \frac{1}{k^2}\right) = -\frac{1}{k^2 \omega_0} \left[\sin(\omega_0 t) \cos(k\omega_0 t)\right]_{-\pi/2\omega_0}^{\pi/2\omega_0}$$

so that

$$I = \frac{-1}{(k^2 - 1)\omega_0} \left[\sin(\omega_0 t) \cos(k\omega_0 t)\right]_{-\pi/2\omega_0}^{\pi/2\omega_0}$$

$$\therefore I = \frac{1}{(1 - k^2)\omega_0} \left\{\sin\left(\frac{\pi}{2}\right) \cos\left(\frac{k\pi}{2}\right) - \sin\left(\frac{-\pi}{2}\right) \cos\left(\frac{-k}{2}\right)\right\}$$

$$\therefore I = \frac{1}{(1 - k^2)\omega_0} \left\{\cos\left(\frac{k\pi}{2}\right) + \cos\left(\frac{-k\pi}{2}\right)\right\} = \frac{2}{(1 - k^2)\omega_0} \cos\left(\frac{k\pi}{2}\right)$$

and we therefore obtain

$$B_k = \frac{2\omega_0}{\pi} \frac{2}{(1 - k^2)\omega_0} \cos\left(\frac{k\pi}{2}\right) = \frac{4}{\pi(1 - k^2)} \cos\left(\frac{k\pi}{2}\right)$$

Now $\cos k\pi/2 = 0$ when k is an odd integer. When k is an even integer, we have

$$\cos\left(\frac{k\pi}{2}\right) = -1, \qquad k = 2, 6, 10, 14 \ldots$$

and

$$\cos\left(\frac{k\pi}{2}\right) = 1, \qquad k = 4, 8, 12, 16 \ldots$$

The nonzero coefficients of the Fourier series are therefore

$$A_0 = \frac{2}{\pi}; \qquad B_2 = \frac{4(-1)}{\pi(-3)} = \frac{4}{3\pi}; \qquad B_4 = \frac{4}{\pi(-15)} = \frac{-4}{15\pi}$$

$$B_6 = \frac{4(-1)}{\pi(-35)} = \frac{4}{35\pi}; \qquad B_8 = \frac{4}{\pi(-63)} = \frac{-4}{63\pi}; \qquad B_{10} = \frac{4(-1)}{\pi(-99)} = \frac{4}{99\pi}$$

and so on. The Fourier Series for the full-wave rectified signal $v_1(t)$ with unit peak amplitude may therefore be written as

$$v_1(t) = \frac{2}{\pi}\Bigg(1 + \frac{2}{3}\cos 2\omega_0 t - \frac{2}{15}\cos 4\omega_0 t + \frac{2}{15}\cos 6\omega_0 t$$

$$- \frac{2}{63}\cos 8\omega_0 t + \frac{2}{99}\cos 10\omega_0 t - \ldots \Bigg)$$

We see that, apart from the DC term, only even-order harmonics are present. This is because we have taken the fundamental period T_0 as that of the sinusoidal signal *before* rectification. The rectified signal $v_1(t)$ is itself periodic, with a period half as great. Had we taken *its* period as the fundamental period, we would have found all harmonics to be present.

We next assess the effect which the power supply's linear filter has on each of the frequencies present in $v_1(t)$. Referring back to figure 4.9(c), we see that the output voltage appears across R and C in parallel. Denoting their parallel impedance by Z, and using the j-notation (reviewed in section 1.4.2), we may write directly

$$\frac{V_2(\omega)}{V_1(\omega)} = \frac{Z}{j\omega L + Z} \tag{4.24}$$

Although the use of the 'potential-divider' principle is not generally recommended for solving circuit problems, there is little danger of making a mistake in such a simple case as this! Now

$$Z = \frac{R(j\omega C)^{-1}}{R + (j\omega C)^{-1}} = \frac{R}{1 + j\omega CR} \tag{4.25}$$

and substitution in equation (4.24) gives

$$\frac{V_2(\omega)}{V_1(\omega)} = \frac{1}{(1 - \omega^2 LC) + (j\omega L/R)} \tag{4.26}$$

It is now a straightforward matter to put ω equal to the various frequencies present in $v_1(t)$, and to assess the magnitude and phase of expression (4.26), given that $L = 5$ H, $C = 10\ \mu$F, and $R = 2$ kΩ. In this case T_0 equals one period of the 50 Hz mains, so $\omega_0 = 2\pi/T_0 = 100\pi$. The frequencies we are interested in are $2\omega_0$, $4\omega_0$, $6\omega_0$, and so on. The first few results may be tabulated as follows

Frequency (radians/s)	$\dfrac{V_2(\omega)}{V_1(\omega)}$	
	magnitude	*phase*
$2\omega_0 = 200\pi$	0.0532	175°
$4\omega_0 = 400\pi$	0.0128	177°
$6\omega_0 = 600\pi$	0.0057	178°
$8\omega_0 = 800\pi$	0.0032	179°

The relative amounts of the various harmonic frequencies present at the filter input, compared with the DC component, are given by the Fourier Series already derived in example E4.3. Thus, if we take the DC component as 1.0, the second harmonic term is of amplitude 2/3, and hence peak-to-peak value 4/3, and so on. Multiplying these values by the magnitude factors in the above table, we obtain the following peak-to-peak ripple percentages

second harmonic (100 Hz): 7.1 per cent

fourth harmonic (200 Hz): 0.34 per cent

sixth harmonic (300 Hz): 0.07 per cent

eighth harmonic (400 Hz): 0.02 per cent

and so on. The ripple is therefore almost entirely at second harmonic frequency, with a peak-to-peak value of just over 7 per cent of the DC output voltage. Higher-order harmonics are much smaller, partly because they have smaller amplitudes at the filter input, and partly because the filter discriminates against them much more strongly.

Although we could superpose the various ripple components to find the actual ripple waveform, in this case it would probably be of little practical interest, because the higher-order harmonics are so small. Incidentally, a ripple of 7 per cent would be regarded as very high for many practical applications—1 per cent or less is a more typical requirement. So a better smoothing filter than the one we have used would probably be required if this power supply were to feed into a 2 kΩ load.

Before leaving discussion of the power supply, we might note that the Fourier Series for $v_1(t)$ shows that a full-wave rectified sinusoid of unit amplitude has a DC component equal to $2/\pi = 0.637$. Since the input mains voltage to the power supply is 220 volts r.m.s., its peak value is $220\sqrt{2} = 311$ volts. Hence, if we ignore the relatively small voltage drops across the conducting diodes in the bridge rectifier, and across the resistance associated with the inductor L, the DC output voltage is expected to be $311 \times 0.637 = 198$ volts.

4.2.2.2 *The exponential form of the series*

We now return to some more theory. Our work on the Fourier Series so far as concentrated on sines and cosines, because this is the approach which most people find easiest to visualise. However, these sines and cosines may be expressed as pairs of imaginary exponential signals (see section 2.2.3). In this way we may obtain an equivalent *exponential form* for the Fourier Series. This is very important, because it leads naturally into the Fourier Transform which we develop and use in the next section.

The general trigonometric form of the Fourier Series has already been expressed in equation (4.12)

$$x(t) = A_0 + \sum_{k=1}^{\infty} B_k \cos k\omega_0 t + \sum_{k=1}^{\infty} C_k \sin k\omega_0 t$$

It may be recast into the following exponential form

$$x(t) = \ldots + a_{-2} \exp(-2j\omega_0 t) + a_{-1} \exp(-j\omega_0 t) + a_0 + a_1 \exp(j\omega_0 t) + a_2 \exp(2j\omega_0 t) + \ldots$$

$$= \sum_{k=-\infty}^{\infty} a_k \exp(jk\omega_0 t) \tag{4.27}$$

These two forms look rather different, but they are in fact exact equivalents. This may be shown using the identities

$$\cos \theta = \frac{1}{2} \{\exp(j\theta) + \exp(-j\theta)\} \quad \text{and} \quad \sin \theta = \frac{-j}{2} \{\exp(j\theta) - \exp(-j\theta)\}$$

with $\theta = k\omega_0 t$. Substitution into equation (4.12) yields equation (4.27) without difficulty. The coefficients of the two forms are related as follows

$$a_0 = A_0; \qquad a_k = \tfrac{1}{2}(B_k - jC_k), \qquad k > 0; \qquad a_k = \tfrac{1}{2}(B_k + jC_k), \qquad k < 0 \tag{4.28}$$

We therefore see that the coefficients a_k of the exponential form are generally complex, and occur in complex conjugate pairs. The introduction of complex coefficients makes equation (4.27) harder to visualise than its counterpart equation (4.12). However, we should remember that the real part of a pair of complex coefficients denotes the magnitude of the cosine component at the relevant harmonic frequency, whereas the imaginary part denotes the magnitude of the sine component. If the signal $x(t)$ is even, it has a cosine series, and all the coefficients a_k in the exponential Fourier Series are real. If $x(t)$ is odd, it has a sine series, and all the coefficients a_k are purely imaginary.

The exponential form of the Fourier Series involves the concept of *negative frequency*, first introduced in section 2.2.3 in our discussion of sinusoidal and exponential signals. Actually, it stems directly from the identities for $\cos \theta$ and $\sin \theta$ quoted above. For example, if we put $\theta = k\omega_0 t$, a cosine signal of amplitude B_k is written as

$$B_k \cos k\omega_0 t = \frac{B_k}{2} \exp(j\{k\omega_0\}t) + \frac{B_k}{2} \exp(j\{-k\omega_0\}t) \tag{4.29}$$

If we plot its *exponential* components on a spectral diagram, the cosine is represented by two spectral lines of height $B_k/2$, one at frequency $(+k\omega_0)$ and the other at frequency $(-k\omega_0)$. The frequency scale is therefore formally extended to include negative as well as positive frequencies, with each cosine component providing *two* spectral lines. Similarly, each sine component is represented by a spectral line at frequency $(+k\omega_0)$ and another at $(-k\omega_0)$. Since these have imaginary coefficients they cannot be plotted on the same diagram as the real coefficients representing the cosines. We therefore see that negative frequencies are a consequence of using pairs of exponential signals to represent sines and cosines.

Although the coefficients a_k of the exponential Fourier Series may be found from the trigonometric coefficients B_k and C_k, this is not normally very economical. It is better to estimate the values of a_k directly. Since, as expression (4.28) shows

$$a_k = \tfrac{1}{2}(B_k - jC_k), \qquad k > 0$$

we may use the expressions for B_k and C_k given earlier by equations (4.15) and (4.16) to yield

$$a_k = \frac{1}{2}\frac{\omega_0}{\pi}\left\{\int_{-\pi/\omega_0}^{\pi/\omega_0} x(t)\cos(k\omega_0 t)\,dt - j\int_{-\pi/\omega_0}^{\pi/\omega_0} x(t)\sin(k\omega_0 t)\,dt\right\}$$

$$= \frac{\omega_0}{2\pi}\int_{-\pi/\omega_0}^{\pi/\omega_0} x(t)(\cos k\omega_0 t - j\sin k\omega_0 t)\,dt$$

$$= \frac{\omega_0}{2\pi}\int_{-\pi/\omega_0}^{\pi/\omega_0} x(t)\exp(-jk\omega_0 t)\,dt \tag{4.30}$$

This result may also be written in terms of the fundamental period T_0 as

$$a_k = \frac{1}{T_0}\int_{-T_0/2}^{T_0/2} x(t)\exp(-2\pi jkt/T_0)\,dt \tag{4.31}$$

It is straightforward to show that these last two equations also hold good when $k < 0$, and when $k = 0$. They are therefore valid for all integer values of k, positive, negative, and zero. Just as equation (4.27) shows how to *synthesise* any signal $x(t)$ by adding together, or superposing, a whole set of weighted imaginary exponentials, so equations (4.30) and (4.31) show how to *analyse* $x(t)$ by finding out 'how much' of each exponential is present in it. These are key results. As we have already intimated, they lead on directly to the extremely important Fourier Transform covered in the following section.

Before ending our discussion of the exponential Fourier Series representation of periodic signals, we should note that integration over half a period is admissible if $x(t)$ exhibits half-wave symmetry, just as it is when using the trigonometric series. On the other hand, the integration interval may *not* be shortened on account of $x(t)$ being either even or odd. This was possible with the trigonometric form because cosine and sine waveforms are themselves even and odd respectively; but $\exp(-jk\omega_0 t)$ is neither even nor odd, and such a simplification is not allowed.

Example E4.4

Find the coefficients a_k of the exponential Fourier Series for the periodic triangular signal shown in figure E4.4(a).

Solution

The signal exhibits half-wave symmetry, so the coefficients a_k must be zero for k even. We may integrate over the half-period between $t = 0$ and $t = \pi/\omega_0$, and multiply the result by 2. Over this half-period the signal is given by

$$x(t) = \frac{2\omega_0 t}{\pi} - 1$$

and using equation (4.30) we obtain

$$a_k = \frac{\omega_0}{\pi}\int_0^{\pi/\omega_0}\left(\frac{2\omega_0 t}{\pi} - 1\right)\exp(-jk\omega_0 t)\,dt, \qquad k = 1, 3, 5, \ldots$$

$$\therefore a_k = \frac{2\omega_0^2}{\pi^2}\int_0^{\pi/\omega_0} t\exp(-jk\omega_0 t)\,dt - \frac{\omega_0}{\pi}\int_0^{\pi/\omega_0} \exp(-jk\omega_0 t)\,dt$$

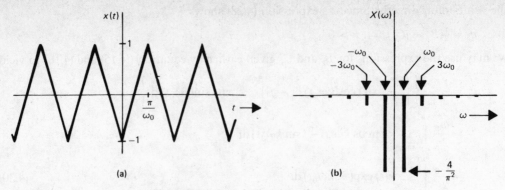

Figure E4.4 A periodic triangular signal.

The first expression may be integrated by parts, giving

$$a_k = \frac{2\omega_0^2}{\pi^2}\left\{\left[\frac{t\exp(-jk\omega_0 t)}{-jk\omega_0}\right]_0^{\pi/\omega_0} - \int_0^{\pi/\omega_0}\frac{\exp(-jk\omega_0 t)}{-jk\omega_0}\,dt\right\}$$

$$- \frac{\omega_0}{\pi}\left[\frac{\exp(-jk\omega_0 t)}{-jk\omega_0}\right]_0^{\pi/\omega_0}$$

$$= \frac{2\omega_0^2}{\pi^2}\left\{\frac{\pi}{\omega_0}\frac{\exp(-jk\pi)}{-jk\omega_0} + \left[\frac{\exp(-jk\omega_0 t)}{k^2\omega_0^2}\right]_0^{\pi/\omega_0}\right\} + \frac{1}{jk\pi}\{\exp(-jk\pi) - 1\}$$

$$= \frac{2}{\pi^2}\left(\frac{\pi\exp(-jk\pi)}{-jk} + \frac{\exp(-jk\pi)}{k^2} - \frac{1}{k^2}\right) + \frac{1}{jk\pi}\{\exp(-jk\pi) - 1\}$$

Now if k is odd, $\exp(-jk\pi) = -1$, and therefore

$$a_k = \frac{2}{\pi^2}\left(\frac{\pi}{jk} - \frac{2}{k^2}\right) - \frac{2}{jk\pi} = -\frac{4}{\pi^2 k^2}\qquad\text{for } k = 1, 3, 5, \ldots$$

As we would expect, all the exponential coefficients are real, corresponding to a cosine series. Also, since a_k is a function of k^2, $a_k = a_{-k}$, and the spectral function $X(\omega)$ is even. It is illustrated in part (b) of figure E4.4. Note that since $X(\omega)$ is purely real in this case it is possible to represent it entirely by a *single* diagram. The fact that all coefficients are negative may appear at first sight a little surprising. However, if we look carefully at the signal $x(t)$, we realise that it could only be synthesised by adding together cosines which are all negative at $t = 0$. In other words, they are all inverted.

4.2.3 *The Fourier Transform*

4.2.3.1 *Analysis and synthesis of aperiodic signals*

In the previous section we have seen how a periodic signal may be expressed as the sum of a set of sinusoidal or exponential functions which are harmonically related. The spectrum of such a signal contains a number of discrete frequencies. Although the analysis of strictly periodic signals gives results which can be of considerable practical value, in fact the great majority of signals are not of this type. Firstly, even those signals which do repeat themselves a large number of times—such as the sinusoidal mains supply—are generally turned on and off. So they may not be assumed to exist for all time, past, present, and future. It may be important to assess the effects which such *time-limitation* has upon their spectra, and upon the systems which transmit or process them. Such transient effects are not covered by the Fourier Series. Secondly, and quite apart from any question of time-limitation, the majority of practical signals are simply not repetititve in nature. For example, speech and TV signals tend to be very nonrepetitive. It is indeed a key concept of communications theory that only signals which are to some extent unpredictable, or *random*, convey useful information.

However, the above comments are not meant to detract from the value or importance of the Fourier Series. Indeed many of its central features form a very good starting point for discussing the spectra of nonrepetitive, or *aperiodic*, signals. These spectra are derived using the Fourier Transform, which may be thought of as a limiting case of the Fourier Series. It was one of Fourier's major achievements to show that an aperiodic signal may, in principle, be built up as an infinite sum—or integral—of sinusoidal or exponential functions which are *not* harmonically related. This is the basic idea behind the Fourier Transform.

A convenient and instructive way of introducing the Fourier Transform is to consider the recurrent pulse waveform shown in figure 4.10(a). Note that the period of the signal is m times the pulse duration, and that the relative amount of time spent at level 1 (the 'high' state) and level 0 (the 'low' state) is therefore set by the parameter m. Our approach is as follows. We first derive the exponential Fourier Series for this signal, considered as a strictly periodic function. Then by allowing the value of m to increase, we may in the limit derive the spectrum of an isolated rectangular pulse at $t = 0$ whose 'neighbours' have moved away to either side towards $t = \pm \infty$. The signal is clearly even so we expect the Fourier coefficients a_k to be purely real, representing a cosine series. Equation (4.30) gives

$$a_k = \frac{\omega_0}{2\pi} \int_{-\pi/\omega_0}^{\pi/\omega_0} x(t) \exp(-jk\omega_0 t)\, dt$$

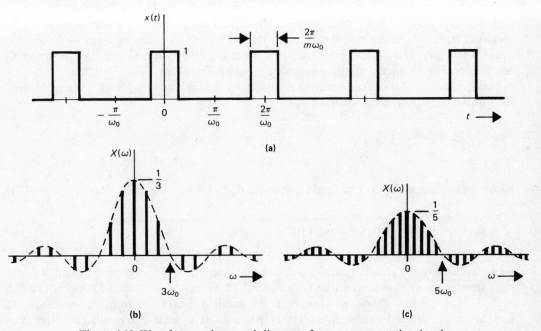

Figure 4.10 Waveform and spectral diagrams for a recurrent-pulse signal.

which in this case reduces to

$$a_k = \frac{\omega_0}{2\pi} \int_{-\pi/m\omega_0}^{\pi/m\omega_0} (1) \exp(-jk\omega_0 t)\, dt = \frac{\omega_0}{2\pi} \left[\frac{\exp(-jk\omega_0 t)}{-jk\omega_0} \right]_{-\pi/m\omega_0}^{\pi/m\omega_0}$$

$$\therefore\ a_k = \frac{1}{2\pi jk} \{ \exp(jk\pi/m) - \exp(-jk\pi/m) \} = \frac{1}{k\pi} \sin(k\pi/m)$$

Hence

$$a_k = \frac{1}{m} \left\{ \frac{\sin(k\pi/m)}{(k\pi/m)} \right\} \tag{4.32}$$

As expected, all the coefficients are real. Their magnitudes follow an envelope of $(\sin x)/x$, or *sinc function*, form, where $x = k\pi/m$. This function is commonly encountered in the theory of signals and linear systems, and takes the form of a decaying oscillation to either side of $x = 0$ (the decay being inversely proportional to x, rather than exponential). It has unit value at $x = 0$, and passes through zero whenever $x = \pm n\pi$, for $n = 1, 2, 3, \ldots$. Parts (b) and (c) of the figure illustrate equation (4.32) for two typical cases, $m = 3$ and $m = 5$ respectively. The sinc function envelope is shown dotted in each case. Although each diagram is labelled as a line spectrum, we may also consider it as a plot of a_k against k.

Two aspects of these spectral diagrams deserve particular attention. Firstly, as m increases from 3 to 5 the fundamental frequency ω_0 reduces, and the coefficients a_k become more closely spaced. Since a reduction in ω_0 corresponds to an increasing period T_0 of the signal, our diagrams illustrate the effects of keeping the pulse duration constant, while altering the spacing between adjacent pulses. The second point to note is that as m increases, and more and more Fourier coefficients bunch together within the sinc function envelope, the magnitude of each coefficient reduces in proportion. Clearly, if m becomes large we obtain a line spectrum with a large number of closely bunched harmonics, all of small amplitude. In the limit as $m \to \infty$, the spectrum represents a single, 'isolated' pulse. Its neighbours have moved away on either side towards $t = \pm\infty$. The spectral lines are now extremely closely spaced, with vanishingly small amplitudes. The Fourier Series has become a Fourier Transform.

Mathematically, this situation may be expressed by modifications to the exponential form of the Fourier Series given by equation (4.27)

$$x(t) = \sum_{k=-\infty}^{\infty} a_k \exp(jk\omega_0 t)$$

where the coefficients a_k may be found using equation (4.30), or the equivalent equation (4.31)

$$a_k = \frac{1}{T_0} \int_{-T_0/2}^{T_0/2} x(t) \exp(-2\pi jkt/T_0)\, dt$$

As we let the period T_0 tend to infinity and each coefficient becomes vanishingly small, it might seem that the above equations are no longer useful. However, the product $a_k T_0$ does not vanish as $T_0 \to \infty$, so we now choose to write this as a variable X. Furthermore, as $T_0 \to \infty$, $\omega_0 \to 0$, and the term $k\omega_0$ tends to a continuous rather than a discrete variable. We will denote this as ω. Since X is a function of this continuous frequency variable ω, we now rewrite the second of the above equations as

$$X(\omega) = a_k T_0 = \int_{-\infty}^{\infty} x(t) \exp(-jk\omega_0 t)\, dt$$

$$\therefore\ X(\omega) = \int_{-\infty}^{\infty} x(t) \exp(-j\omega t)\, dt \tag{4.33}$$

Returning to the first equation which expresses $x(t)$ as the sum of an infinite set of harmonic components, we have

$$x(t) = \sum_{k=-\infty}^{\infty} \frac{X(\omega)}{T_0} \exp(jk\omega_0 t) = \sum_{k=-\infty}^{\infty} X(\omega) \frac{\omega_0}{2\pi} \exp(jk\omega_0 t)$$

Once again the term $k\omega_0$ is replaced by the continuous variable ω. The fundamental frequency ω_0 (which is now vanishingly small) is written as $d\omega$. The summation becomes an integration in the limit, so that

$$x(t) = \frac{1}{2\pi} \int_{-\infty}^{\infty} X(\omega) \exp(j\omega t)\, d\omega \tag{4.34}$$

The two equations (4.33) and (4.34) are of central importance in the theory of signals and systems, and are known as the *Fourier Transform pair*. $X(\omega)$ is the Fourier Transform of $x(t)$, and $x(t)$ is the inverse Fourier Transform of $X(\omega)$. It is very important to grasp the significance of these equations. The first tells us how the spectral energy of the signal $x(t)$ is continuously distributed in the frequency domain. The second shows how, in effect, an aperiodic signal may be synthesised from an infinite set of exponential functions of the form $\exp(j\omega t)$, each weighted by the relevant value of $X(\omega)$.

Let us straight away illustrate the Fourier Transform by a simple example. Consider the single, isolated, rectangular pulse shown in figure 4.11(a). The frequency spectrum of this signal may be found using equation (4.33)

$$X(\omega) = \int_{-\infty}^{\infty} x(t) \exp(-j\omega t)\, dt = \int_{-t_1}^{t_1} (1) \exp(-j\omega t)\, dt$$

$$\therefore\ X(\omega) = -\frac{1}{j\omega}\left[\exp(-j\omega t)\right]_{-t_1}^{t_1} = \frac{1}{j\omega}\{\exp(j\omega t) - \exp(-j\omega t)\}$$

$$\therefore\ X(\omega) = \frac{2}{\omega} \sin \omega t_1 = 2t_1 \left\{\frac{\sin \omega t_1}{\omega t_1}\right\} \tag{4.35}$$

As would be expected from the above discussion, this function is of sinc form, and is also illustrated in figure 4.11(a). Note that a double-ended arrow is drawn between $x(t)$ and $X(\omega)$, to show that they are a Fourier Transform pair. The spectrum passes through zero whenever $\sin \omega t_1 = 0$, which occurs when ω is an integer multiple of π/t_1. It may seem strange that the pulse contains no energy at certain frequencies, but this is not in fact hard to demonstrate. Consider, for example, the frequency $\omega = \pi/t_1$, or $f = 1/2t_1$ Hz. If we wish to find out 'how much' of this frequency is contained in the pulse, the rule is to multiply the pulse by a sinusoid at the relevant frequency, and integrate over the interval of interest (as explained in our discussion of signal orthogonality in section 4.2.1). It is clear that the result must be zero because in this case the product is simply equal to the sinusoid itself, and the integral of the sinusoid over any interval equal to $2t_1$ is zero. Therefore the pulse contains no energy at $1/2t_1$ Hz.

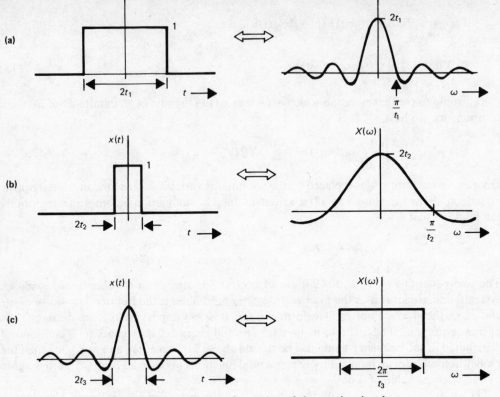

Figure 4.11 Fourier transformation of three pulse signals.

The above result for an isolated rectangular pulse allows us to illustrate two important general ideas. Firstly, equation (4.35) and figure 4.11(a) show that the frequency at which the spectrum first crosses zero ($\omega = \pi/t_1$) is inversely proportioned to the pulse duration ($2t_1$). Therefore a narrower pulse of duration $2t_2$, such as that in part (b) of the figure, must have a wider spread of spectral energy. This demonstrates a valuable principle. A signal which is very *time-limited* occupies a wide spectral bandwidth, but a signal which is very *bandlimited* has a wide spread in the time-domain—in other words it tends to be of long duration.

The second idea concerns an essential *symmetry* between the time and frequency domains, as shown by the Fourier Transform pair

$$X(\omega) = \int_{-\infty}^{\infty} x(t)\exp(-j\omega t)\,\mathrm{d}t$$

and

$$x(t) = \frac{1}{2\pi}\int_{-\infty}^{\infty} X(\omega)\exp(j\omega t)\,\mathrm{d}\omega$$

Apart from the $1/2\pi$ multiplier in the second equation (which arises from the use of angular frequency ω rather than frequency expressed in Hz), and the change of sign in the exponential index, the equations are symmetrical in form. The symmetry becomes perfect for even functions, such as the rectangular pulses and their spectra shown in parts (a) and (b) of figure 4.11. This may be deduced mathematically using the identity

$$\exp(j\theta) = \cos\theta + j\sin\theta$$

and writing the Fourier Transform pair as

$$X(\omega) = \int_{-\infty}^{\infty} \{x(t)\cos\omega t - jx(t)\sin\omega t\}\, dt \tag{4.36}$$

and

$$x(t) = \frac{1}{2\pi} \int_{-\infty}^{\infty} \{X(\omega)\cos\omega t + jX(\omega)\sin\omega t\}\, d\omega \tag{4.37}$$

Now the product of an even function and an odd function is itself odd, and integrates to zero between $\pm\infty$. The function $\sin\omega t$ is odd, and therefore if both $x(t)$ and $X(\omega)$ are even, the equations reduce to

$$X(\omega) = \int_{-\infty}^{\infty} x(t)\cos(\omega t)\, dt \tag{4.38}$$

and

$$x(t) = \frac{1}{2\pi} \int_{-\infty}^{\infty} X(\omega)\cos(\omega t)\, d\omega \tag{4.39}$$

This produces a perfect symmetry between time and frequency domains. For example, just as an even rectangular pulse in the time-domain has a spectrum of sinc form, so a sinc function 'pulse' in the time-domain *must* have a rectangular distribution of spectral energy. This is illustrated by figure 4.11(c). Such equivalence between time and frequency domains is often referred to as the *duality property* of the Fourier Trarnsform.

Before we evaluate more Fourier Transforms, it is perhaps helpful to consider rather more carefully the physical meaning of a continuous spectrum $X(\omega)$. There is no doubt that many people find the idea of a signal being composed of an infinite set of exponentials, all of vanishingly small amplitudes, rather hard to envisage. The more familiar situations illustrated by figure 4.12 may help. Figure 4.12(a) shows a simply supported beam loaded at several points. In part (b) of the figure the beam is continuously loaded along its length by, say, gravel or sand. In the first case it is clear that the loading is applied only at discrete points, just as a periodic signal contains only discrete frequencies. However, if one is asked what the load on the continuously loaded beam is at a point such as P, the answer must be that at that point (or any other) the applied load is vanishingly small. The sensible approach is to ask what the *average* loading is over a small distance such as Q–R, and to give the answer as a loading density in kilograms per metre. In an analogous way, a continuous frequency spectrum $X(\omega)$ implies that

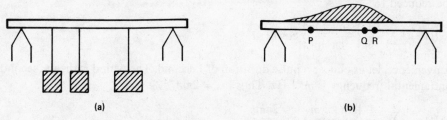

(a) (b)

Figure 4.12 Two types of beam-loading: (a) discrete, and (b) continuous.

the component at any point-frequency is vanishingly small, and that we should talk instead about the energy contained over a small band of frequencies centred around that point. $X(\omega)$ is therefore best thought of as a *frequency density* function.

This is a good point to reconsider Parseval's Theorem, quoted in section 4.2.2 for the case of periodic signals and the Fourier Series (see equation (4.22)). In essence, the theorem states that the power or energy in a signal may be found either in terms of its time-domain waveform, or in terms of its frequency spectrum. When dealing with a strictly periodic signal which (at least in theory) continues forever, it is appropriate to consider the signal's *average power*. However, in the case of a time-limited aperiodic signal the average power over all time tends to zero, so Parseval's relation is written in terms of total energy

$$\int_{-\infty}^{\infty} |x(t)|^2 \, dt = \frac{1}{2\pi} \int_{-\infty}^{\infty} |X(\omega)|^2 \, d\omega \tag{4.40}$$

This equation may be interpreted as follows. We consider $x(t)$ to represent a voltage across, or current through, a 1 ohm resistor. The total energy dissipated then equals the instantaneous power $x^2(t)$, integrated over all time (note that $x^2(t)$ may also be written as $|x(t)|^2$, thereby emphasising the symmetry between time and frequency in the above equation). The left-hand side therefore gives the signal's total energy, evaluated in the time-domain. This must equal the sum of energies in all the signal's frequency components. Now the energy in a frequency component depends only upon the square of its amplitude, not on its phase. Since $X(\omega)$ is a frequency density function, $|X(\omega)|^2/2\pi$ is effectively *spectral energy density*, representing the amount of energy per unit frequency. If this function is integrated over all frequencies, as on the right-hand side of the above equation, we again obtain the signal's total energy.

A further way of 'putting some flesh on the bones' of the Fourier transform is to carry out a simulation on a digital computer. A computer cannot, of course, add together an *infinite* number of frequency components to synthesise an aperiodic signal perfectly, but a modern machine can add together a large number in a short time, producing a good approximation. Let us return to equation (4.32), which specifies the exponential Fourier Series coefficients for a recurrent pulse signal in which the period is m times the pulse duration

$$a_k = \frac{1}{m} \left\{ \frac{\sin k\pi/m}{k\pi/m} \right\}$$

As we have seen, by letting m become large we may, in the limit, approach the Fourier Transform of a single rectangular pulse centred at $t = 0$. Conversely, such a pulse may in principle be synthesised using equation (4.27)

$$x(t) = \sum_{k=-\infty}^{\infty} a_k \exp(jk\omega_0 t) = \sum_{k=-\infty}^{\infty} \frac{1}{m} \left\{ \frac{\sin k\pi/m}{k\pi/m} \right\} \exp(jk\omega_0 t) \tag{4.41}$$

In this case the signal is even, all coefficients a_k are real, and $a_k = a_{-k}$ for all k. So equation (4.41) may be reduced to

$$x(t) = \sum_{k=-\infty}^{\infty} \frac{1}{m} \left\{ \frac{\sin k\pi/m}{k\pi/m} \right\} \cos k\omega_0 t \tag{4.42}$$

For convenience, let us choose a pulse duration of 1 second. The period is then m seconds, and the fundamental frequency is m^{-1} Hz. Thus $\omega_0 = 2\pi m^{-1}$, giving

$$x(t) = \sum_{k=-\infty}^{\infty} \frac{1}{m} \left\{ \frac{\sin k\pi/m}{k\pi/m} \right\} \cos \frac{2\pi kt}{m}$$

Clearly, we can only sum a finite set of frequency components in a practical simulation. Suppose we restrict ourselves to n equally spaced harmonics, covering the range up to 10 Hz. Hence

$$\omega_0 = \frac{2\pi}{m} = 2\pi\left(\frac{10}{n}\right), \quad \text{giving } n = 10m$$

Our simulation equation is now

$$x(t) = \sum_{k=-n}^{n} \frac{10}{n} \left\{ \frac{\sin 10k\pi/n}{10k\pi/n} \right\} \cos \frac{20k\pi t}{n} \tag{4.43}$$

We expect that as n is increased while keeping the total frequency range fixed at 10 Hz, the signal $x(t)$ will more and more closely resemble a single, aperiodic pulse at $t = 0$.

BASIC program listing no. 3 implements equation (4.43) for values of t in the range ± 5, with a step size of 0.02 s. The program loads 500 values of the synthesised signal $x(t)$ into array X. The simulation is well within the capabilities of a small personal computer, although some patience may be needed while waiting for the result! Optional program lines 160 and 170 give a screen print-out of the time value currently being processed (between -5 and 5 seconds), to indicate progress. Just one further detailed point should be explained. Line 190 adds 0.001 to the calculated value of $10k\pi$, to avoid a division by zero when $k = 0$.

```
100 REM ***   PROGRAM NO.3        SYNTHESIS OF RECTANGULAR PULSE   **
110 REM
120 DIM X(500):PRINT "REQUIRED NO. OF HARMONICS?":INPUT N
130 FOR S=1 TO 500:T=((S-1)/50)-5:X(S)=0
140 REM
150 REM **********   LINES 160 AND 170 ARE OPTIONAL   ************
160 CLS:PLOT 10,300
170 TAG:PRINT "TIME VALUE BEING PROCESSED=";T;" SECS.";:TAGOFF
180 FOR K=-N TO N
190 A=10*K*PI+0.001:X(S)=X(S)+10*SIN(A/N)*COS(2*A*T/N)/A:NEXT K
200 NEXT S
210 REM *******************  PLOT OPTION  *******************
220 CLS:PLOT 500,100:DRAW 1,100:PLOT 1,100+X(1)*200
230 FOR J=2 TO 500:DRAW J,100+X(J)*200:NEXT J
240 REM
250 REM ******************  PRINT OPTION  ******************
260 FOR K=1 TO 500:PRINT X(K);:NEXT K
270 REM ****************************************************
```

Figure 4.13 shows some typical computed results. The 500 values of array X are joined together in each case to give a continuous waveform. In part (a) of the figure $n = 20$, corresponding to a harmonic spacing of 0.5 Hz over the chosen range 0 to 10 Hz, and a fundamental frequency of 0.5 Hz. Since $m = n/10 = 2$, and the pulse duration is 1 second, we expect a recurrent pulse signal of period 2 seconds, with equal amounts of time spent in its 'high' and 'low' states. This is confirmed by the computer output.

Parts (b) and (c) of the figure show the effects of increasing the number of frequency components to 43 and 77 respectively. As expected, the pulses move apart as n increases; when $n = 77$ only the central pulse at $t = 0$ is visible within the plotted time interval. The simulation is clearly approaching the inverse Fourier Transform of an isolated pulse quite well in this case. It is interesting to see that the simulated pulses are all more or less the same shape, regardless of the value of n. This is because we have kept the total bandwidth of the simulation fixed at 10 Hz. Note also that the bandwidth restriction prevents the pulse edges from being sharply defined, and gives rise to a clear example of the Gibbs phenomenon.

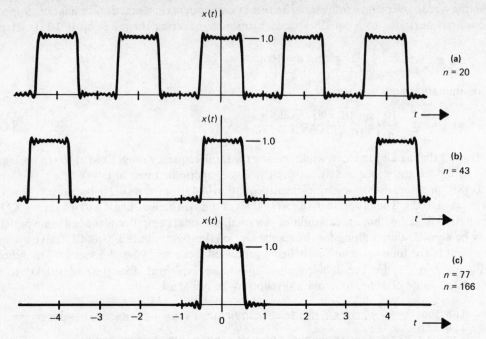

Figure 4.13 Computer simulation of an inverse Fourier Transform.

We have spent some time on the above computer simulation, in an attempt to give the Fourier Transform—and its close relationship with the Fourier Series—a clearer and more tangible interpretation. However, it is important to remember that a digital computer can only *approximate* the transform, or inverse transform, of continuous functions, because it can work only with sampled versions of signals and spectra. We have in fact been straying over the boundary between the Fourier analysis of continuous and discrete signals. This topic will be covered much more fully in chapter 5.

It is time to consider an engineering application of the ideas developed in the last few pages. An important consideration in the design of TV systems—including TV cameras, transmission channels, and receivers—is the bandwidth requirement of TV signals. It has already been mentioned in section 1.3 that monochrome (or black and white) TV signals typically occupy a frequency range of a few megahertz. We now show by a few simple calculations, and using our knowledge of Fourier analysis, why this is so. A good approach is to consider the receiving end of the system, and ask what sharpness of images is required on a typical TV screen. As readers are probably aware, TV receivers generally work on the *raster-scan* principle, in which a 'flying spot' electron beam travels across the screen, tracing out a large number of horizontal lines. The incoming video signal changes, or *modulates*, the instantaneous brightness of the spot. Provided the horizontal lines are closely spaced, and the picture is traced out often enough to avoid visible *flicker*, the human eye and brain integrate the displayed information into a complete picture. In the following discussion, we assume the following typical parameters

Number of horizontal lines	= 625
Repetition frequency of complete picture	= 25 Hz
Screen dimensions: horizontal	= 40 cm
vertical	= 30 cm

Suppose that the system specification calls for a vertical line of thickness 1 mm (either a white line against a dark background, or vice versa) to be clearly visible on the display. Of course, TV pictures do not generally consist of isolated vertical lines. However, the problem of display resolution is well illustrated and tackled by this approach.

Let us first estimate the scanning speed of the flying spot. It repeats each horizontal line, of length 40 cm, 25 times per second, and there are 625 lines. Ignoring the relatively small *flyback time* needed to return the spot to its starting position for the next scan, its speed is

$$625 \times 25 \times 40 \,\text{cm/s} = 6.25 \times 10^6 \,\text{mm/s}$$

(as a point of interest, this is more than 20 000 km/h). The time taken to travel 1 mm horizontally is therefore

$$\frac{1}{6.25 \times 10^6} \,\text{s} = 0.16 \,\mu\text{s}$$

The video signal which controls the brightness of the spot would ideally be a rectangular pulse of this duration, giving a sharply defined 1 mm line on the screen. However, we have seen that the Fourier Transform of a true rectangular pulse is a sinc function of unlimited bandwidth. So a compromise is necessary (one must not be upset by the word *compromise*: it is an essential ingredient of virtually all real engineering design). Bandwidth must be conserved as much as possible, while allowing the vertical line to be 'clearly visible'. It is easier to make an informed decision if we consider the distortion caused by bandlimiting an isolated rectangular pulse (actually the pulse is not truly isolated, because one must be generated during each horizontal line scan, but successive pulses are well separated).

The computer program already given in this section is useful for exploring this problem. Although originally written for a pulse duration of 1 second, it is valid for *any* duration if we label axes in terms of time *units* and frequency *units*, rather than seconds and hertz respectively. In this case one time unit will be taken as the pulse duration of 0.16 μs, and one frequency unit as its inverse, equal to 6.25 MHz. The reader probably recalls that the simulation equation (4.43) applied to a bandwidth of 0–10 Hz, or 0–10 frequency units; however, it is simple to allow for *any* bandwidth by replacing the constant 10 in line 190 of program no. 3 by a variable.

Figure 4.14 shows some computed results for bandwidths (denoted by B) of 0.5, 1.0, 1.5, and 2.0 frequency units. The number of harmonics (n) was set to 50 in each case, giving a good approximation to the inverse Fourier Transform. The plotted time scale was shortened to cover

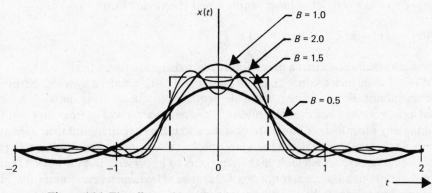

Figure 4.14 The effects of bandlimiting an isolated rectangular pulse.

the range ± 2 time units. The 'ideal' rectangular pulse is also shown dotted, for comparison. It is clear that a bandwidth of 0.5 units causes much spreading of the pulse, and a reduction in its amplitude. This could not be expected to produce a bright, sharply defined line on the TV screen. With $B = 1$ unit, the rise and fall of the pulse are much faster, and it achieves a good peak value. When $B = 1.5$ or 2.0 the pulse edges are further improved, but it is doubtful whether the benefits justify such a large bandwidth penalty. Also, the simulations show a 'double-hump' at the top of the pulse, which might cause brightness modulation of the displayed line. All in all, it seems that a bandwidth of about 1 frequency unit, or 6.25 MHz, represents a good design compromise. Interestingly, such a figure is fairly typical of high-quality monochrome TV channels.

The reader may have noticed parallels between this discussion and an earlier one, in section 4.2.2.1, on the transmission of a periodic square wave through a bandlimited cable or system. In both cases we have assumed a sudden cut-off in the frequency domain, and have ignored any additional signal distortion due to the effects of phase shift. However, in the earlier example we were dealing with a true line spectrum. In the case of the TV pulse, we have *approximated* a continuous spectrum by a set of closely spaced discrete frequencies for the purposes of computer simulation.

So far, we have used the Fourier Transform equation to find the spectrum of only one type of aperiodic signal—an isolated rectangular pulse. To give practice in Fourier Transformation and to illustrate some important aspects of continuous spectra, we now consider some further examples. The first of these is of general interest and relevance, and is tackled in the main text; the others are covered by a worked example. At the end of this chapter, our 'library' of Fourier Transforms is supplemented by including a table of signals and their transforms. Such tables are widely used in engineering practice, and save the trouble of evaluating transforms of commonly used functions.

We first find the Fourier Transforms of the continuous unit impulse function $\delta(t)$, and its shifted version $\delta(t - t_0)$. These signals are shown in figure 4.15

Using equation (4.33) the spectrum of the impulse $\delta(t)$ is given by

$$X(\omega) = \int_{-\infty}^{\infty} x(t) \exp(-j\omega t)\, dt = \int_{-\infty}^{\infty} \delta(t) \exp(-j\omega t)\, dt$$

This integral is readily solved using the *sifting property* of the unit impulse, first discussed in section 3.2. When the impulse is multiplied by another function, and the product integrated between $\pm \infty$, the result is to *sift out* the value of the second function where the impulse occurs. Since $\delta(t)$ occurs at $t = 0$, $X(\omega)$ must simply equal the value of $\exp(-j\omega t)$ at $t = 0$. Thus

$$X(\omega) = \exp(-j\omega t)|_{t=0} = \exp(0) = 1 \qquad (4.44)$$

This important result shows that a unit impulse centred at $t = 0$ theoretically contains an equal 'amount' of *all* frequencies. Since $X(\omega)$ is purely real, $\delta(t)$ could be synthesised by adding together an infinite set of cosines, with all frequencies equally represented. This may be visualised as follows. At $t = 0$ every infinitesimal cosine, regardless of its frequency, has its peak value. But at any other instant, some are positive and others negative, and their sum averages out to zero. So the synthesised signal has a large peak at $t = 0$, and is zero elsewhere. In practice, of course, we cannot expect *infinitely* high frequencies to be present. But the notion that a very narrow pulse contains an equal amount of a wide range of frequencies remains a valid, and very valuable, one. The spectrum $X(\omega)$ is illustrated in figure 4.15(a). It is said to be *white*, because all

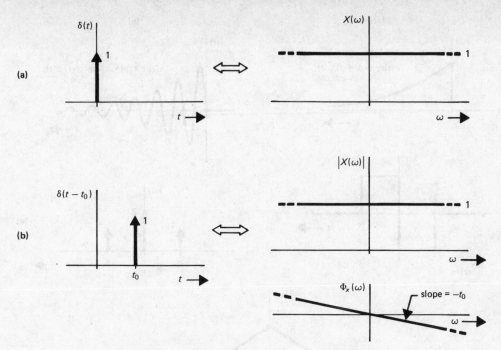

Figure 4.15 Fourier Transforms of impulse signals.

spectral components are equally represented (just as white light contains an equal mixture of all the colours of the rainbow).

The spectrum of the shifted unit impulse shown in part (b) of figure 4.15 may be found in similar fashion. We have

$$X(\omega) = \int_{-\infty}^{\infty} \delta(t - t_0) \exp(-j\omega t) \, dt = \exp(-j\omega t)|_{t=t_0} = \exp(-j\omega t_0) \tag{4.45}$$

This spectrum is also white, because the *magnitude* of $\exp(-j\omega t_0)$ is likewise unity for all values of ω. This is what we should expect, because a mere time-shift cannot alter the amount of the various frequencies present. What *has* changed is the phase, which is now proportional to ω. The magnitude $|X(\omega)|$ and phase $\Phi_x(\omega)$,of this spectrum are shown in figure 4.15(b). We shall have reason to return to these important results later. Let us for the moment just note one interesting point, namely that an impulse function represents the ultimate time-limited signal, and we now see that its spectrum is, in theory, infinitely wide. This nicely illustrates a general principle we discussed earlier. A signal which is severely time-limited has a wide spectral distribution, and vice versa.

Example E4.5

Evaluate, and sketch, the Fourier Transforms of the four signals shown in parts (a) to (d) of figure E4.5.1, and the inverse Fourier Transform of the spectrum shown in part (e).

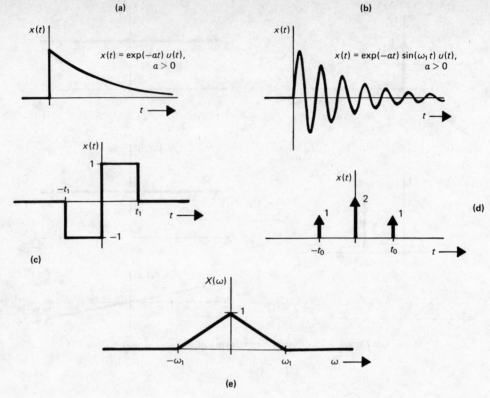

Figure E4.5.1

Solution

(a)

$$X(\omega) = \int_{-\infty}^{\infty} x(t) \exp(-j\omega t)\, dt = \int_{0}^{\infty} \exp(-\alpha t) \exp(-j\omega t)\, dt$$

$$\therefore\ X(\omega) = \int_{0}^{\infty} \exp(-\{\alpha + j\omega\} t)\, dt = \left[\frac{\exp(-\{\alpha + j\omega\}t)}{-(\alpha + j\omega)}\right]_{0}^{\infty}$$

$$\therefore\ X(\omega) = \left\{0 - \frac{\exp(0)}{-(\alpha + j\omega)}\right\} = \frac{1}{(\alpha + j\omega)}$$

This spectrum is complex, implying that both sine and cosine waves would be needed to synthesise the decaying exponential signal. $X(\omega)$ cannot be represented on a single diagram, and the most usual approach is to plot its magnitude and phase separately. The magnitude is given by

$$|X(\omega)| = \frac{1}{|\alpha + j\omega|} = \frac{1}{(\alpha^2 + \omega^2)^{1/2}}$$

The phase angle in radians represented by the term $(\alpha + j\omega)$ is $\tan^{-1}(\omega/\alpha)$. Since this appears in the *denominator*, and the numerator is real, the phase of $X(\omega)$ is simply

$$\Phi_x(\omega) = -\tan^{-1}(\omega/\alpha)$$

Magnitude and phase are separately shown in part (a) of figure E4.5.2. Although these spectral diagrams do extend to negative frequencies, we generally show only the positive frequency range. In fact, the spectral magnitude function of any real signal or time function is always even, and the phase function is always odd. In this particular case it is clear that the signal is relatively rich in low-frequency components. When $\omega = \alpha$, the magnitude function has already fallen to $1/\sqrt{2}$ of its peak value at $\omega = 0$, and the phase is $-\pi/4$. As $\omega \to \infty$, the phase asymptotically approaches $-\pi/2$ (or $-90°$).

(b)

$$X(\omega) = \int_{-\infty}^{\infty} x(t) \exp(-j\omega t) \, dt = \int_{0}^{\infty} \exp(-\alpha t) \sin \omega_1 t \exp(-j\omega t) \, dt$$

Using the identity

$$\sin \omega_1 t = \frac{1}{2j} \{\exp(j\omega_1 t) - \exp(-j\omega_1 t)\}$$

we obtain

$$X(\omega) = \frac{1}{2j} \int_{0}^{\infty} \{\exp(j\omega_1 t) - \exp(-j\omega_1 t)\} \exp(-\{\alpha + j\omega\}t) \, dt$$

$$\therefore \ X(\omega) = \frac{1}{2j} \left\{ \int_{0}^{\infty} \exp(-\{\alpha + j\omega - j\omega_1\}t) \, dt - \int_{0}^{\infty} \exp(-\{\alpha + j\omega + j\omega_1\}t) \, dt \right\}$$

$$\therefore \ X(\omega) = \frac{1}{2j} \left\{ \left[\frac{\exp(-\{\alpha + j\omega - j\omega_1\}t)}{-(\alpha + j\omega - j\omega_1)} \right]_{0}^{\infty} - \left[\frac{\exp(-\{\alpha + j\omega + j\omega_1\}t)}{-(\alpha + j\omega + j\omega_1)} \right]_{0}^{\infty} \right\}$$

$$\therefore \ X(\omega) = \frac{1}{2j} \left\{ \frac{-1}{-(\alpha + j\omega - j\omega_1)} + \frac{1}{-(\alpha + j\omega + j\omega_1)} \right\}$$

$$\therefore \ X(\omega) = \frac{1}{2j} \left\{ \frac{2j\omega_1}{\alpha^2 + \omega_1^2 + 2j\alpha\omega - \omega^2} \right\} = \frac{\omega_1}{\alpha^2 + \omega_1^2 + 2j\alpha\omega - \omega^2}$$

Once again the spectrum is a complex function of ω, which is to be expected since the signal $x(t)$ is neither even nor odd. The magnitude and phase are respectively

$$|X(\omega)| = \frac{\omega_1}{\{(\alpha^2 + \omega_1^2 - \omega^2)^2 + (2\alpha\omega)^2\}^{1/2}}$$

and

$$\Phi_x(\omega) = -\tan^{-1} \left\{ \frac{2\alpha\omega}{(\alpha^2 + \omega_1^2 - \omega^2)} \right\}$$

It is difficult to sketch these functions as they stand, because their shapes depend markedly on the values of α and ω_1. Note, however, that the signal shown in figure E4.5.1(b) displays several oscillations of the sinusoid within one time constant of its exponential decay, so that $\omega_1 \gg \alpha$. If we take $\alpha = 1$ and $\omega_1 = 20$ as an example, then clearly $\omega_1^2 \gg \alpha^2$, and to a good approximation we may write

$$|X(\omega)| \approx \frac{\omega_1}{\{(\omega_1^2 - \omega^2)^2 + (2\alpha\omega)^2\}^{1/2}} = \frac{20}{\{(400 - \omega^2)^2 + 4\omega^2\}^{1/2}}$$

and

$$\Phi_x(\omega) = -\tan^{-1}\left\{\frac{2\alpha\omega}{\omega_1^2 - \omega^2}\right\} = -\tan^{-1}\left\{\frac{2\omega}{400 - \omega^2}\right\}$$

These functions are plotted in part (b) of figure E4.5.2. The most important point they reveal is that frequencies close to ω_1 are very strongly represented in $|X(\omega)|$. This is what we would expect, since the signal is essentially a sinusoid at this frequency. The spreading of spectral energy to either side of ω_1 is due to time-limitation of the sinewave—caused by 'switching it on' at $t = 0$, and by the subsequent exponential decay. The sharpness of the resonant peak is very dependent on the value of α. The plot of $\Phi_x(\omega)$ shows that there is a sudden phase change of π radians as resonance is passed. The phase of frequency components close to ω_1 is near $\pm\pi/2$, denoting sines rather than cosines. Again, this is what would be expected.

(c)

$$X(\omega) = \int_{-\infty}^{\infty} x(t) \exp(-j\omega t)\,dt = \int_{-t_1}^{0} (-1) \exp(-j\omega t)\,dt + \int_{0}^{t_1} (1) \exp(-j\omega t)\,dt$$

$$\therefore X(\omega) = \left[\frac{\exp(-j\omega t)}{j\omega}\right]_{-t_1}^{0} - \left[\frac{\exp(-j\omega t)}{j\omega}\right]_{0}^{t_1}$$

$$\therefore X(\omega) = \frac{1}{j\omega}\{1 - \exp(j\omega t_1) - \exp(-j\omega t_1) + 1\} = \frac{2}{j\omega}(1 - \cos \omega t_1)$$

In this case $X(\omega)$ is purely imaginary for all values of ω. This implies that $x(t)$ contains only sines, which is correct since it is an odd function. $X(\omega)$ can therefore be entirely represented by a single spectral diagram, as shown in part (c) of figure E4.5.2. There is no spectral energy close to zero frequency, since the mean, or DC, component of the signal is zero.

(d)

$$X(\omega) = \int_{-\infty}^{\infty} x(t) \exp(-j\omega t)\,dt$$

$$\therefore X(\omega) = \int_{-\infty}^{\infty} \{\delta(t + t_0) + 2\delta(t) + \delta(t - t_0)\} \exp(-j\omega t)\,dt$$

which, by the sifting property of the impulse function, becomes

$$X(\omega) = \exp(j\omega t_0) + 2 + \exp(-j\omega t_0) = 2(1 + \cos \omega t_0)$$

Since $x(t)$ is an even time function, $X(\omega)$ is real and represents a cosine spectrum. It may be represented by a single spectral diagram, as shown in part (d) of figure E4.5.2. This result emphasises the important point that, although a single impulse function has a constant, or white, spectral magnitude characteristic, a group or sequence of impulses does not. Note that $X(\omega)$ is strictly periodic in ω, and extends theoretically up to infinitely high frequencies

(e)

$$x(t) = \frac{1}{2\pi}\int_{-\infty}^{\infty} X(\omega) \exp(j\omega t)\,d\omega$$

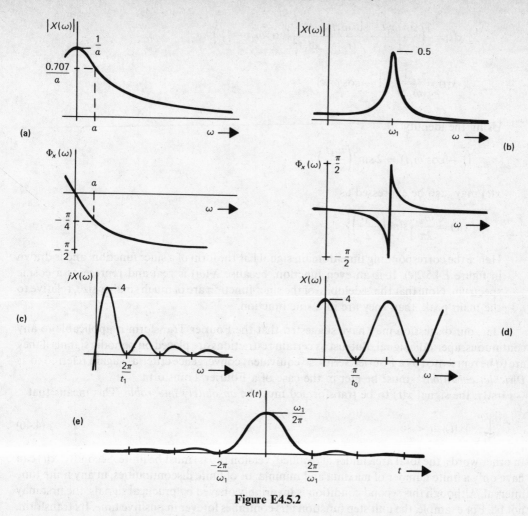

Figure E4.5.2

Since $X(\omega)$ is a real spectrum and an even function of ω, the above equation reduces to

$$x(t) = \frac{1}{2\pi} \int_{-\infty}^{\infty} X(\omega) \cos(\omega t)\, d\omega$$

Also, since the area under the product $X(\omega) \cos \omega t$ between $\omega = -\omega_1$ and $\omega = 0$ is clearly equal to its area between $\omega = 0$ and ω_1, we may further simplify to give

$$x(t) = \frac{1}{\pi} \int_{0}^{\infty} X(\omega) \cos(\omega t)\, d\omega = \frac{1}{\pi} \int_{0}^{\omega_1} \left(1 - \frac{\omega}{\omega_1}\right) \cos(\omega t)\, d\omega$$

(this step is not *necessary*, but it simplifies the integration). Hence

$$x(t) = \frac{1}{\pi} \left\{ \int_{0}^{\omega_1} \cos(\omega t)\, d\omega - \frac{1}{\omega_1} \int_{0}^{\omega_1} \omega \cos(\omega t)\, d\omega \right\}$$

$$\therefore\ x(t) = \frac{1}{\pi} \left[\frac{\sin \omega t}{t} \right]_{0}^{\omega_1} - \frac{1}{\pi \omega_1} \left\{ \left[\frac{\omega \sin \omega t}{t} \right]_{0}^{\omega_1} - \int_{0}^{\omega_1} \frac{(1) \sin(\omega t)}{t}\, d\omega \right\}$$

$$\therefore \quad x(t) = \frac{1}{\pi}\left(\frac{\sin\omega_1 t}{t} - \frac{\sin\omega_1 t}{t} - \frac{1}{\omega_1 t^2}\{\cos\omega_1 t - 1\}\right)$$

$$\therefore \quad x(t) = \frac{1}{\omega_1 \pi t^2}(1 - \cos\omega_1 t)$$

Using the identity

$$(1 - \cos\omega_1 t) = 2\sin^2\left(\frac{\omega_1 t}{2}\right)$$

$x(t)$ may also be expressed as

$$x(t) = \frac{\omega_1}{2\pi}\left\{\operatorname{sinc}\left(\frac{\omega_1 t}{2}\right)\right\}^2$$

Hence the corresponding time-domain signal has the form of a sinc^2 function, and is drawn in figure E4.5.2(e). It is an even function, because $X(\omega)$ is real and represents a cosine spectrum. Note that the 'sidelobes' of the sinc^2 function are of much smaller size, relative to the main peak, than they are in a sinc function.

So far, our discussion may have suggested that the Fourier Transform is applicable to any continuous, aperiodic signal. But just as certain restrictions are placed on periodic signals if they are to be reprsented by a Fourier Series, so equivalent convergence criteria—again referred to as *Dirichlet conditions*—must be met in the case of a Fourier Transform.

Firstly, the signal $x(t)$ to be transformed must be *absolutely integrable*. This means that

$$\int_{-\infty}^{\infty} |x(t)|\,\mathrm{d}t < \infty \tag{4.46}$$

In other words, the total area under a 'rectified' version of $x(t)$ must be finite. Secondly, $x(t)$ can have only a finite number of maxima and minima, or of finite discontinuities, in any finite time interval. Although this second condition is invariably obeyed by practical signals, the first may not be. For example, the unit step function $u(t)$ continues forever in positive time. Its transform, specified by the Fourier integral (equation (4.33)) does not converge. Nor does that of a ramp function. Similarly, *eternal* sine and cosine signals (which are considered to continue forever) do not meet the condition specified by expression (4.46). Therefore we see that a number of quite basic signals present difficulties when it comes to Fourier transformation.

There are various ways round such problems. In some cases it is better to seek a frequency-domain representation of a continuous signal using the Laplace Transform. This is closely related to the Fourier Transform, and will be described in chapter 6. In other cases, the Fourier Transform of a signal which fails to meet the condition of absolute integrability may be inferred as the limiting case of a signal which *does* meet it. A good example of this is the unit step function $u(t)$. If we start with the decaying exponential signal

$$x(t) = \exp(-\alpha t), \quad t > 0; \qquad x(t) = 0, \quad t < 0$$

where α is real and positive, then its Fourier Transform may easily be found (see worked example E4.5, part (a))

$$X(\omega) = \frac{1}{\alpha + j\omega} \tag{4.47}$$

The transform of $u(t)$ may now be inferred by letting $\alpha \to 0$, giving

$$X(\omega) \to \frac{1}{j\omega} \tag{4.48}$$

Considerable care is needed when interpreting this result, because there is a singularity at $\omega = 0$, where $|X(\omega)| \to \infty$. This implies that $u(t)$ contains a *discrete* spectral component at $\omega = 0$, corresponding to its DC value (which is equal to 1/2 over the complete interval $-\infty < t < \infty$). Such a discrete frequency can be represented in a Fourier Transform only by an infinitely narrow *impulse function* concentrated at $\omega = 0$. Since the inverse Fourier Transform equation includes a multiplier equal to $1/2\pi$, the value of the impulse function must in this case be π. Over the frequency range away from $\omega = 0$, $X(\omega)$ is 'well behaved', having a spectral density inversely proportional to ω as indicated by expression (4.48) above. This discussion shows that the Fourier Transform of the unit step function $u(t)$ is given by

$$X(\omega) = \frac{1}{j\omega} + \pi\delta(\omega) \tag{4.49}$$

The idea that a Fourier Transform may contain one or more frequency-domain impulses also offers a very useful representation of eternal sine and cosine signals (and of other strictly *periodic* signals which are not absolutely integrable). Consider, for example, the real spectral function

$$X(\omega) = \pi\delta(\omega - \omega_0) + \pi\delta(\omega + \omega_0) \tag{4.50}$$

Its inverse Fourier Transform, given by equation (4.34), specifies the corresponding signal

$$x(t) = \frac{1}{2\pi} \int_{-\infty}^{\infty} X(\omega) \exp(j\omega t)\, d\omega = \frac{1}{2} \int_{-\infty}^{\infty} \{\delta(\omega - \omega_0) + \delta(\omega + \omega_0)\} \exp(j\omega t)\, d\omega$$

Using the sifting property of the continuous unit impulse function, we obtain directly

$$x(t) = \tfrac{1}{2}\{\exp(j\omega_0 t) + \exp(-j\omega_0 t)\} = \cos \omega_0 t \tag{4.51}$$

Therefore an eternal cosine signal of unit amplitude has a Fourier Transform consisting of a pair of frequency-domain 'impulses', each weighted by π. Similarly, an eternal sine signal transforms into a pair of impulse functions, but in this case the spectrum is imaginary because a sinewave is odd.

These important spectral representations are shown in figure 4.16. They provide a further confirmation of the antithesis between time limitation and band limitation. Eternal sinusoids, being completely unlimited in the time-domain, have all their spectral energy compressed into a single, discrete frequency. This is in complete contrast to the isolated time-domain impulse, with a spectrum which is (in theory) infinitely wide. Note that the spectra of figure 4.16 are shown for negative, as well as positive, frequencies. This helps emphasise once again that the cosine signal, being even, has a spectrum which is both real and even; whereas the sine signal, which is odd, has a spectrum which is both imaginary and odd.

4.2.3.2 *Properties of the transform*

The Fourier Transform, considered as a mathematical operation, possesses a number of important properties. Among the most valuable of these from the point of view of electronic signals and systems are the following: linearity, time-shifting and scaling, differentiation and integration, convolution, and modulation. These properties give further insight into the nature of Fourier transformation, and the relationships between the time and frequency domains.

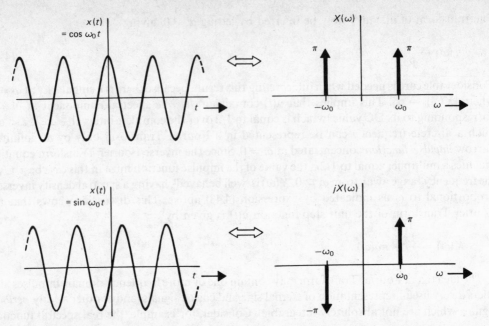

Figure 4.16 The spectral representation of eternal cosine and sine signals.

From the engineer's point of view they often simplify or reduce the amount of work involved in solving practical problems, and we shall find several of them very useful in later chapters of this book.

We have in fact already mentioned two general properties of the Fourier Transform pair: its essential *symmetry*, which is most obvious for even signals having real, even, spectra; and the related idea of the *duality* between the time and frequency domains. In this section we cover the additional properties listed above. Rather than use the Fourier Transform and inverse Fourier Transform equations (4.33) and (4.34) each time we need to define or discuss a property, it is helpful to introduce the following shorthand notation

$\mathscr{F}\{x(t)\}$ denotes the Fourier Transform of a signal $x(t)$

$\mathscr{F}^{-1}\{X(\omega)\}$ denotes the inverse transform of a spectrum $X(\omega)$

$x(t) \leftrightarrow X(\omega)$ signifies that $x(t)$ and $X(\omega)$ are a Fourier Transform pair

The *linearity* of the Fourier Transform is an important property which stems directly from its mathematical definition. It may be summarised as follows

If $x_1(t) \leftrightarrow X_1(\omega)$ and $x_2(t) \leftrightarrow X_2(\omega)$

then $ax_1(t) + bx_2(t) \leftrightarrow aX_1(\omega) + bX_2(\omega)$ (4.52)

Thus the Fourier Transform of a composite signal, formed by the addition of weighted individual signals $x_1(t)$, $x_2(t)$, ... equals the sum of their individual transforms, duly weighted. It must be emphasised straightaway that since spectra are generally complex functions of ω, a frequency-domain summation must take proper account of relative phase as well as magnitude. This is well illustrated by the signal covered in part (d) of worked example E4.5, which consisted of three time-domain impulses. The spectrum of each impulse, considered separately, has a constant, white, magnitude characteristic. However, it would be quite wrong to assume that the *composite* signal is also white, because of interactions between the phases of the component spectra.

The Fourier Transform also has an important *time-shifting* property, which may be expressed as follows

If $\quad x(t) \leftrightarrow X(\omega)$

then $\quad x(t - t_0) \leftrightarrow X(\omega) \exp(-j\omega t_0)$ (4.53)

This result may readily be proved by writing

$$\mathscr{F}\{x(t - t_0)\} = \int_{-\infty}^{\infty} x(t - t_0) \exp(-j\omega t)\, dt$$

Substituting $\alpha = (t - t_0)$, we obtain

$$\mathscr{F}\{x(t - t_0)\} = \int_{-\infty}^{\infty} x(\alpha) \exp(-j\omega\{\alpha + t_0\})\, d\alpha$$

$$= \exp(-j\omega t_0) \int_{-\infty}^{\infty} x(\alpha) \exp(-j\omega\alpha)\, d\alpha$$

Since α is an auxiliary variable and disappears when the limits are inserted, we may write

$$\mathscr{F}\{x(t - t_0)\} = \exp(-j\omega t_0) X(\omega)$$ (4.54)

This is equivalent to expression (4.53) above. Since $\exp(-j\omega t_0)$ has unit magnitude for all values of ω, it follows that time-shifting does not affect the magnitude of a Fourier Transform. But it does affect the phase characteristic, introducing a phase-shift proportional to frequency. This point has already been made several times in this text—for example, in our derivation of the transforms of the unit impulse function $\delta(t)$ and its shifted version $\delta(t - t_0)$ in equations (4.44) and (4.45). The time-shifting property can be very useful. If we already know the Fourier Transform of a signal, we may at once write down the transform of its time-shifted version without further analysis.

The *time-scaling* property of the transform means that if a signal $x(t)$ is expanded in time, then its spectrum $X(\omega)$ is compressed in proportion, and vice versa. We have already met an example of this effect in the synthesis by computer simulation of an isolated rectangular pulse, described in the previous section. Although the computer program was written for a pulse duration of one second, we subsequently applied it to a TV bandwidth problem in which the pulse duration was 0.16 μs. It was then necessary to change the frequency scale in inverse proportion. Another example of time-scaling, probably familiar to many readers, is the playback of a tape or disc recording at a speed other than the recording speed. For example, if the time-scale is *expanded* by reducing the playback speed, the frequency scale is shortened or *compressed* by the same factor, reducing the frequency (or pitch) of musical notes and speech. This property is summarised as

If $\quad x(t) \leftrightarrow X(\omega)$

then $\quad x(at) \leftrightarrow \dfrac{1}{a} X\left(\dfrac{\omega}{a}\right)$ (4.55)

where the constant a is real and positive. Note that the spectrum undergoes a simple change of amplitude, as well as of frequency scale. This may be explained quite easily. Suppose, for example, $a = 0.5$, corresponding to a doubling of the signal's total duration and hence of its total energy. Since the spectrum is compressed by a factor of 2, $X(\omega/a)$ has half the total energy of $X(\omega)$. In order to obey Parseval's Theorem, equation (4.40), the energy in $X(\omega/a)$ must therefore be increased by a factor of 4. But energy is proportional to the square of amplitude, so the amplitude must be doubled, or multipied by $(1/a)$.

When a signal is *differentiated* or *integrated*, the effect on its Fourier Transform is readily predictable. This is a particularly useful property of the transform. As we have seen in section 2.3.3, the performance of continuous LTI systems is often described in terms of differential or integral equations relating input and output signals. Therefore the frequency-domain effects of time-domain differentiation or integration are of special interest for the analysis of signal flow through such systems. The *differentiation property* of the Fourier Transform may be deduced as follows

If $x(t) \leftrightarrow X(\omega)$

then $x(t) = \dfrac{1}{2\pi} \displaystyle\int_{-\infty}^{\infty} X(\omega) \exp(j\omega t)\, d\omega$

Since $X(\omega)$ is not a function of time, differentiation of both sides with respect to time gives

$$\frac{dx(t)}{dt} = \frac{1}{2\pi} \int_{-\infty}^{\infty} X(\omega) j\omega \exp(j\omega t)\, d\omega = \mathscr{F}^{-1}\{j\omega X(\omega)\}$$

therefore

$$\mathscr{F}\left\{\frac{dx(t)}{dt}\right\} = j\omega X(\omega) \tag{4.56}$$

This shows that the transform of a differentiated signal is just the transform of the signal itself, multiplied by $j\omega$. The relatively complicated process of *differentiation* in the time-domain is therefore equivalent to a much simpler *multiplication* in the frequency domain.

Since differentiation is equivalent to multiplication by $j\omega$, the reader may suspect that *integration* is equivalent to *division* by $j\omega$. This is so, but unfortunately it is not quite the whole story, because such a division does not take account of any DC level possessed by the signal. The mathematical argument here is a little complicated, but we may illustrate the problem by referring back to the unit step function $u(t)$ and its Fourier Transform, given in equation (4.49)

$$u(t) \leftrightarrow \frac{1}{j\omega} + \pi\delta(\omega)$$

If we differentiate $u(t)$ we obtain the unit impulse function $\delta(t)$—see equation (2.7); and the Fourier Transform of $\delta(t)$ has been shown by equation (4.44) to equal unity. Clearly, if we now divide this latter transform by $j\omega$ in an attempt to derive the spectrum of a unit step, we get the result $1/j\omega$. This is correct except that the term $\pi\delta(\omega)$ is missing. As we have shown previously, the latter term represents the step function's finite DC level. So integration in the time-domain is equivalent to division by $j\omega$ in the frequency-domain, *plus* the addition of a frequency-domain impulse at $\omega = 0$ if the signal has a finite DC level. The precise relationship may be shown to be

$$\int_{-\infty}^{t} x(\tau)\, d\tau \leftrightarrow \frac{X(\omega)}{j\omega} + X(0)\pi\delta(\omega) \tag{4.57}$$

where the left-hand side denotes the running integral of $x(t)$, and $X(0)$ is the zero-frequency, or DC, value of $X(\omega)$.

We now turn to the very important *convolution property* of the Fourier Transform. As will become clear below, this property is responsible for the widespread use of frequency-domain methods to analyse and predict signal flow through LTI systems. Like other properties already mentioned, it is essentially a consequence of the mathematical definition of the Fourier Transform. We may introduce it in general terms by considering the convolution of two time functions or signals $x_1(t)$ and $x_2(t)$, producing a third time function $x_3(t)$. The form of the convolution integral, developed in the previous chapter (see equation (3.18)), allows us to write

$$x_3(t) = \int_{-\infty}^{\infty} x_1(\tau) x_2(t - \tau)\, d\tau$$

Now if

$$x_3(t) \leftrightarrow X_3(\omega)$$

then

$$X_3(\omega) = \int_{-\infty}^{\infty} \int_{-\infty}^{\infty} \{x_1(\tau) x_2(t - \tau)\, d\tau\} \exp(-j\omega t)\, dt \tag{4.58}$$

$x(\tau)$ is not a function of t, so by changing the order of integration we obtain

$$X_3(\omega) = \int_{-\infty}^{\infty} x_1(\tau) \left\{ \int_{-\infty}^{\infty} x_2(t - \tau) \exp(-j\omega t)\, dt \right\} d\tau$$

Using the shifting property of the Fourier Transform, if

$$x_2(t) \leftrightarrow X_2(\omega)$$

then

$$\int_{-\infty}^{\infty} x_2(t - \tau) \exp(-j\omega t)\, dt = \exp(-j\omega\tau) X_2(\omega) \tag{4.59}$$

and hence

$$X_3(\omega) = \int_{-\infty}^{\infty} x_1(\tau) \exp(-j\omega\tau) X_2(\omega)\, d\tau \tag{4.60}$$

Finally, if

$$x_1(t) \leftrightarrow X_1(\omega)$$

then

$$X_3(\omega) = X_1(\omega) X_2(\omega) \tag{4.61}$$

Equation (4.61) shows that the spectrum of $x_3(t)$ equals the product of the individual spectra of $x_1(t)$ and $x_2(t)$. Since $x_1(t)$ and $x_2(t)$ have been convolved to produce $x_3(t)$, we conclude that *time-domain convolution is equivalent to frequency-domain multiplication*. In mathematical terms we may therefore write

$$x_3(t) = x_1(t) * x_2(t) \leftrightarrow X_3(\omega) = X_1(\omega) X_2(\omega) \tag{4.62}$$

This is a perfectly general result which applies to any time and frequency functions, but it has a special relevance to our work on signals and systems. For, as we have seen in the last chapter, the output signal from an LTI system may be found by convolution of the input signal with the system's impulse response. Equation (4.62) shows that this must be precisely equivalent to *multiplying* the corresponding spectral functions. The first of these is the spectrum of the input signal. The second is another frequency-domain function equal to the Fourier Transform of the system's impulse response. As will become clear in the next section, this latter function is the *frequency response* of the system. We shall find many opportunities to apply the above result in later chapters of this book.

The last property to be discussed is *modulation*. Closely related to the convolution property, it is of particular relevance to the field of electronic communications, where *modulation processes* are widely used for the transmission of signals by such means as cable, or optical fibre. Although it is quite straightforward to derive the modulation property mathematically (as we have done with the convolution property) we may instead infer it from the other features of the Fourier Transform already described. It may be stated as follows. If two time functions are multiplied together, then the Fourier Transform of their product may be found by convolving their individual transforms. In other words, just as time-domain convolution is equivalent to frequency-domain multiplication, so *time-domain multiplication is equivalent to frequency-domain convolution*. Thus

$$x_3(t) = x_1(t)x_2(t) \leftrightarrow X_3(\omega) = \frac{1}{2\pi}\{X_1(\omega)*X_2(\omega)\} \tag{4.63}$$

In view of the symmetry of the Fourier Transform pair, and the duality between time and frequency domains, this result is surely what we should expect.

We may illustrate an important practical implication of expression (4.63) by considering two cosine waveforms, of different frequencies ω_1 and ω_2. These are multiplied together in the time-domain to produce the signal

$$x(t) = \cos(\omega_1 t)\cos(\omega_2 t) \tag{4.64}$$

If $\omega_2 \gg \omega_1$, then $\cos \omega_1 t$ may be thought of as a relatively slowly-varying envelope which *modulates*, or changes, the amplitude of $\cos \omega_2 t$. Although we wish to avoid further analytical detail at this stage, convolution of the spectra of $\cos \omega_1 t$ and $\cos \omega_2 t$ shows that $x(t)$ contains no energy at frequencies ω_1 and ω_2, but only at the *sum and difference* frequencies $\omega_2 \pm \omega_1$. The major effect of such time-domain multiplication, or modulation, is therefore to produce *frequency shifts*. As we shall see later, this effect is of great value in signal processing. Actually, in this particular case we can also demonstrate the frequency shift effect by using the trigonometric identity

$$\cos(\omega_1 t)\cos(\omega_2 t) = \tfrac{1}{2}\cos(\omega_2 + \omega_1)t + \tfrac{1}{2}\cos(\omega_2 - \omega_1)t \tag{4.65}$$

which indicates, once again, that *additive* frequency components of $x(t)$ are present only at the sum and difference frequencies.

We should finally relate this discussion to earlier remarks on convolution, made in section 3.7. It was noted there that convolution is associative, commutative, and distributive, and that it is sometimes appropriate to convolve frequency functions rather than time functions. We now see that Fourier transformation, too, has important features which follow from its mathematical definition—and that its convolution and modulation properties, summarised by equations (4.62) and (4.63), are very closely connected to our previous work on time-domain convolution.

Example E4.6

Equation (4.35) in the main text shows that the spectrum of an isolated, even, rectangular pulse of duration $2t_1$ and unit amplitude is given by

$$X(\omega) = \frac{2t_1 \sin(\omega t_1)}{\omega t_1} = 2t_1 \operatorname{sinc}(\omega t_1)$$

Using only this information, and the known properties of the Fourier Transform, infer the spectrum of the isolated signal shown in figure E4.6(a).

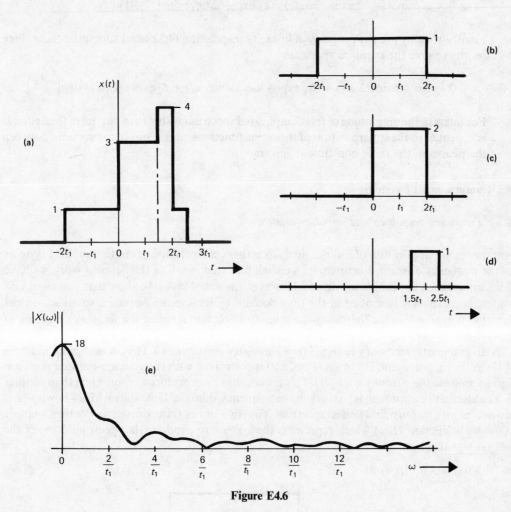

Figure E4.6

Solution

The signal shown in part (a) of the figure may be formed by the addition of the three rectangular pulses shown in parts (b),(c), and (d). Using the time-scaling property of the Fourier Transform (expression (4.55)), we may write the spectrum of the pulse shown in part (b) as

$$\left(\frac{1}{0.5}\right)2t_1 \operatorname{sinc}\left(\frac{\omega t_1}{0.5}\right) = 4t_1 \operatorname{sinc}(2\omega t_1)$$

Using the time-shifting property (expression (4.53)), the pulse in figure E4.6(c) transforms to

$$2 \times 2t_1 \,\text{sinc}(\omega t_1)\exp(-j\omega t_1) = 4t_1\exp(-j\omega t_1)\,\text{sinc}(\omega t_1)$$

Using both the time-shifting and time-scaling properties, the spectrum of the pulse in part (d) of the figure is

$$\frac{1}{2} \times 2t_1\,\text{sinc}\!\left(\frac{\omega t_1}{2}\right)\exp(-j\omega 2t_1) = t_1\exp(-2j\omega t_1)\,\text{sinc}\!\left(\frac{\omega t_1}{2}\right)$$

Finally, we may use the property of linearity (expression (4.52)) and superpose these three results to give the required spectrum

$$X(\omega) = 4t_1\,\text{sinc}(2\omega t_1) + 4t_1\exp(-j\omega t_1)\,\text{sinc}(\omega t_1) + t_1\exp(-2j\omega t_1)\,\text{sinc}\!\left(\frac{\omega t_1}{2}\right)$$

For interest, the magnitude of this complicated spectrum is shown in part (e) of the figure. It is *not* equal to the superposition of three sinc functions, as a result of interactions between the phases of the three constituent spectra.

4.3 Continuous LTI systems

4.3.1 *Frequency responses and impulse responses*

Another major application of Fourier analysis is the representation of continuous LTI systems in the frequency-domain. Fortunately, we shall find that much of the detailed work we have done on signals is applicable to systems. However, the initial task is to show that, just as an LTI system is completely described in the time-domain by its impulse response, so an equivalent function is available in the frequency-domain. This function is called the *frequency response* of the system.

A diagrammatic summary of signal flow through a continuous LTI system is given in figure 4.17. In the time-domain, the input signal $x(t)$ is convolved with the system's impulse response $h(t)$ to produce the output signal $y(t)$. This process has been explored at some length in chapter 3. The alternative approach is to work in the frequency-domain. If we start with a known signal waveform $x(t)$, we must first find its spectrum $X(\omega)$ by Fourier transformation. We then *multiply* $X(\omega)$ by a function $H(\omega)$ which represents the system, to produce the spectrum $Y(\omega)$ of the output signal. Thus

$$Y(\omega) = X(\omega)H(\omega) \tag{4.66}$$

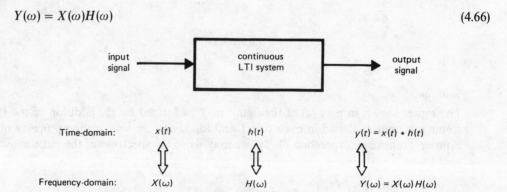

Figure 4.17 Signal flow through a continuous LTI system.

or

$$H(\omega) = \frac{Y(\omega)}{X(\omega)} \tag{4.67}$$

Therefore the system function $H(\omega)$ equals the Fourier Transform of the output signal divided by that of the input. Finally, if we need to know the time-domain waveform of the output signal, $Y(\omega)$ must be inverse-transformed to produce $y(t)$. If this seems a complicated way to the answer, remember that Fourier Transforms and inverse Transforms are widely tabulated in texts and reference books. The important advantage of the frequency-domain method is that $X(\omega)$ and $H(\omega)$ are *multiplied* together to produce $Y(\omega)$. This is generally a simpler operation than the equivalent time-domain convolution.

We next show that the frequency response $H(\omega)$, which characterises the system in the frequency-domain, is the Fourier Transform of the impulse response $h(t)$. Suppose that the input signal is a unit impulse function $\delta(t)$. Then, as we have seen in section 4.2.3.1 and equation (4.44), $X(\omega) = 1$. Hence

$$Y(\omega) = X(\omega)H(\omega) = H(\omega) \tag{4.68}$$

However, in this case the output signal $y(t)$ is by definition the system's impulse response $h(t)$. Therefore, $h(t)$ and $H(\omega)$ *must be related as a Fourier Transform pair*. The impulse response gives a complete description of the LTI system in the time-domain, and its frequency response $H(\omega)$ gives a complete description in the frequency-domain. This is a satisfying result, which ties in neatly with our earlier work on the Fourier Transform. For, as we have seen, all practical signals and time functions have their frequency-domain counterparts, and an impulse response is no exception. *Its* counterpart is $H(\omega)$, which describes the system's response in both magnitude and phase to all frequency components present in an input signal.

Before proceeding, we must be clear about the nature of frequency responses which describe LTI systems. The main point to note is that, whereas in this book we concern ourselves with *real* time functions, their spectral counterparts are very often *complex* functions of ω. Thus, a function $H(\omega)$ may in general be expressed in terms of real and imaginary parts

$$H(\omega) = H_r(\omega) + H_i(\omega) \tag{4.69}$$

where $H_r(\omega)$ is an even function and $H_i(\omega)$ is an odd function. The magnitude of $H(\omega)$ at any frequency is then given by

$$|H(\omega)| = \{H_r^2(\omega) + H_i^2(\omega)\}^{1/2} \tag{4.70}$$

and its phase by

$$\Phi_H(\omega) = \tan^{-1}\frac{H_i(\omega)}{H_r(\omega)} \tag{4.71}$$

A convenient alternative to equation (4.69) is to express $H(\omega)$ directly in terms of magnitude and phase, using the so-called *polar representation*

$$H(\omega) = |H(\omega)| \exp(j\Phi_H(\omega)) \tag{4.72}$$

Note that the exponential has unit magnitude, and represents just the phase of $H(\omega)$. The representation of a spectral function in terms of magnitude and phase is generally simpler to visualise than the alternative based on real and imaginary parts, and we use it extensively in this book. Since in our present discussion $H(\omega)$ denotes the *frequency response of a system*, we interpret $|H(\omega)|$ as the factor by which the system multiplies the *magnitude* of any sinusoidal component present at its input. This factor is widely referred to as the *gain* of the system. $\Phi_H(\omega)$ represents the *phase-shift* imposed by the system as a function of the sinusoidal input frequency.

Let us now consider the multiplication of an input signal spectrum $X(\omega)$ by $H(\omega)$ to produce the output signal spectrum $Y(\omega)$, as specified by equation (4.66). Using the polar representation, we may write

$$Y(\omega) = |X(\omega)| \exp(j\Phi_X(\omega))|H(\omega)| \exp(j\Phi_H(\omega))$$

$$\therefore\ Y(\omega) = |X(\omega)||H(\omega)| \exp(j\Phi_X(\omega) + j\Phi_H(\omega)) = |Y(\omega)| \exp(j\Phi_Y(\omega)) \tag{4.73}$$

The magnitude of the output spectrum at any value of ω therefore equals the *product* of the magnitudes of input spectrum and system frequency response. Its phase equals the *sum* of the individual phase contributions of $\Phi_X(\omega)$ and $\Phi_H(\omega)$. This follows the normal rules of complex arithmetic. To find the product of two complex numbers, we multiply their magnitudes, and add their phase angles.

The polar representation of frequency-domain functions has already been used in this book. However, most of the spectra so far considered—such as those in figures 4.4, 4.10, 4.11 and 4.16—are either purely real (cosines only) or purely imaginary (sines only), and it has therefore been possible to represent them by single diagrams. But in the following pages we will meet a number of complex frequency responses, which need two diagrams to represent them fully.

A number of points have been made in earlier sections and chapters which bear directly on the present discussion. As far back as section 1.4.2, we derived an expression for the frequency-domain performance of a tuned *RLC* circuit (equation (1.10)). Magnitude and phase were plotted separately in figure 1.12. This is effectively a frequency response, plotted in polar form and expressed in terms of input and output voltages. We now realise that its inverse Fourier Transform would give the response of the circuit to a unit impulse of voltage. In chapter 2 several references were made to the possibility of using a linear filter for separating two signals, or a signal from noise, on the basis of their different frequency content. Clearly, the notion of frequency response is central here, since it describes the selectivity of a filter or system in the frequency domain. Section 2.3 mentioned the associative property of LTI systems, pointing out that there are straightforward rules by which a number of subsystems may be interconnected, or *associated*, to make up an overall system. Our work on convolution in chapter 3, and on the properties of the Fourier Transform in section 4.2.3.2, has shown what these rules are. When subsystems are cascaded, their individual impulse responses must be *convolved* to find the overall impulse response. Alternatively, the individual frequency responses must be *multiplied*, using the normal rules of complex arithmetic. On the other hand if subsystems are connected in parallel, the overall impulse response or frequency response may be found by adding, or superposing, the appropriate individual responses. In the case of frequency responses, such superposition must of course take due account of phase as well as magnitude.

With these general ideas in mind, it is now time to consider some practical systems. We will focus here on several basic filter circuits which are widely used in electronic engineering. These nicely demonstrate the connections between frequency responses and impulse responses.

Figure 4.18 shows two simple filters—one low-pass, the other high-pass—with voltage input and output signals. As usual, the output terminals are assumed to be open-circuited. The reader will probably recognise the filter in part (a) of the figure as an 'old friend', which we have already met several times in this book! For example, in section 3.5 it was used as a simplified model for a transmission cable, and in worked example E3.2 as a low-pass filter to reduce high-frequency noise in the signal obtained from a thermocouple. In our analysis of the transmission cable problem in section 3.5, we used the differential equation of the circuit to derive its step and

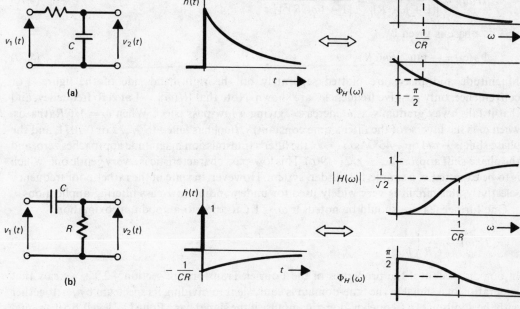

Figure 4.18 First-order *RC* filters: (a) low-pass, and (b) high-pass.

impulse responses. The latter is of real exponential form

$$h(t) = \frac{1}{CR} \exp(-t/CR), \qquad t > 0 \tag{4.74}$$

If we now take the Fourier Transform of $h(t)$ we obtain the filter's frequency response

$$H(\omega) = \int_{-\infty}^{\infty} h(t) \exp(-j\omega t)\, dt = \frac{1}{CR} \int_{0}^{\infty} \exp(-t/CR) \exp(-j\omega t)\, dt$$

$$\therefore\ H(\omega) = \frac{1}{CR} \left[\frac{\exp\left(-\left\{\dfrac{1}{CR} + j\omega\right\}t\right)}{-\left(\dfrac{1}{CR} + j\omega\right)} \right]_{0}^{\infty} = \frac{1}{CR} \left(-\frac{1}{-\left(\dfrac{1}{CR} + j\omega\right)} \right)$$

$$\therefore\ H(\omega) = \frac{1}{(1 + j\omega CR)} \tag{4.75}$$

It is worth noting the similarity between this result and the spectrum of a real decaying exponential signal, evaluated in part (c) of worked example E4.5. This emphasises an important point. A time function may, in principle, represent *either* a signal *or* the impulse response of a system. The corresponding frequency function may represent either the spectrum of a signal, or the frequency response of a system. In this sense, signals and LTI systems are analogous. At the end of the chapter we include a table of signals and their Fourier Transforms. But we may also regard it as a table of impulse responses and frequency responses of LTI systems.

We may recast equation (4.75) into a polar representation. The magnitude of the frequency response is

$$|H(\omega)| = \left| \frac{1}{(1 + j\omega CR)} \right| = \frac{1}{\{1 + (\omega CR)^2\}^{1/2}} \tag{4.76}$$

and its phase is given by

$$\Phi_H(\omega) = -\tan^{-1}(\omega CR) \tag{4.77}$$

Magnitude and phase are plotted separately on the right-hand side of the figure. For convenience, only positive frequencies are shown. Note that $|H(\omega)| = 1$ at zero frequency, and that it falls away gradually as ω increases, giving a low-pass effect. When $\omega = 1/CR$ (that is, when ω is the inverse of the filter's time constant), $|H(\omega)|$ has fallen to $1/\sqrt{2}$ or 0.7071, and the phase shift is $-\pi/4$ or $-45°$. As $\omega \to \infty$, the filter's transmission magnitude approaches zero, and the phase-shift approaches $-\pi/2\,(-90°)$. This low-pass characteristic is a very gentle one, which is to be expected of a simple, first-order, system. However, in spite of the rather poor frequency selectivity, this circuit is very widely used for undemanding low-pass filtering applications.

One further feature should be noted. If $\omega \gg 1/CR$, then to a good approximation

$$H(\omega) \to \frac{1}{CR}\left(\frac{1}{j\omega}\right) \tag{4.78}$$

In our discussion of the properties of the Fourier Transform in section 4.2.3.2, we saw that integration of a signal in the time-domain is equivalent to dividing its spectrum by $j\omega$ (together with the addition of a frequency-domain impulse if the signal has a finite DC level). So if a signal is passed through a system with a frequency response equal to $1/j\omega$, the output will be an integrated version of the input. Since this low-pass filter's frequency response tends to $(1/CR)(1/j\omega)$ at high frequencies (CR being a constant scaling factor), we may expect the filter to produce a *running integral* of any input signal whose significant frequency components are all well above $\omega = 1/CR$. This filter is indeed quite widely referred to as an *integrator* circuit. However, the description is only valid at high enough frequencies.

Part (b) of figure 4.18 shows a high-pass filter, again composed of a single resistor and capacitor. Its impulse response takes a somewhat unusual form, consisting of a unit impulse at $t = 0$, together with an inverted decaying exponential. Accepting for the moment that it *is* the correct form of impulse response, let us derive the corresponding frequency response

$$H(\omega) = \int_{-\infty}^{\infty} h(t)\exp(-j\omega t)\,dt$$

$$= \int_{-\infty}^{\infty} \delta(t)\exp(-j\omega t)\,dt + \int_{0}^{\infty} \frac{1}{CR}\exp(-t/CR)\exp(-j\omega t)\,dt \tag{4.79}$$

The first of these integrals is just the spectrum of a unit impulse, which equals unity (see equation (4.44)). The second may be inferred directly from the result already derived for the low-pass filter. Therefore

$$H(\omega) = 1 - \frac{1}{(1 + j\omega CR)} = \frac{j\omega CR}{1 + j\omega CR} \tag{4.80}$$

The magnitude response of the high-pass filter is

$$|H(\omega)| = \frac{\omega CR}{\{1 + (\omega CR)^2\}^{1/2}} \tag{4.81}$$

We may find its phase response by rationalising the denominator of $H(\omega)$. Thus

$$H(\omega) = \frac{j\omega CR(1 - j\omega CR)}{1 + (\omega CR)^2} = \frac{j\omega CR + (\omega CR)^2}{1 + (\omega CR)^2} \tag{4.82}$$

The denominator is now real and makes no phase-shift contribution. Hence $\Phi_H(\omega)$ is just due to the phase-shift represented by the numerator

$$\Phi_H(\omega) = \tan^{-1} \frac{\omega CR}{(\omega CR)^2} = \tan^{-1} \frac{1}{(\omega CR)} \tag{4.83}$$

Magnitude and phase are again separately plotted on the right-hand side of the figure. The filter acts as a complete block to DC ($\omega = 0$), but as $\omega \to \infty$ its transmission magnitude tends to unity. This represents a high-pass performance. The phase-shift of the filter is close to 90° at low frequencies, tending towards 0° at high frequencies. As in the case of the low-pass filter, the response at $\omega = 1/CR$ is easy to remember. Its magnitude is $1/\sqrt{2}$ or 0.7071, and its phase is $\pi/4$, or 45°. This frequency, equal to the inverse of the circuit's time constant, is widely referred to as the nominal *cut-off frequency*.

We have already seen that the low-pass filter in part (a) of the figure acts approximately like an *integrator* at *high* frequencies. The high-pass filter, on the other hand, behaves as a *differentiator* if the frequency is sufficiently *low*. This may be shown as follows. If $\omega \ll 1/CR$, so that $\omega CR \ll 1$, then

$$H(\omega) = \frac{j\omega CR}{1 + j\omega CR} \to j\omega CR \tag{4.84}$$

which equals $j\omega$ together with a constant scaling factor CR. One of the properties of the Fourier Transform is that differentiation of a signal in the time-domain is equivalent to multiplication by $j\omega$ in the frequency-domain. Therefore at low enough frequencies the first-order high-pass filter acts like a differentiator, giving an output signal whose instantaneous value is proportional to the *rate of change* of the input.

So far, we have found each frequency response by evaluating the Fourier Transform of the appropriate impulse response. However, it is generally much faster and easier to find $H(\omega)$ directly. There are two main methods. The first and more fundamental is to use the differential equation which defines the system. For example, in section 2.33 and equation (2.44) we derived the differential equation relating input to output voltage signals of the first-order low-pass filter as

$$v_2(t) = v_1(t) - CR \frac{dv_2(t)}{dt} \tag{4.85}$$

Since differentiation in time is equivalent to multiplication by $j\omega$ in frequency, we may transform this equation into the frequency-domain by inspection

$$V_2(\omega) = V_1(\omega) - CRj\omega V_2(\omega) \tag{4.86}$$

Here $V_1(\omega)$ and $V_2(\omega)$ represent the Fourier Transforms of $v_1(t)$ and $v_2(t)$ respectively. Hence

$$V_2(\omega)\{1 + j\omega CR\} = V_1(\omega)$$

giving

$$H(\omega) = \frac{V_2(\omega)}{V_1(\omega)} = \frac{1}{(1 + j\omega CR)} \tag{4.87}$$

This is a very neat and rapid way to the answer, and illustrates an important aspect of the Fourier Transform. Since time-domain differentiation and integration correspond, in the frequency-domain, to multiplication or division by $j\omega$, the transform converts a *differential* equation in the variable t into an *algebraic* equation in the variable ω.

The j-notation offers an alternative and very convenient method for finding the frequency response of a continuous LTI circuit. It is valid because it describes the steady-state sinusoidal performance of lumped, linear, circuit elements. Also Fourier analysis is, of course, concerned with the decomposition of signals into eternal sinusoids. The circuits of the two filters in figure 4.18 are so simple that we may use the 'potential-divider' principle to write down their frequency responses directly (remembering that the output terminals are considered to be open-circuit). For the low-pass filter we obtain

$$H(\omega) = \frac{V_2(\omega)}{V_1(\omega)} = \frac{1/j\omega C}{R + (1/j\omega C)} = \frac{1}{(1 + j\omega CR)} \tag{4.88}$$

and for the high-pass filter

$$H(\omega) = \frac{R}{R + (1/j\omega C)} = \frac{j\omega CR}{(1 + j\omega CR)} \tag{4.89}$$

These are the results derived above by Fourier transformation.

Example E4.7

By connecting a first-order low-pass filter to a high-pass filter it is possible to make an elementary bandpass filter, as shown in figure E4.7(a). Although this circuit does not possess a sharply defined passband, it does find occasional practical use, and we shall also meet it in our discussion of the Wien oscillator in chapter 7.

Find the frequency response of the filter and sketch its magnitude and phase in the range $0 < \omega < 5\omega_1$, where $\omega_1 = 1/CR$. Also find, and sketch, its impulse response.

Solution

We may label voltages and circulating currents as shown, remembering that they are frequency functions. It is convenient to denote the impedance of each capacitor by Z. Since the output terminals are assumed to be open circuit, we have

$$V_1 = I_1(R + Z) - I_2 Z$$
$$0 = I_2(R + 2Z) - I_1 Z$$

and

$$V_2 = I_2 R$$

It is straightforward to eliminate the two currents I_1 and I_2, giving

$$\frac{V_2}{V_1} = \frac{RZ}{R^2 + 3RZ + Z^2}$$

and hence

$$H(\omega) = \frac{V_2(\omega)}{V_1(\omega)} = \frac{R/j\omega C}{R^2 + (3R/j\omega C) - (1/\omega^2 C^2)}$$

$$\therefore H(\omega) = \frac{j\omega CR}{1 + 3j\omega CR - (\omega CR)^2} = \frac{j\left(\dfrac{\omega}{\omega_1}\right)}{1 + 3j\left(\dfrac{\omega}{\omega_1}\right) - \left(\dfrac{\omega}{\omega_1}\right)^2}$$

where $\omega_1 = 1/CR$.

We should note straight away that $H(\omega)$ is *not* equal to the product of the frequency responses of the first-order low-pass and high-pass filters previously derived (see equations (4.88) and (4.89)). This is because the two filter sections *interact*. The high-pass one loads the low-pass one by drawing current from it. To obtain an overall frequency response equal to the product of the individual responses (a true *cascading*), it would be necessary to place a buffer between the two filters—such as a voltage follower circuit based upon an operational amplifier, as described in section 1.4.3.

The magnitude of $H(\omega)$ is given by

$$|H(\omega)| = \frac{\left(\dfrac{\omega}{\omega_1}\right)}{\left\{\left(1 - \dfrac{\omega^2}{\omega_1^2}\right)^2 + \dfrac{9\omega^2}{\omega_1^2}\right\}^{1/2}}$$

The phase-shift represented by the numerator of $H(\omega)$ is $+\pi/2$; that represented by the denominator is

$$\tan^{-1} \frac{3\omega/\omega_1}{\{1 - (\omega^2/\omega_1^2)\}}$$

Hence

$$\Phi_H(\omega) = (\pi/2) - \tan^{-1} \frac{3\omega/\omega_1}{\{1 - (\omega^2/\omega_1^2)\}}$$

These are drawn in part (b) of figure E4.7. $|H(\omega)|$ is zero at $\omega = 0$, and tends to zero again as $\omega \to \infty$. It reaches its peak value of $1/3$ when $\omega = \omega_1$. The phase-shift characteristic starts at $\pi/2$ and tends to $-\pi/2$ as $\omega \to \infty$, passing through zero when $\omega = \omega_1$.

To obtain the impulse response of the circuit, we need to find the inverse Fourier Transform of $H(\omega)$. In this case we are unlikely to find it included in a table of standard Fourier Transform pairs. But instead of attempting to evaluate the Fourier integral directly, it is often simpler to use the method of *partial fractions*. This involves decomposing $H(\omega)$ into two or more parts, each of which has an inverse transform which *does* appear in such a table. The present example offers a good illustration of this approach. For convenience, let us first write the frequency response in the form

$$H(\alpha) = \frac{j\alpha}{1 + 3j\alpha - \alpha^2}, \quad \text{where } \alpha = \omega CR = \frac{\omega}{\omega_1}$$

The aim is to express $H(\alpha)$ in terms of *partial fractions*, each of which has a simpler denominator. We therefore write the following equation

$$\frac{j\alpha}{1 + 3j\alpha - \alpha^2} = \frac{A}{(1 + j\beta_1)} + \frac{B}{(1 + j\beta_2)} = \frac{A(1 + j\beta_2) + B(1 + j\beta_1)}{(1 + j\beta_1)(1 + j\beta_2)}$$

where A, B, β_1 and β_2 are constants. Now

$$(1 + j\beta_1)(1 + j\beta_2) = 1 + j(\beta_1 + \beta_2) - \beta_1\beta_2$$

and since this must be identically equal to the denominator of $H(\alpha)$, we obtain

$$(\beta_1 + \beta_2) = 3\alpha \quad \text{and} \quad \beta_1\beta_2 = \alpha^2$$

Hence

$$\beta_1 + \frac{\alpha^2}{\beta_1} = 3\alpha \quad \text{or} \quad \beta_1^2 - 3\alpha\beta_1 + \alpha^2 = 0$$

Solving this last equation as a quadratic gives

$$\beta_1 = \frac{3\alpha \pm (9\alpha^2 - 4\alpha^2)^{1/2}}{2} = 2.618\alpha \quad \text{or} \quad 0.382\alpha$$

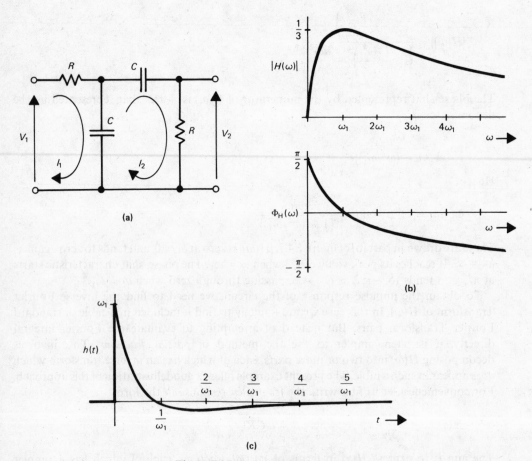

Figure E4.7 A simple bandpass filter.

Note that if $\beta_1 = 0.382\alpha$ then $\beta_2 = 2.618\alpha$, and vice versa. Therefore these two values satisfy the identity requirements of the denominator. As far as the numerator is concerned, we require that

$$j\alpha = A(1 + j\beta_2) + B(1 + j\beta_1) = A + B + j(A\beta_2 + B\beta_1)$$

giving

$$A = -B \quad \text{and} \quad \alpha = A\beta_2 - A\beta_1 = 2.236A$$

Therefore

$$A = 0.447 \quad \text{and} \quad B = -0.447$$

We may finally write the frequency response as the sum of two partial fractions

$$H(\alpha) = \frac{0.447}{(1 + j0.382\alpha)} - \frac{0.447}{(1 + j2.618\alpha)}$$

or

$$H(\omega) = \frac{0.447}{1 + j\omega(0.382CR)} - \frac{0.447}{1 + j\omega(2.618CR)}$$

If we consult a standard table of Fourier Transforms, we find that

$$\frac{1}{(1 + j\omega CR)} \leftrightarrow \frac{1}{CR}\exp(-t/CR), \quad t > 0$$

It therefore follows that the inverse transform of $H(\omega)$, which equals the circuit's impulse response, is

$$h(t) = 0.447\left\{\frac{1}{0.382CR}\exp(-t/0.382CR)\right\}$$

$$- 0.447\left\{\frac{1}{2.618CR}\exp(-t/2.618CR)\right\}, \quad t > 0$$

$$\therefore h(t) = \frac{1.17}{CR}\exp(-2.618t/CR) - \frac{0.17}{CR}\exp(-0.382t/CR), \quad t > 0$$

or

$$h(t) = 1.17\omega_1\exp(-2.618\omega_1 t) - 0.17\omega_1\exp(-0.382\omega_1 t), \quad t > 0$$

This impulse response, which is drawn in part (c) of figure E4.7, consists of the difference of two real, decaying exponentials. The technique of partial fractions, although not particularly short, has provided quite a straightforward method to the answer and has avoided the need to solve a potentially awkward Fourier integral.

We next turn to second-order continuous LTI systems. Although more complicated than the first-order circuits so far discussed, they can provide much more selective frequency responses with well-defined resonant peaks. In the time-domain, the impulse responses of second-order systems are often oscillatory, denoting a strong natural tendency to favour particular frequencies or frequency ranges. By cascading a number of such circuits or systems together it is possible to build up a wide variety of useful electronic systems. We shall meet examples of this later—particularly in our more detailed discussion of filters in chapter 8.

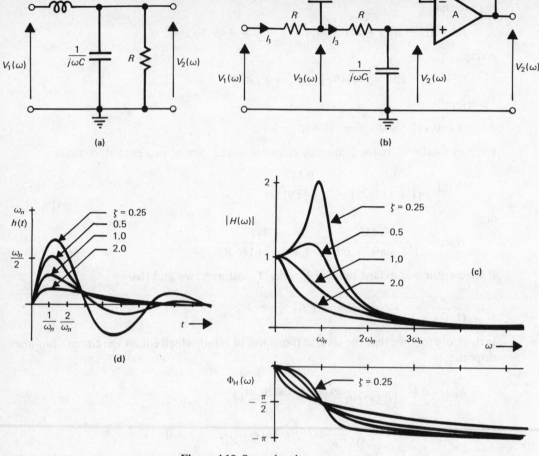

Figure 4.19 Second-order systems.

In the review of basic AC circuits in section 1.4.2, we considered the frequency response of a second-order series *RLC* circuit, taking the output signal as the voltage developed across the resistor. It was shown that such a circuit can display a sharp resonant peak, at a centre frequency determined by the product *LC*. We now develop this important theme further, by analysing the two second-order systems shown in figure 4.19.

The performance of the passive *RLC* circuit shown in figure 4.19(a) is broadly similar to that of the circuit discussed in chapter 1, although the three elements are differently arranged. The output signal is now defined as the voltage across the paralleled resistor and capacitor. In fact we have recently met this circuit in a different guise—as the smoothing filter for a DC power supply (see figure 4.9 and worked example E4.3)—and we shall have more to say later about this particular application. The circuit is quite a simple one, and if the impedance of the parallel combination of *R* and *C* is denoted by *Z*, we may safely use the 'potential-divider' principle to write directly

$$H(\omega) = \frac{V_2(\omega)}{V_1(\omega)} = \frac{Z}{j\omega L + Z}$$

where

$$Z = \frac{R/j\omega C}{R + (1/j\omega C)} = \frac{R}{(1 + j\omega CR)}$$

$$\therefore \ H(\omega) = \frac{R}{(1 + j\omega CR)} \times \frac{1}{j\omega L + R(1 + j\omega CR)^{-1}}$$

which gives

$$H(\omega) = \frac{1}{1 + j\omega\left(\dfrac{L}{R}\right) - \omega^2 LC} \tag{4.90}$$

This is the result derived earlier in equation (4.26) during our discussion of the DC power supply. For present purposes it is helpful to write this frequency response in the form

$$H(\omega) = \frac{1}{\left(\dfrac{j\omega}{\omega_n}\right)^2 + 2\zeta\left(\dfrac{j\omega}{\omega_n}\right) + 1} \tag{4.91}$$

The parameters ω_n and ζ depend on the values of the circuit elements, as follows

$$\omega_n = (LC)^{-1/2} \tag{4.92}$$

and

$$\zeta = \frac{\omega_n L}{2R} = \frac{L}{2R}(LC)^{-1/2} = \frac{1}{2R}\left(\frac{L}{C}\right)^{1/2} \tag{4.93}$$

The angular frequency ω_n is known as the *undamped natural frequency* of the system, and the parameter ζ as the *damping factor*. Note that if ζ is very small, then so also is the imaginary part of the denominator of $H(\omega)$. This means that when the input signal frequency equals, or is close to, the system's natural frequency ω_n, the magnitude of $H(\omega)$ rises sharply. This gives a well-defined resonant peak. A small value of ζ therefore corresponds to a high Q-factor. Indeed, the Q-factor of this circuit may be defined as the ratio between $|H(\omega)|$ at resonance and its value at low frequency. Since $|H(\omega)| \to 1$ as $\omega \to 0$, whereas it equals $(2\zeta)^{-1}$ when $\omega = \omega_n$, we have

$$Q = \frac{1}{2\zeta} \tag{4.94}$$

Another second-order system with the same form of frequency response (and hence impulse response) is shown in figure 4.19(b). For many practical applications, such circuits offer the important advantage of using operational amplifiers in place of inductors. This can be especially valuable for relatively low-frequency applications (say below a few hundred kilohertz), when inductors tend to be bulky, expensive, and non-ideal. Circuits which use amplifiers, resistors, and capacitors to achieve a high degree of frequency selectivity are widely referred to as *active filters*. The particular circuit illustrated is just one example of a second-order active filter, and incorporates an operational amplifier connected as a voltage follower (see section 1.4.3). Its frequency response may be derived using the *j*-notation. Let us, for convenience, denote the impedances of C_1 and C_2 by Z_1 and Z_2 respectively. Then, recalling that the algebraic sum of currents entering (or leaving) a circuit node must always be zero, we may write

$$I_1 + I_2 - I_3 = 0 \tag{4.95}$$

and hence

$$\frac{(V_1 - V_3)}{R} + \frac{(V_2 - V_3)}{Z_2} - \frac{(V_3 - V_2)}{R} = 0$$

Rearranging, we obtain

$$V_1 Z_2 + V_2 (R + Z_2) = V_3 (R + 2Z_2) \tag{4.96}$$

Now a voltage follower has an extremely high input impedance so that, for all likely choices of the circuit elements, we may assume that the whole of I_3 flows through capacitor C_1. The right-hand resistor R and capacitor C_1 therefore act as a potential divider, giving

$$\frac{V_2}{V_3} = \frac{Z_1}{R + Z_1} \quad \text{or} \quad V_3 = V_2 \frac{(R + Z_1)}{Z_1} \tag{4.97}$$

Substitution for V_3 in equation (4.96) yields

$$\frac{V_2}{V_1} = \frac{Z_1 Z_2}{R^2 + 2RZ_2 + Z_1 Z_2} \tag{4.98}$$

Finally, putting $Z_1 = (j\omega C_1)^{-1}$ and $Z_2 = (j\omega C_2)^{-1}$, we obtain

$$H(\omega) = \frac{V_2(\omega)}{V_1(\omega)} = \frac{1}{1 + j\omega(2RC_1) - \omega^2 R^2 C_1 C_2} \tag{4.99}$$

This is clearly similar to equation (4.90). It too may be recast into the form of equation (4.91), with undamped natural frequency and damping factor given by

$$\omega_n = \frac{1}{R(C_1 C_2)^{1/2}} \quad \text{and} \quad \zeta = \omega_n R C_1 = \left(\frac{C_1}{C_2}\right)^{1/2} \tag{4.100}$$

The Q-factor of the circuit is

$$Q = \frac{1}{2\zeta} = \left(\frac{C_2}{4C_1}\right)^{1/2} \tag{4.101}$$

We therefore see that this circuit, although containing no inductors, can provide the type of second-order frequency response specified by equation (4.91). The parameters ω_n and ζ may, in principle, be varied over wide ranges by suitable choice of the passive circuit elements.

It is now time to explore the frequency-domain performance of this important class of LTI system rather more carefully. The magnitude and phase of $H(\omega)$ are respectively

$$|H(\omega)| = \frac{1}{\left[\left\{1 - \left(\frac{\omega}{\omega_n}\right)^2\right\}^2 + \left(2\zeta \frac{\omega}{\omega_n}\right)^2\right]^{1/2}} \tag{4.102}$$

and

$$\Phi_H(\omega) = -\tan^{-1}\left\{\frac{2\zeta\left(\frac{\omega}{\omega_n}\right)}{1 - \left(\frac{\omega}{\omega_n}\right)^2}\right\} \tag{4.103}$$

These are plotted separately in part (c) of figure 4.19, for several values of the damping factor ζ

between 0.25 and 2.0. Note that the frequency axis is scaled in units of ω_n, making the plots valid for *any* second-order system with this form of response. $|H(\omega)|$ shows a resonant peak for values of ζ less than unity, and as $\zeta \to 0$ the resonant frequency tends to the undamped natural frequency ω_n. The phase-shift characteristic of such a system always covers the same total range (0 to $-\pi$ radians), but occurs over a more restricted frequency range when the damping is small (see the case $\zeta = 0.25$ marked on the figure). In the limit, as $\zeta \to 0$, the resonant peak becomes very high and narrow, and the complete phase change is concentrated into a small range of frequencies close to $\omega = \omega_n$.

If the damping factor ζ is less than unity, the system is said to be *underdamped*; if $\zeta = 1$, it is *critically damped*; whereas if $\zeta > 1$, it is *overdamped*. As we have seen, an underdamped system displays a resonant peak in its frequency response. It also has an oscillatory impulse response. A critically damped system, on the other hand, just fails to display these features. Many automatic control systems are designed to be approximately critically damped, representing a good compromise between the ability to *respond quickly* to an input signal or demand, while avoiding any undesirable tendency to show oscillations or *overshoot* in the response. Overdamped systems with $\zeta > 1$ tend to be rather 'sluggish', but are very stable. On the whole it is probably fair to say that underdamped second-order systems are more valuable to the electronic engineer than overdamped ones—principally on account of their frequency-selectivity.

The above comments may be explained quantitatively by referring back to equation (4.91). For convenience let us rewrite it in the form

$$H(\alpha) = \frac{1}{\alpha^2 + 2\zeta\alpha + 1} \quad \text{where } \alpha = j\frac{\omega}{\omega_n} \tag{4.104}$$

The roots of the denominator quadratic are given by

$$\alpha = \frac{-2\zeta \pm (4\zeta^2 - 4)^{1/2}}{2} = -\zeta \pm (\zeta^2 - 1)^{1/2} \tag{4.105}$$

and $H(\alpha)$ may therefore also be expressed as

$$H(\alpha) = \frac{1}{\{\alpha + \zeta + (\zeta^2 - 1)^{1/2}\}\{\alpha + \zeta - (\zeta^2 - 1)^{1/2}\}} \tag{4.106}$$

If $\zeta < 1$, corresponding to an underdamped system, the roots are complex, and by consulting a table of Fourier Transforms it is seen that the equivalent time function—which is the system's impulse response $h(t)$—is a decaying sinusoidal oscillation (there are very close relationships between this finding and the Fourier Transform evaluated in part (b) of worked example E4.5). If $\zeta = 1$, however, the two roots are real and *equal*. This corresponds to critical damping, and the inverse transform takes the non-oscillatory form

$$h(t) = \omega_n^2 t \exp(-\omega_n t), \qquad t > 0 \tag{4.107}$$

If $\zeta > 1$ the system is overdamped and the roots are both real, but *unequal*. A partial fraction expansion of $H(\alpha)$ may then be used to show that $h(t)$ is made up of two decaying, real, exponentials, and is relatively 'sluggish', with slow rates of change.

Although these various cases are not analysed in detail here, the reader should appreciate the general effects which the damping factor ζ has on the form of $h(t)$. These are illustrated by figure 4.19(d). Note that the time axis is normalised in terms of ω_n, making the curves applicable to a wide range of continuous, second-order, LTI systems.

We now return briefly to the DC power supply problem illustrated by figure 4.9. As already noted, its smoothing filter and resistive load form an identical second-order circuit to the one shown in figure 4.19(a). The circuit values are $L = 5\,\text{H}$, $C = 10\,\mu\text{F}$, and $R = 2\,\text{k}\Omega$. Using equations (4.92) and (4.93), we find that

$$\omega_n = (LC)^{-1/2} = 141\ \text{radians/s}\quad\text{(equivalent to 22.5 Hz)}$$

and

$$\zeta = \frac{1}{2R}\left(\frac{L}{C}\right)^{1/2} = 0.18$$

The circuit is therefore very underdamped, and must have a sharp resonance at 22.5 Hz. At first this may seem a strange result, because the filter is required to act as a low-pass system. However, if we consider the frequencies actually present in its input signal, the situation becomes clearer. These frequencies are zero (the required DC component), and unwanted harmonics at multiples of 100 Hz. Since *all* these harmonics lie well above resonance, they are severely reduced in magnitude by the filter.

So far we have used the j-notation to find the frequency response of second-order systems. However, for the sake of completeness we should note that the differential equation provides a more fundamental time-domain description of such a system. It may be quite simply converted into a frequency response, using the differentiation and integration properties of the Fourier Transform described in section 4.2.3.2. For example, second-order systems such as those shown in figure 4.19 have a differential equation of the form

$$\frac{d^2 y(t)}{dt^2} + 2\zeta\omega_n\frac{dy(t)}{dt} + \omega_n^2 y(t) = \omega_n^2 x(t) \tag{4.108}$$

where $y(t)$ and $x(t)$ are the output and input signals respectively. In most electronic applications these are voltages. Since differentiation in the time-domain is equivalent to multiplying by $j\omega$ in the frequency-domain, we may write the following frequency-domain description by inspection

$$(j\omega)^2 Y(\omega) + 2\zeta\omega_n j\omega Y(\omega) + \omega_n^2 Y(\omega) = \omega_n^2 X(\omega) \tag{4.109}$$

where $Y(\omega)$ and $X(\omega)$ are, as usual, the Fourier Transforms of $y(t)$ and $x(t)$. Hence

$$Y(\omega)\{(j\omega)^2 + 2\zeta\omega_n j\omega + \omega_n^2\} = \omega_n^2 X(\omega)$$

and therefore the system's frequency response is

$$H(\omega) = \frac{Y(\omega)}{X(\omega)} = \frac{\omega_n^2}{(j\omega)^2 + 2\zeta\omega_n j\omega + \omega_n^2} = \frac{1}{\left(\dfrac{j\omega}{\omega_n}\right)^2 + 2\zeta\left(\dfrac{j\omega}{\omega_n}\right) + 1} \tag{4.110}$$

This last result is the same as equation (4.91). The derivation shows, once again, the power of the Fourier Transform in converting a time-domain differential equation into an algebraic equation in the frequency-domain.

Example E4.8

(*Note:* This example is based on the active filter shown in figure 4.19(b) of the main text, and illustrates some of the factors affecting the choice of component values for a particular application.)

Electroencephalograms (EEGs), representing the electrical activity of the brain, are often used in medical diagnosis. EEG signals may be picked up from the surface of the scalp, and require amplification, suitable signal processing, and display. Although they appear random in form, their energy often falls within one or more quite well-defined spectral bands. For example, the so-called *alpha-rhythm* of the EEG is normally centred at about 12 Hz.

In a particular case, an EEG signal has a magnitude up to about 1 volt r.m.s. after initial amplification, but is unfortunately contaminated by 50 Hz mains supply interference at a level of about 0.25 volt r.m.s. The EEG signal is known to contain a strong alpha-rhythm at about 12 Hz. It is therefore required to preserve frequency components in the range 10–14 Hz, while discriminating strongly against the 50 Hz interference. A *relative* discrimination of about 50:1 is needed between 12 Hz and 50 Hz. Recommend the component values for a second-order active filter to achieve this performance.

Solution

It is important to realise that design problems rarely have a single, 'correct' solution. Some sensible choices generally have to be made. The degree of filtering required here suggests the need for an underdamped system with a well-defined resonant peak. If we choose the filter's natural frequency as 12 Hz, then the alpha-rhythm will be accentuated. The 50 Hz interference then corresponds to $\omega = 4.17\omega_n$. Using the circuit shown in figure 4.19(b), $|H(\omega)|$ is given by equation (4.102) as

$$|H(\omega)| = \frac{1}{\left[\left\{1 - \left(\dfrac{\omega}{\omega_n}\right)^2\right\}^2 + \left(2\zeta\dfrac{\omega}{\omega_n}\right)^2\right]^{1/2}}$$

when $\omega/\omega_n = 1$, $|H(\omega)| = 1/2\zeta$; and when $\omega/\omega_n = 4.17$, we have

$$|H(\omega)| = \frac{1}{[\{1 - 4.17^2\}^2 + (8.34\zeta)^2]^{1/2}} = \frac{1}{(269 + 69.6\zeta^2)^{1/2}}$$

For a *relative* discrimination of 50:1 against the 50 Hz interference we therefore require that

$$\frac{1}{2\zeta} = \frac{50}{(269 + 69.6\zeta^2)^{1/2}}$$

$$\therefore \ 269 + 69.6\zeta^2 = 10\,000\zeta^2$$

which gives $\zeta = 0.165$ and hence $Q = 1/2\zeta = 3.03$.

Equations (4.100) and (4.101) in the main text specify relationships between ω_n, ζ, Q, and the filter's components. Since this is a low-frequency application, the capacitor and resistor values are likely to be quite large. However, it is often helpful to keep capacitor values below about 1 μF, to save on cost and size. Let us therefore try $C_2 = 1\ \mu$F. Equation (4.101) gives

$$3.03^2 = \frac{C_2}{4C_1}, \quad \text{so that} \quad C_1 = 0.027C_2 = 0.027\ \mu\text{F}$$

Equation (4.100) now gives

$$R = \frac{1}{\omega_n(C_1 C_2)^{1/2}} = \frac{1}{2\pi \times 12(0.027 \times 10^{-12})^{1/2}} = 8.09 \times 10^4\ \Omega$$

A value of 80.9 kΩ for the circuit's two resistors is quite appropriate, since we would probably wish to keep them within the range (say) 5 kΩ to 500 kΩ (if their value is too low, the circuit's input impedance becomes low, too; if too high, the assumption that the voltage follower's input impedance is effectively infinite breaks down). To summarise, the following passive component values might be expected to give a performance close to the predicted one, using a typical, inexpensive, operational amplifier

$$C_1 = 0.027\ \mu F; \qquad C_2 = 1.00\ \mu F; \qquad R = 80.9\ k\Omega$$

Finally, we should check that this filter, which is quite sharply tuned, will adequately transmit the whole range of required EEG frequencies (10 to 14 Hz). At 10 Hz, we have

$$|H(\omega)| = \frac{1}{\left[\left\{1 - \left(\frac{10}{12}\right)^2\right\}^2 + \left(0.33 \times \frac{10}{12}\right)^2\right]^{1/2}} = 2.43$$

and at 14 Hz

$$|H(\omega)| = \frac{1}{\left[\left\{1 - \left(\frac{14}{12}\right)^2\right\}^2 + \left(0.33 \times \frac{14}{12}\right)^2\right]^{1/2}} = 1.89$$

The lower of these two figures is only 62 per cent of the peak gain of 3.03 occurring at 12 Hz. In the present application, this would probably be acceptable, although the specification of the problem is unclear on this point. If a higher gain at the band 'edges' were required, it would be necessary to reduce the filter's Q-factor somewhat, and to accept a relative discrimination factor against the 50 Hz interference of rather less than 50. The alternative would be to use a more complicated filter of higher order. However this possibility is outside the scope of the present example. The important point to note is that such practical problems almost always involve compromises between technical performance, complexity, and cost.

4.3.2 *Bode and Nyquist plots*

The frequency–response plots so far presented in this book have all been drawn to linear scales. However, logarithmic scales are often used in practice, both for the magnitude of a spectral function and for the frequency axis. To see the reasons for this, let us reconsider equation (4.73), which describes signal flow through a continuous LTI system

$$Y(\omega) = |X(\omega)||H(\omega)| \exp(j\Phi_X(\omega) + j\Phi_H(\omega)) = |Y(\omega)| \exp(j\Phi_Y(\omega)) \qquad (4.111)$$

If logarithmic scales are used for the magnitude functions, we may find the output magnitude by *adding*, rather than multiplying, the corresponding input and system functions. Also, if two or more LTI systems are cascaded together, the overall frequency–response magnitude equals the product of the individual functions. Once again, this is simplified to addition with logarithmic scales.

The frequency axis is often logarithmic as well. This produces a relative expansion of its low-frequency end which can be valuable for clarifying the performance of a system close to zero frequency (DC). It also means that frequency scaling—such as is produced by altering the time constants of a system—does not affect the *shape* of a particular frequency–response curve. Another advantage of using a logarithmic frequency scale is that frequency–response plots may be approximated with reasonable accuracy by straight-line sections. We shall meet examples of this a little later.

When using a logarithmic scale for the response magnitude or *gain* of a system, it is usual to plot the quantity $20 \log_{10}|H(\omega)|$, measured in *decibels* (dB). In some ways the decibel is an unfortunate unit for this purpose, since it is basically defined as a *power ratio*. Thus if we have two values of power P_1 and P_2, their ratio may be expressed as

$$\left(10 \log_{10} \frac{P_2}{P_1}\right) \text{decibels (dB)} \tag{4.112}$$

Now in an electrical circuit or system the power dissipated in any resistor R equals V^2/R, where V is the r.m.s. voltage across it. If P_1 and P_2 represent powers *dissipated in equal resistors*, we may therefore write

$$10 \log_{10} \frac{P_2}{P_1} = 10 \log_{10} \frac{V_2^2}{V_1^2} = 20 \log_{10} \frac{V_2}{V_1} \text{ dB} \tag{4.113}$$

Strictly, we should measure a voltage ratio (or gain) in dB only if the voltages are developed across equal resistive loads. However, in practice the decibel has proved to be a unit of such convenient size that it is widely used in electronic engineering to measure voltage ratios—even though the above condition is rarely satisfied. Note that 1 dB corresponds to a voltage ratio given by

$$20 \log_{10} \frac{V_2}{V_1} = 1, \quad \text{or} \quad \frac{V_2}{V_1} = \text{antilog } 0.05 = 1.122 \tag{4.114}$$

20 dB corresponds to a voltage ratio of 10, 40 dB to a ratio of 100, and so on.

The above ideas are incorporated in *Bode plots*, named after H.W. Bode who used them for his work on electronic feedback amplifiers at the Bell laboratories in the 1920s. In such plots, $20 \log_{10}|H(\omega)|$ and $\Phi_H(\omega)$ are separately shown against log frequency. Their main features are illustrated using the examples in figure 4.20. Part (a) of the figure is a Bode plot for the first-order low-pass filter discussed previously and shown in figure 4.18(a). Here, the cut-off frequency $1/CR$ is denoted by ω_1. The magnitude plot is scaled in dB and approaches the 0 dB line as $\omega \to 0$. It approaches another straight-line asymptote as $\omega \to \infty$. This may be explained in the following way. The earlier equation (4.76) may be written as

$$|H(\omega)| = \frac{1}{\left\{1 + \left(\dfrac{\omega}{\omega_1}\right)^2\right\}^{1/2}} \tag{4.115}$$

and hence

$$20 \log_{10}|H(\omega)| = 20(-0.5) \log_{10}\left\{1 + \left(\frac{\omega}{\omega_1}\right)^2\right\} \text{ dB} \tag{4.116}$$

As $\omega \to 0$, this tends to

$$-10 \log_{10}(1) = 0 \tag{4.117}$$

which is the horizontal 0 dB line. Conversely if ω is very large, we obtain

$$-10 \log_{10}\left(\frac{\omega}{\omega_1}\right)^2 = -20 \log\left(\frac{\omega}{\omega_1}\right) = -20 \log \omega + 20 \log \omega_1 \tag{4.118}$$

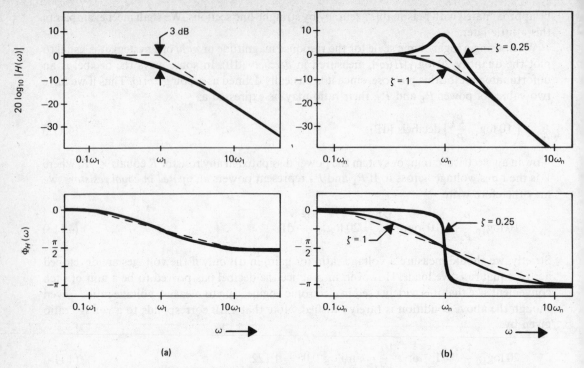

Figure 4.20 Bode plots for first and second-order systems.

Plotted against $\log_{10}\omega$, this represents a line of constant negative slope which intersects the 0 dB line when $\omega = \omega_1$. The two straight-line asymptotes are shown dotted in the figure. For obvious reasons, the frequency ω_1 is also known as the *break frequency*, or *corner frequency*.

The actual response of the system, shown as a full line, departs substantially from the asymptotes only in the region of $\omega = \omega_1$. It may in fact be proved that the maximum departure is 3 dB at ω_1 (more accurately, it corresponds to a $\sqrt{2}$ ratio, or 3.010 dB). For this reason the point $\omega = \omega_1$ is often referred to as the *3 dB point*. Fortunately, the straight-line approximation is adequate for many practical purposes. We should finally note that the high-frequency asymptote for this first-order system has a slope of -20 dB/decade. In other words, for every tenfold increase in frequency there is a tenfold reduction of response magnitude. This is a rather elaborate way of saying that the response magnitude becomes inversely proportional to ω. (The slope is alternatively quoted as '-6 dB/octave', representing a *halving* of the response magnitude for a *doubling* of frequency.)

The phase plot is shown in the lower part of figure 4.20(a). The phase tends asymptotically to zero at low frequency, and to $-\pi/2$ radians at high frequency. At intermediate frequencies it may be usefully approximated by the function

$$\Phi_H(\omega) \approx -\frac{\pi}{4}\left\{\log_{10}\left(\frac{\omega}{\omega_1}\right) + 1\right\}, \qquad 0.1\omega_1 \leqslant \omega \leqslant 10\omega_1 \tag{4.119}$$

This is also a straight line when plotted against $\log \omega$, and is shown dotted on the figure. It decreases from 0 to $-\pi/2$ over the specified frequency range, agreeing with the actual value of $-\pi/4$ at the break frequency.

Similar considerations may be used to construct a Bode plot for the first-order high-pass filter previously shown in figure 4.18(b). In this case the high-frequency asymptote is the 0 dB line, and the low-frequency one has a positive slope of 20 dB/decade. Once again, the break frequency is given by $\omega_1 = 1/CR$, and the maximum departure of the actual plot from the straight-line approximation is 3 dB at this point. We do not work out the Bode plot for the high-pass filter in detail here, but it is included as a problem at the end of the chapter.

Typical Bode plots for second-order systems are drawn in figure 4.20(b). These correspond to linear plots already shown in figure 4.19. However, to avoid confusion only two values of the damping factor ζ are illustrated (0.25 and 1.0, corresponding to an underdamped and critically damped system respectively). Once again, the magnitude curves tend to the 0 dB line at low frequency, and to a straight-line of negative slope at high frequency. However, since these are systems of second order, the slope is doubled to -40 dB/decade, or -12 dB/octave. This is because $|H(\omega)|$ becomes inversely proportional to ω^2, rather than ω, as $\omega \to \infty$ (see equation (4.102)). The two asymptotes meet at the break frequency $\omega = \omega_n$, which is the undamped natural frequency. The actual response magnitude lies quite close to the straight-line approximation for values of ζ between about 0.5 and 1.5. However, severely underdamped or overdamped responses depart considerably from it in the region of ω_n.

As far as phase is concerned, the plots approach zero phase shift as $\omega \to 0$, and $-\pi$ radians as $\omega \to \infty$. For overdamped or critically damped systems, the phase characteristic is quite well approximated at intermediate frequencies by the function

$$\Phi_H(\omega) \approx -\frac{\pi}{2}\left\{\log_{10}\left(\frac{\omega}{\omega_n}\right) + 1\right\}, \qquad 0.1\omega_n \leqslant \omega \leqslant 10\omega_n \tag{4.120}$$

This is also a straight-line on a Bode plot, shown dotted in the figure.

As suggested at the start of this section, Bode plots have the important advantage of being additive for cascaded systems. We may illustrate this by considering a continuous LTI system with the frequency response

$$H(\omega) = \frac{50(j\omega + 2)}{(j\omega + 1)\{(j\omega)^2 + 5j\omega + 25\}} \tag{4.121}$$

The reader may object that, since this is clearly not the response of a simple low-pass, high-pass, or bandpass filter, it is hard to imagine what the system might be used for! However, it is important to appreciate that many practical systems do have complicated frequency responses, and cannot be categorised as simple filters. It follows from the differential equations describing any continuous LTI system that $H(\omega)$ is always a *rational function*, that is to say, a ratio of polynomials in $j\omega$. The numerator and denominator polynomials may always be recast as the product of a number of first and second-order factors together with a constant gain term, or multiplier—as in the above example. This means that such a system could, in principle, be synthesised by cascading the appropriate first and second-order subsystems. In the context of Bode plots, it also means that the plot for the overall system may be found by adding together a number of much simpler plots.

A good way of proceeding is to express the various numerator and denominator factors of $H(\omega)$ in the form

$$\left\{\left(j\frac{\omega}{\omega_1}\right) + 1\right\} \quad \text{or} \quad \left\{\left(j\frac{\omega}{\omega_n}\right)^2 + 2\xi\left(j\frac{\omega}{\omega_n}\right) + 1\right\} \tag{4.122}$$

In the present sample, we have

$$H(\omega) = \frac{50 \times \left(j\dfrac{\omega}{2} + 1\right) \times 2}{(j\omega + 1)\left\{\left(j\dfrac{\omega}{5}\right)^2 + \left(j\dfrac{\omega}{5}\right) + 1\right\}25} = \frac{4\left(j\dfrac{\omega}{2} + 1\right)}{(j\omega + 1)\left\{\left(j\dfrac{\omega}{5}\right)^2 + 2(0.5)\left(j\dfrac{\omega}{5}\right) + 1\right\}}$$

(4.123)

Four separate contributions to the overall Bode plot magnitude characteristic may be identified

(a) A constant gain term of 4, equivalent to $20\log_{10}4 = 12.04$ dB.
(b) A first-order numerator term with a break frequency of 2 radians/s, and a high-frequency asymptote of slope $+20$ dB/decade.
(c) A first-order denominator term with a break frequency of 1 radian/s, and a high-frequency asymptote of slope -20 dB/decade.
(d) A second-order denominator term with a break frequency of 5 radians/s, a damping factor of 0.5, and a high-frequency asymptote of slope -40 dB/decade.

The asymptotic approximations for these four individual Bode plots are shown in figure 4.21, labelled (a) to (d) respectively. Their sum, which represents the Bode plot approximation for the overall system, is indicated by a thicker line and labelled (e). Since in this example the second-order factor has $\zeta = 0.5$, the actual plot would not display a sharp resonance near $\omega = \omega_n$. So the straight-line approximation must be quite close to the actual plot. To avoid confusion, the latter is omitted from the figure. We could, of course, also build up a phase plot for the system, using a very similar approach. However, in many practical situations phase plots are less important than magnitude plots, so we do not give them further space here. We shall have some further remarks to make about the relative significance of amplitude and phase responses at the end of this section.

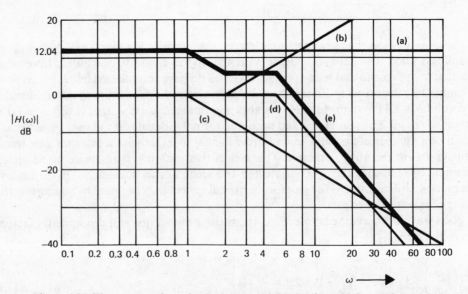

Figure 4.21 The construction of a Bode magnitude plot for a high-order system.

Nyquist plots are named after H. Nyquist who also worked at the Bell laboratories in the USA in the 1930s. His research was very much concerned with feedback, control, and stability. In a Nyquist plot, the magnitude and phase of a spectral function are both shown on a single diagram. However, the frequency is only indicated indirectly, by labelling various points on the plot with values of ω. As a simple example, let us take the frequency response of a first-order low-pass filter, first given in equation (4.75)

$$H(\omega) = \frac{1}{(1 + j\omega CR)} = \frac{1}{1 + j\left(\dfrac{\omega}{\omega_1}\right)} \tag{4.124}$$

The magnitude and phase of $H(\omega)$ are respectively

$$|H(\omega)| = \frac{1}{\left\{1 + \left(\dfrac{\omega}{\omega_1}\right)^2\right\}^{1/2}} \quad \text{and} \quad \Phi_H(\omega) = -\tan^{-1}\left(\frac{\omega}{\omega_1}\right) \tag{4.125}$$

For any value of ω we may plot $H(\omega)$ as a vector in the complex plane. The length of the vector is $|H(\omega)|$, and the angle it makes with the positive real axis is $\Phi_H(\omega)$. This is illustrated for several values of ω in figure 4.22(a). When $\omega = 0$, the response has unit magnitude and zero phase-shift, so the vector lies along the real axis (labelled Re). When $\omega = \omega_1$, the vector's length is $1/\sqrt{2}$ and its phase angle is $-45°$ $(-\pi/4)$. As $\omega \to \infty$, the vector becomes very small, with a phase approaching $-90°$ $(-\pi/2)$. The locus of the tips of all such vectors is the *Nyquist plot*, and is shown dotted in the figure. In this particular case it begins on the real axis, ends at the origin, and is semicircular. It is usual to indicate the direction of increasing frequency by a small arrow on the plot itself. This particular plot corresponds to the Bode plot of figure 4.20(a).

The plot for a first-order high-pass filter is shown in part (b) of the figure. Starting at the origin, it moves initially very close to the positive imaginary axis (labelled Im). This denotes a small response magnitude, and a phase-shift close to $+90°$ at low frequency. As $\omega \to \infty$ the plot approaches the real axis with a magnitude of unity. Once again it is semicircular.

Figure 4.22(c) shows Nyquist plots for two second-order systems with damping factors $\zeta = 0.25$ and $\zeta = 1$. These correspond to the Bode plots of figure 4.20(b). Starting on the positive real axis, they both cut the imaginary axis when $\omega = \omega_n$, and approach the origin along the negative real axis as $\omega \to \infty$. This is because the phase-shift of both systems tends to $-180°$ at high frequency. At intermediate frequencies, the two plots are very different. That for $\zeta = 0.25$ is much more open, reflecting the larger gain of the underdamped system close to resonance. A few frequency values are marked against it. These show that much of the plot is traced out over quite a narrow range of frequency around resonance.

Although Nyquist plots show essentially the same information as Bode plots, their form is very different. They are especially valuable for the analysis of stability in feedback and control systems. However, in other fields they are less widely used than separate linear or logarithmic plots of magnitude and phase against frequency. Before leaving the topic of Nyquist plots, it is worth noting that the ones drawn in figure 4.22 only cover positive frequencies. We could readily extend them to negative frequencies. However, since $|H(\omega)|$ is always even, and $\Phi_H(\omega)$ is always odd, no further information would be conveyed. In fact, any Nyquist plot for negative frequencies $(-\infty < \omega < 0)$ is simply a reflection, or 'mirror image', about the real axis of the plot for positive frequencies.

It was mentioned a little earlier that the phase response of an LTI system is often considered

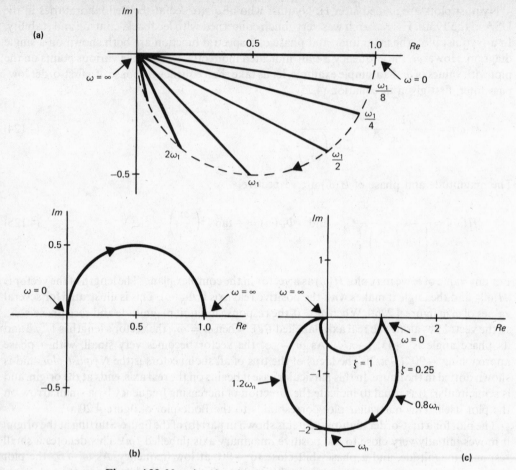

Figure 4.22 Nyquist plots for first and second-order systems.

less important than its magnitude response. We therefore end this section by considering briefly the relative practical importance of these two aspects of a frequency response.

It is quite often said that the human ear is insensitive to phase. Although this is rather an oversimplification, it is true that the design of audio frequency amplifiers and systems generally needs to focus more on the magnitude of a frequency response than on its phase. For example, if a system has a poor bass response, most listeners are far more likely to notice the effect than if the relative phases of the low-frequency sounds are rearranged. On the other hand, gross distortion of phase relationships may well make music unenjoyable, and speech unintelligible. A good illustration of this is provided by playing a tape recording of speech backwards. Time reversal alters only the phase spectrum of a signal, not its magnitude. But it is quite sufficient to confuse the human ear and brain!

Although some degree of phase distortion may be quite acceptable in most audio systems, there are other practical situations where phase response is far more critical. A good example is the transmission and processing of two-dimensional pictorial information—TV signals, maps from weather satellites, and so on. Here the detailed *waveshapes* of signals are generally very important, becuase they control the edges and regions of contrast of the image. Since time-

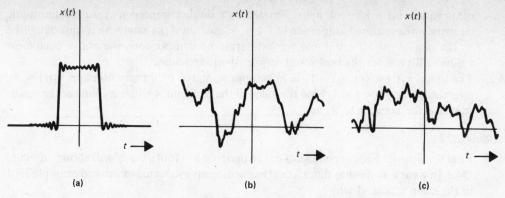

Figure 4.23 Some effects of phase-change on a signal waveform.

domain waveshapes can be dramatically affected by phase changes, phase response may be just as important as magnitude response.

Some effects of phase change on waveshape are shown in figure 4.23, using the computer simulation program described earlier in this chapter (section 4.2.3.1 and figure 4.13). In part (a) of the figure the program has been used, as before, to synthesise a rectangular pulse. 50 harmonics were specified, in accordance with equation (4.43). Parts (b) and (c) represent two additional runs of the program, with each harmonic component phase-shifted by a random amount between 0 and 2π. This was done using the computer's random number generator. The amplitude of each component was not altered. The results give a striking illustration of the effects which can be produced by phase changes. Of course, the changes produced by practical LTI systems would rarely, if ever, be as severe as these. Nevertheless, they can be a major design consideration for the type of application mentioned above. Also, in those cases where the phase response of a system is unacceptable, it may be appropriate to cascade it with a phase-correcting system or network, known as a *phase-equaliser*.

There is one type of phase adjustment which produces no distortion of a signal waveshape in the time-domain. This is the so-called *linear-phase* characteristic. If a system imposes a phase-shift proportional to frequency, then each frequency component in an input signal is delayed by a fixed amount of time. There is said to be no *phase distortion*, the output signal being simply a delayed version of the input. Since all realisable frequency-dependent LTI systems must introduce some phase-shift, this type of phase response is often considered the practical ideal. When a phase-equaliser is incorporated, it is generally with the aim of producing an overall phase characteristic which is close to linear.

The above remarks are intended to counteract the commonly held view that phase is relatively unimportant. However, we must beware of overstating the case. It remains true that in a great many practical situations amplitude response is more important than phase response to the system designer.

Problems to chapter 4

Section 4.2.1

Q4.1. If the sawtooth signal shown in figure 4.1 of the main text is approximated by a single sinusoid at the fundamental frequency, the amplitude of the sinusoid giving the least mean square error is $2/\pi$. If approximated by a single component at second-harmonic frequency, the required amplitude is $-1/\pi$. Show that if the sawtooth is approximated as the *sum* of fundamental *and* second-harmonic components, the above coefficient values still produce the best result in a least-squares sense.

Q4.2.   The signal $x_1(t) = \{\exp(t) - 1\}$ is to be approximated by a ramp function $x_2(t) = At$, over the interval $0 < t < 1$. Find the value of the constant A which minimises the mean-square error between $x_1(t)$ and $x_2(t)$.

Section 4.2.2.1

Q4.3.   Find the Fourier Series coefficients of the periodic sawtooth waveform shown in figure Q4.3. In what way do they differ from the coefficients evaluated in worked example E4.1 in the main text, and why?

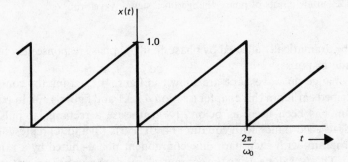

Figure Q4.3

Q4.4.   Find the magnitudes of the first three nonzero Fourier coefficients of the periodic triangular signal shown in figure Q4.4.

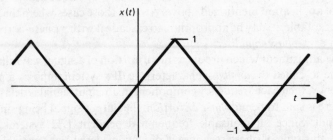

Figure Q4.4

Q4.5.   The Fourier Series of a full-wave rectified cosine signal has been evaluated in worked example E4.3. Find the DC term and the first four nonzero cosine coefficients of the half-wave rectified signal shown in figure Q4.5.

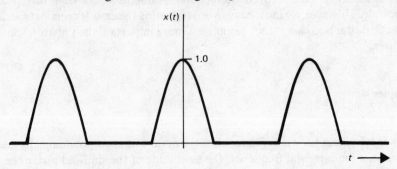

Figure Q4.5

Q4.6.   Figure Q4.6 shows a signal in the interval $0 < t < T_0/4$. Complete the signal over the full period from $t = -T_0/2$ to $t = T_0/2$ in such a way that, if repeated

(a) its Fourier Series would contain only cosine terms
(b) its Fourier Series would contain only sine terms
(c) the signal would display half-wave symmetry, but be neither even nor odd.

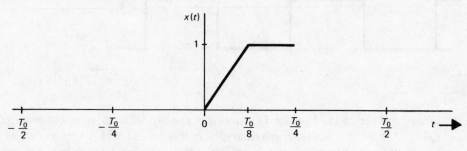

Figure Q4.6

Q4.7.   Determine from symmetry considerations which terms must be absent from the Fourier Series of the periodic signal shown in figure Q4.7.

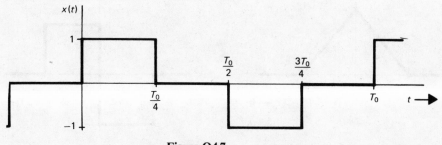

Figure Q4.7

Q4.8.   Show that approximately 90 per cent of the total power of a periodic square wave having zero mean value is contained in its first and third harmonic components.

Section 4.2.2.2

Q4.9.   Find the exponential Fourier Series of the periodic signal shown in figure Q4.9.

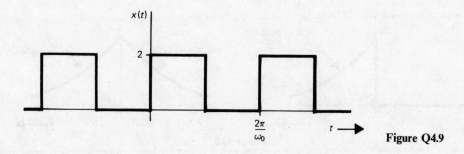

Figure Q4.9

Q4.10. Find the coefficients of the exponential Fourier Series of the periodic signal shown in figure Q4.10. In what ways do they differ from those found in Q4.9, and why?

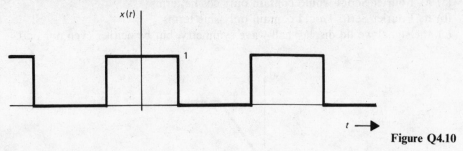

Figure Q4.10

Section 4.2.3.1

Q4.11. Derive and sketch the Fourier Transforms of the two isolated signals shown in figure Q4.11. Are the spectra real, imaginary, or complex, and why? Approximately what bandwidth would be required to transmit such signals via a linear cable or network, assuming that the time axis in case (a) is scaled in milliseconds, and in case (b) in microseconds?

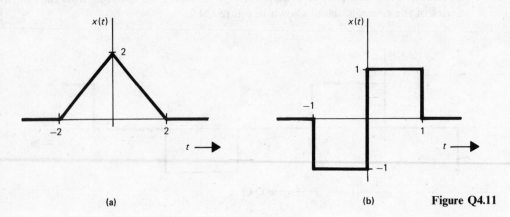

(a)   (b)   **Figure Q4.11**

Q4.12. Evaluate the Fourier spectra of the single-sided and double-sided decaying exponential signals illustrated in figure Q4.12. Denoting these by $X_1(\omega)$ and $X_2(\omega)$ respectively, show that

$$X_2(\omega) = 2Re[X_1(\omega)]$$

where *Re* denotes the real part.

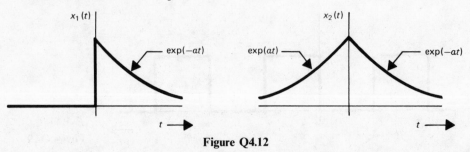

Figure Q4.12

Q4.13. A BASIC computer program for synthesis of a rectangular pulse has been given in section 4.2.3.1 of the main text. Modify the program to include a graphical or printed output of the simulated pulse, according to the computer facilities at your disposal (if appropriate, rewrite the program in another programming language). Use the program to investigate the effects of different degrees of signal bandlimiting.

Q4.14. A long-range radar system transmits a train of pulses with a rectangular envelope and a duration of 2 μs, and infers the range of aircraft targets by measuring the time taken for echoes to return to the receiver. What approximate receiver bandwidth would you expect, assuming that echoes are merely to be *detected* (that is, without necessarily preserving their waveshape)? Can you think of any reason—apart from questions of receiver cost and complexity—why it might be a disadvantage to increase the receiver bandwidth?

Q4.15. Find the Fourier Transform of the signal shown in figure Q4.15(a), and the inverse transform of the spectrum shown in figure Q4.15(b).

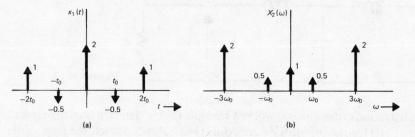

(a) (b) **Figure Q4.15**

Section 4.2.3.2

Q4.16. The spectrum of a symmetrical triangular pulse of peak value 2, and total duration 4 time units, has been found in problem Q4.11(a). Using only this information, and the properties of the Fourier Transform described in the text, infer the spectra of the two signals shown in figure Q4.16.

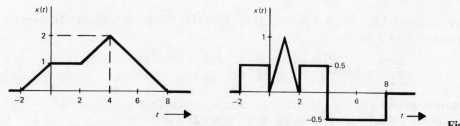

Figure Q4.16

Section 4.3.1

Q4.17. A signal with the spectrum

$$X(\omega) = \frac{1}{1 + 0.5j\omega}$$

forms the input to a first-order high-pass filter having the frequency response

$$H(\omega) = \frac{j\omega}{1 + j\omega}$$

Sketch the magnitude and phase of the output signal spectrum over the range $0 < \omega < 5$. Use linear scales.

Q4.18. A continuous LTI bandpass filter has the frequency response

$$H(\omega) = \frac{1}{1 + 0.1j\omega - \omega^2}$$

Using linear scales, sketch the magnitude of its response over the range $0 < \omega < 5$. What is the filter's Q-factor? What phase-shift does it impose on an input signal of frequency (a) 0.5 radians/s, and (b) 3 radians/s.

Q4.19. A signal source is connected to a resistive load via an LC filter, as shown in figure Q4.19. Derive an expression for the frequency response $H(\omega) = V_2(\omega)/V_1(\omega)$. If $L = 50\,\mu H$ and $C = 1\,nF$ ($10^{-9}\,F$), at what frequencies does the circuit display resonant effects? If $R = 1\,k\Omega$, what is the response magnitude and phase at the lower of these frequencies?

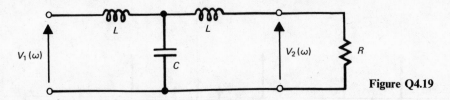

Figure Q4.19

Q4.20. Use a partial fraction expansion (see worked example E4.7 in the main text) to derive the output signal $y(t)$ for the problem described in Q4.17 above. Sketch the form of this signal over the range $0 < t < 3$ seconds.

Q4.21. Figure 4.19(b) in the main text shows an active filter circuit. For reasons external to this problem, the value $R = 10\,k\Omega$ is suitable in a particular application. It is also required that the circuit's Q-factor is 5, and its centre-frequency is 1 kHz. Specify values for the capacitors C_1 and C_2.

Section 4.3.2

Q4.22. A continuous LTI system is described by the following differential equation relating its input and output signals

$$y(t) + \frac{dy(t)}{dt} + 0.16\frac{d^2y(t)}{dt^2} = 2x(t) + 0.2\frac{dx(t)}{dt}$$

Find an expression for the system's frequency response $H(\omega)$, and construct a Bode plot (magnitude only) for the system, representing its gain in decibels.

Q4.23. Construct a Bode plot (magnitude and phase) for the first-order high-pass filter shown in figure 4.18(b) of the main text.

Q4.24. Construct a Bode plot (magnitude and phase) for the simple bandpass filter described in worked example E4.7 in the main text. Assume that the product CR equals 1 second, and show values of frequency in the range $0.1 < \omega < 10$ radians/s.

Q4.25. Sketch a Nyquist plot for the frequency response of (a) the system described in problem Q4.22, and (b) the bandpass filter of problem Q4.24.

Table 4A The continuous-time Fourier Transform: properties

Property or operation	Aperiodic signal	Fourier Transform
transformation	$x(t)$	$\int_{-\infty}^{\infty} x(t)\exp(-j\omega t)dt$
inverse transformation	$\frac{1}{2\pi} \int_{-\infty}^{\infty} X(\omega)\exp(j\omega t)d\omega$	$X(\omega)$
linearity	$a_1 x_1(t) + a_2 x_2(t)$	$a_1 X_1(\omega) + a_2 X_2(\omega)$
time-reversal	$x(-t)$	$X(-\omega)$ $= X^*(\omega), x(t)$ real
time-shifting	$x(t - t_0)$	$\exp(-j\omega t_0)X(\omega)$
time-scaling	$x(at)$	$\frac{1}{\|a\|} X\left(\frac{\omega}{a}\right)$
time-differentiation	$\frac{d^n}{dt^n} x(t)$	$(j\omega)^n X(\omega)$
time-integration	$\int_{-\infty}^{t} x(t)\, dt$	$\frac{1}{j\omega} X(\omega) + \pi X(0)\delta(\omega)$
frequency-differentiation	$t^n x(t)$	$(j)^n \frac{d^n}{d\omega^n} X(\omega)$
convolution	$x_1(t) * x_2(t)$	$X_1(\omega)X_2(\omega)$
modulation	$x_1(t)\, x_2(t)$	$\frac{1}{2\pi}\{X_1(\omega) * X_2(\omega)\}$
real time-function	$x(t)$	$X(\omega) = X^*(-\omega)$ $Re\,\{X(\omega)\} = Re\,\{X(-\omega)\}$ $Im\,\{X(\omega)\} = -Im\,\{X(-\omega)\}$ $\|X(\omega)\| = \|X(-\omega)\|$ $\Phi_x(\omega) = -\Phi_x(-\omega)$
duality	if $g(t)$ ⟺ then $f(t)$ ⟺	$f(\omega)$ $2\pi g(-\omega)$

Table 4B The continuous-time Fourier Transform: pairs

Waveform	Signal $x(t)$	Spectrum $X(\omega)$
1 DC level	1	$2\pi\,\delta(\omega)$
2 unit impulse	$\delta(t)$	1
3 shifted unit impulse	$\delta(t-t_0)$	$\exp(-j\omega t_0)$
4 unit step	$u(t)$	$\pi\,\delta(\omega)+\dfrac{1}{j\omega}$
5 signum function	$\text{sgn}(t)=\dfrac{t}{\|t\|}$	$\dfrac{2}{j\omega}$
6 rectangular pulse	$u(t+T)-u(t-T)$	$2T\,\dfrac{\sin(\omega T)}{\omega T}=2T\,\text{sinc}(\omega T)$
7 triangular pulse	$1-\dfrac{\|t\|}{T},\ \|t\|<T$ 0 elsewhere	$T\left[\dfrac{\sin\frac{\omega T}{2}}{\frac{\omega T}{2}}\right]^2=T\,\text{sinc}^2\left(\dfrac{\omega T}{2}\right)$
8 exponential	$\exp(-\alpha t)\,u(t)$	$\dfrac{1}{\alpha+j\omega}$
9	$\dfrac{1}{\beta-\alpha}\left\{\exp(-\alpha t)-\exp(-\beta t)\right\}u(t)$	$\dfrac{1}{(\alpha+j\omega)\,(\beta+j\omega)}$
10 double exponential	$\exp(-\|\alpha\|t)$	$\dfrac{2\alpha}{\alpha^2+\omega^2}$

Table 4B *continued*

	Waveform	Signal $x(t)$	Spectrum $X(\omega)$
11	gaussian pulse	$\exp(-a^2 t^2)$	$\dfrac{\pi^{\frac{1}{2}}}{a} \exp\!\left(\dfrac{-\omega^2}{4a^2}\right)$
12		$t\exp(-at)\,u(t)$	$\dfrac{1}{(a+j\omega)^2}$
13		$\dfrac{t^{n-1}}{(n-1)!}\exp(-at)\,u(t)$	$\dfrac{1}{(a+j\omega)^n}$
14	eternal cosine	$\cos\omega_0 t$	$\pi\left[\delta(\omega-\omega_0)+\delta(\omega+\omega_0)\right]$
15	eternal sine	$\sin\omega_0 t$	$\dfrac{\pi}{j}\left[\delta(\omega-\omega_0)-\delta(\omega+\omega_0)\right]$
16	damped sine	$\exp(-at)\sin(\omega_0 t)\,u(t)$	$\dfrac{\omega_0}{(a+j\omega)^2+\omega_0^2}$
17	damped cosine	$\exp(-at)\cos(\omega_0 t)\,u(t)$	$\dfrac{a+j\omega}{(a+j\omega)^2+\omega_0^2}$
18	cosine pulse	$\cos\omega_0 t\left[u(t+T)-u(t-T)\right]$	$T\left[\dfrac{\sin(\omega-\omega_0)T}{(\omega-\omega_0)T}+\dfrac{\sin(\omega+\omega_0)T}{(\omega+\omega_0)T}\right]$
19	sinc pulse	$\dfrac{\omega_0}{\pi}\operatorname{sinc}\!\left(\dfrac{\omega_0 t}{\pi}\right)$	$u(\omega+\omega_0)-u(\omega-\omega_0)$
20	impulse train	$\displaystyle\sum_{n=-\infty}^{\infty}\delta(t-nT)$	$\dfrac{2\pi}{T}\displaystyle\sum_{n=-\infty}^{\infty}\delta\!\left(\omega-\dfrac{2\pi n}{T}\right)$

5   Fourier Analysis: Discrete Signals and Systems

"Plus ça change, plus c'est la même chose."
Alphonse Karr (1808–1890)

5.1 Introduction

The application of Fourier analysis to continuous-time phenomena has a history going back nearly two hundred years. As we saw in the previous chapter, it has exerted a major influence on the ways in which electronic engineers think about continuous signals and systems. However, recent years have seen dramatic developments in digital electronics, and there has been a corresponding growth of interest in discrete-time Fourier techniques. It is now commonplace to use digital computers for the Fourier analysis of signals, and for investigating the frequency-domain performance of linear systems.

Back in the 1950s, the practical possibilities appeared far more limited. Digital computers were generally too slow and expensive to tackle the large amount of numerical computation involved. This picture was changed during the following decade by two main factors: the ever-increasing performance of digital hardware, and the development of highly efficient programming algorithms, known collectively as the *fast Fourier Transform*. Subsequent advances in integrated circuit technology have made discrete Fourier techniques even more attractive. Also, 'dedicated' Fourier Transform circuits are now available for applications where operating speed is paramount.

Our discussion of analog-to-digital and digital-to-analog conversion in section 1.3 emphasised the essential equivalence of the continuous and discrete-time approaches to signal representation and processing. Broadly speaking, any continuous-time technique has its discrete-time counterpart. We have already seen this in the case of convolution in chapter 3. Fourier analysis is no exception. However, despite the many similarities between continuous and discrete Fourier techniques, there are a few important differences. These will become clear in the following pages.

5.2 The discrete-time Fourier Series

A strictly periodic discrete signal may be analysed in terms of a Fourier Series. Like its

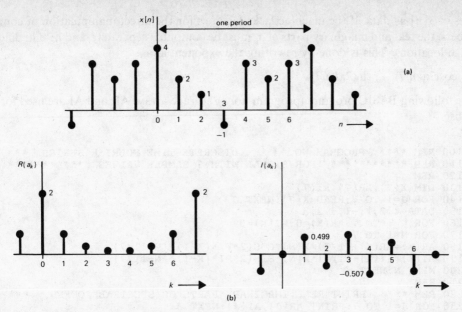

Figure 5.1 (a) A discrete periodic signal, and (b) the real and imaginary parts of its spectral coefficients.

continuous-time counterpart, it has a line spectrum. The special features of such a line spectrum form a good starting point for our discussion of discrete Fourier analysis. This leads on without difficulty to the discrete-time Fourier Transform. Rather than getting involved in mathematical derivations and details, we will start with a definition, and illustrate it with a simple example based upon a computer program.

Suppose we wish to assess the frequency-domain characteristics of a periodic discrete signal $x[n]$, such as the one shown in figure 5.1(a). The various coefficients of its line spectrum may be found using the following equation

$$a_k = \frac{1}{N} \sum_{n=0}^{N-1} x[n] \exp(-j2\pi kn/N) \tag{5.1}$$

Here a_k represents the kth spectral component or harmonic, and N is the number of sample values within each period of the signal. This is known as the *analysis equation* of the discrete-time Fourier Series. Conversely, if we know the coefficients a_k, we may regenerate the signal $x[n]$ using the *synthesis equation*

$$x[n] = \sum_{k=0}^{N-1} a_k \exp(j2\pi kn/N) \tag{5.2}$$

As we might expect from our work on the continuous Fourier Transform in the previous chapter, there is an essential symmetry between the above two equations.

The signal illustrated has 7 sample values per period, so that $N = 7$. The analysis equation therefore becomes

$$a_k = \frac{1}{7} \sum_{n=0}^{6} x[n] \exp(-j2\pi kn/7) \tag{5.3}$$

A digital computer may easily be programmed to calculate the various coefficients a_k, given the values of $x[n]$ as data. If the machine lacks facilities for the direct manipulation of complex numbers, the real and imaginary parts of a_k must be computed separately, and held in different storage locations. This is done by rewriting the exponential as

$$\cos(2\pi kn/7) - j\sin(2\pi kn/7)$$

In the following BASIC program (program no. 4), storage arrays AR and AI are used for this purpose.

```
100 REM ****  PROGRAM NO.4       DISCRETE-TIME FOURIER SERIES  ***
110 REM **********  FOR SIGNAL WITH 7 SAMPLE VALUES  **********
120 REM
130 DIM X(7),AR(7),AI(7)
140 FOR J=1 TO 7:READ X(J):NEXT J
150 DATA 4,2,1,-1,3,2,3
160 FOR K=1 TO 7:AR(K)=0:AI(K)=0
170 FOR N=1 TO 7
180 AR(K)=AR(K)+(1/7)*X(N)*COS(2*PI*(K-1)*(N-1)/7)
190 AI(K)=AI(K)-(1/7)*X(N)*SIN(2*PI*(K-1)*(N-1)/7)
200 NEXT N:NEXT K
210 REM
220 REM ****  PRINT REAL,IMAGINARY PARTS OF SPECTRAL COEFFS.  ***
230 FOR J=1 TO 7:PRINT AR(J),AI(J):NEXT J
240 REM ********************************************************
```

The values of $x[n]$ are read into array X in lines 140 and 150. Having first cleared arrays AR and AI, they are incremented by the appropriate amounts in lines 180 and 190. The print-out produces the following results

k	Spectral coefficient a_k	
	real part	*imaginary part*
0	2	0
1	0.663992639	0.498899192
2	0.204495477	− 0.369468822
3	0.131511886	0.507394844
4	0.131511885	− 0.507394843
5	0.204495477	0.369468823
6	0.663992634	− 0.498899193

Ignoring the very small arithmetic errors in the last decimal place, these values display a 'mirror-image' pattern. This happens whenever $x[n]$ is real. For example, the real parts of a_1 and a_6 are equal, so are those of a_2 and a_5. Apart from a change of sign, the imaginary parts show a similar pattern. Next, suppose that we used equation (5.3) and the computer program no. 4 to estimate *additional* coefficients, outside the range a_0 to a_6. We would find that they form part of a repetitive, periodic, sequence. Thus the next 7 coefficients, a_7 to a_{13} inclusive, are identical to the set a_0 to a_6—and so on. This is because the exponential term in equation (5.3) is, like $x[n]$, a periodic function. It may also be shown that the repetition extends to negative values of k, such that the real parts of a_k form an even function of k, and the imaginary parts form an odd function. The spectral coefficients for the signal we have chosen are illustrated in figure 5.1(b).

We therefore arrive at an important conclusion. A repetitive discrete signal with N samples per period is completely specified in the frequency domain by a set of N consecutive harmonics. When the signal is real, half this number of harmonics is adequate, because of the mirror-image pattern we have already noted. For example, coefficients a_0 to a_3 may be used to define the spectrum of the signal in figure 5.1(a). There is an intuitively appealing reason for this. Our signal possesses 7 independently adjustable sample values, and is therefore said to have 7 *degrees of freedom* in the time-domain. We may therefore expect it to have 7 degrees of freedom in the frequency-domain. Each harmonic contributes 2 of these (independent real and imaginary parts, or amplitude and phase). The zero-frequency coefficient a_0, which always has zero imaginary part, contributes 1. So we arrive at the expected total of 7.

We therefore see that discrete periodic signals—unlike their continuous-time counterparts—have spectra which repeat indefinitely along the frequency axis. This feature is closely related to the *ambiguity* of sampled sinusoids, discussed in section 2.2.4. Figure 2.19 illustrated the fact that a given set of samples can represent more than one underlying sinusoidal waveform. Equations (2.36) and (2.37) generalised the idea, showing that a discrete imaginary exponential of frequency $\pm\Omega_0$ is identical to others of frequency $\Omega_0 \pm 2\pi$, $\Omega_0 \pm 4\pi$, and so on. As we have said before, Fourier analysis of any signal is equivalent to asking 'how much' of a particular frequency is present. This question is ambiguous in the discrete case, since a whole series of spectral representations are possible. Discrete-time Fourier analysis acknowledges this by producing spectra which repeat indefinitely at frequency intervals of 2π. However, this need not cause confusion. Provided the Sampling Theorem has been obeyed, it is only the *first* of these repetitions which reflects frequencies present in the underlying continuous signal. The others are simply a consequence of sampling. A more rigorous justification of this conclusion will be found in chapter 8.

There are close connections between the discrete-time Fourier Series and the exponential form of the series developed for continuous signals in section 4.2.2.2. This may be readily appreciated if we compare their analysis and synthesis equations.

Continuous-time exponential Fourier Series	*Discrete-time Fourier Series*
analysis: $$a_k = \frac{1}{T_0} \int_{-T_0/2}^{T_0/2} x(t) \exp(-j2\pi kt/T_0)\, dt \qquad (4.31)$$	$$a_k = \frac{1}{N} \sum_{n=0}^{N-1} x[n] \exp(-j2\pi kn/N) \qquad (5.1)$$
synthesis: $$x(t) = \sum_{k=-\infty}^{\infty} a_k \exp(jk\omega_0 t)$$ $$= \sum_{k=-\infty}^{\infty} a_k \exp(j2\pi kt/T_0)\, dt \qquad (4.27)$$	$$x[n] = \sum_{k=0}^{N-1} a_k \exp(j2\pi kn/N) \qquad (5.2)$$

The analysis equations specify integration, or summation, over one complete period of the signal, and are very similar in form. The synthesis equations are almost identical. The only substantial difference is that we sum between $k = \pm\infty$ in the continuous case, but only between $k = 0$ and $(N - 1)$ in the discrete case. This is because the line spectrum of a continuous periodic signal is not repetitive, and all harmonics must be included in the synthesis. But the spectrum of a discrete signal is periodic, and complete information about the signal is contained in just one of the repetitions.

The reader may have noticed a slight change in the presentation of line spectra in figure 5.1(b). Earlier line spectra (see, for example, figures 4.1 and 4.10) used plain vertical bars to indicate the values of spectral coefficients, but we are now using bars with 'blobs' on them—symbols previously reserved for time-domain samples. By representing discrete spectral coefficients as frequency-domain 'samples', we help emphasise the symmetry of Fourier transformation. Analysis and synthesis, as defined by equations (5.1) and (5.2), involve essentially the same numerical computations. Therefore a set of numerical values may in principle represent either a signal, or a spectrum.

The signal values in figure 5.1 were selected arbitrarily, and it is hard to explain the values of the resulting spectral coefficients. We may illustrate the relationships between a discrete signal and its spectrum more clearly, by deliberately choosing a signal with a few known frequency components. This forms the basis of the following worked example.

Example E5.1

Sketch the discrete periodic signal

$$x[n] = 1 + 2 \sin \frac{\pi n}{4} + 3 \cos \frac{\pi n}{2}$$

Find its Fourier Series coefficients a_k, and sketch these in the form of real and imaginary parts, and also magnitude and phase.

Solution

As we have seen in section 2.2.3 (equations (2.27) and (2.28)), a discrete signal $\sin n\Omega_0$ is periodic if $2\pi/\Omega_0$ is the ratio of two integers. In this case, the signal $x[n]$ contains a discrete sinusoid with $\Omega_0 = 2\pi/8$, giving exactly 8 samples per cycle, and a discrete cosinusoid with $\Omega_0 = 2\pi/4$, giving 4 samples per cycle. There is also a constant, zero-frequency, term. We may tabulate the values of $x[n]$ over one complete period ($n = 0$ to 7 inclusive) as follows.

n	$2 \sin \dfrac{\pi n}{4}$	$3 \cos \dfrac{\pi n}{2}$	$x[n]$
0	0	3	4
1	1.414	0	2.414
2	2	-3	0
3	1.414	0	2.414
4	0	3	4
5	-1.414	0	-0.414
6	-2	-3	-4
7	-1.414	0	-0.414

The signal is sketched in figure E5.1(a). Its values could be used as data in computer program no. 4 (modifying it to accommodate 8 samples per period), to calculate the Fourier Series coefficients a_k. However, since $x[n]$ has been expressed as a sum of sines and cosines, it may readily be expanded as a complex exponential series. This yields the values of a_k directly. We have

$$x[n] = 1 + 2 \sin \frac{\pi n}{4} + 3 \cos \frac{\pi n}{2}$$

$$\therefore \ x[n] = 1 + \frac{1}{2j} \{ \exp(j\pi n/4) - \exp(-j\pi n/4) \}$$

$$+ \frac{3}{2} \{ \exp(j\pi n/2) + \exp(-j\pi n/2) \}$$

$$\therefore \ x[n] = \frac{3}{2} \exp(2j\pi n/4) - \frac{j}{2} \exp(j\pi n/4) + 1 + \frac{j}{2} \exp(-j\pi n/4) + \frac{3}{2} \exp(2j\pi n/4)$$

The Fourier Series coefficients are therefore

$$a_2 = \frac{3}{2}; \qquad a_1 = -\frac{1}{2}j; \qquad a_0 = 1; \qquad a_{-1} = \frac{1}{2}j; \qquad a_{-2} = \frac{3}{2}$$

Note that since $x[n]$ has 8 samples per period, its Fourier Series must repeat every 8 harmonics. Since the above analysis gives only 5 finite terms, the other 3 must be zero. The real and imaginary parts of the various coefficients are therefore as shown in figure E5.1(b). More that one complete repetition of the spectrum is drawn, to emphasise its periodic

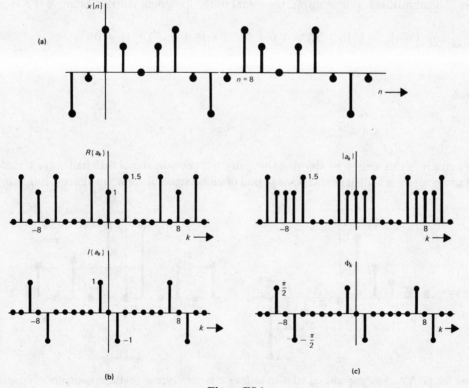

Figure E5.1

nature. Since $x[n]$ is a real time function, the real parts of a_k form an even function of k, and the imaginary parts of a_k form an odd function of k. In part (c) of the figure, the results are recast in terms of magnitude and phase. The three known frequency components of $x[n]$— its zero frequency component, fundamental, and second harmonic—are clearly shown by these spectral diagrams.

In the early sections of chapter 4, we not only showed how to analyse a continuous periodic signal into a Fourier Series, but also discussed a number of related issues—such as the Dirichlet conditions, Parseval's Theorem, and the effects of half-wave symmetry. Rather than giving a detailed treatment of the same topics again, we will confine ourselves to some general remarks in section 5.3.2, when we discuss the properties of the discrete Fourier Transform. At this point we merely illustrate (rather than prove) Parseval's Theorem and half-wave symmetry in relation to discrete periodic signals. The purpose is to emphasise, once again, the close parallels between many aspects of continuous and discrete signal analysis.

Parseval's Theorem equates the total mean power or energy of a signal in the time and frequency domains (see equations (4.22) and (4.40)). In the case of discrete periodic signals it takes the form

$$\frac{1}{N} \sum_{n=0}^{N-1} \{x[n]\}^2 = \sum_{k=0}^{N-1} |a_k|^2 \tag{5.4}$$

The left-hand side represents the average energy per sample value, measured over one period in the time-domain. The right-hand side is a measure of the signal's total spectral energy, measured over one complete repetition, or 'period', in the frequency-domain. The validity of the equation is easily demonstrated. For example, the signal in the foregoing worked example (E5.1) gives

$$\frac{1}{N} \sum_{n=0}^{N-1} \{x[n]\}^2 = \tfrac{1}{8}\{16 + 5.828 + 0 + 5.828 + 16 + 0.172 + 16 + 0.172\}$$

$$= \tfrac{60}{8} = 7.5 \tag{5.5}$$

and also

$$\sum_{k=0}^{N-1} |a_k|^2 = \{1 + 1 + 2.25 + 0 + 0 + 0 + 2.25 + 1\} = 7.5 \tag{5.6}$$

We conclude this section by showing that a discrete periodic signal with half-wave symmetry contains no even-order harmonics. One period of such a signal is shown in figure 5.2(a). Samples

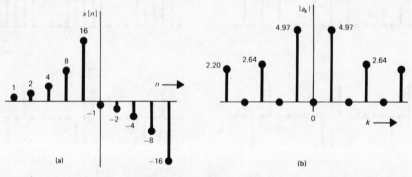

Figure 5.2 (a) A discrete periodic signal with half-wave symmetry, and (b) the magnitudes of its spectral coefficients.

separated by half a period are equal in magnitude but opposite in sign. Computer program no. 4, described earlier in this section, was modified to accept 10 samples per period and used to calculate the spectral coefficients, a_k. Their magnitudes are shown in figure 5.2(b). As expected, all even-order terms are zero.

5.3 The discrete-time Fourier Transform

5.3.1 *Analysis and synthesis of discrete aperiodic signals*

Practical discrete-time signals, like their continuous-time counterparts, are rarely periodic. As we mentioned in section 4.2.3.1, a degree of uncertainty is necessary if a signal is to convey useful information. The discrete temperature record shown in figure 3.8 is a good example of this. So are speech and TV signals, and a wide range of other signals transmitted via communications and data networks. It is therefore important to understand the techniques of Fourier Analysis, as they apply to discrete aperiodic signals.

In the previous chapter we developed the continuous-time Fourier Transform from the Fourier Series by analysing a recurrent pulse waveform. This was illustrated in figure 4.10. By allowing the spacing between adjacent pulses to increase towards infinity, we derived the transform of a single, isolated, pulse centred at $t = 0$. A very similar approach may be used in discrete time. Figure 5.3(a) shows a discrete recurrent pulse signal, in which each 'pulse' consists of $(2N_1 + 1)$ unit sample values. The period is N sampling intervals. Since the signal is even,

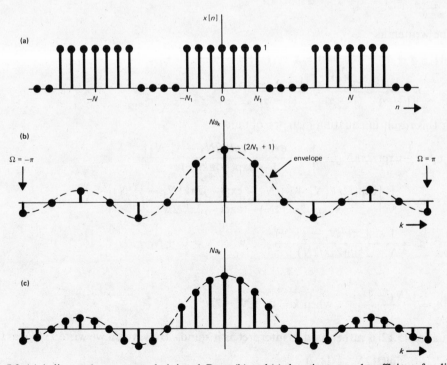

Figure 5.3 (a) A discrete 'recurrent-pulse' signal. Parts (b) and (c) show its spectral coefficients for different values of the period N.

equation (5.1) is conveniently rewritten to produce summation over half a period to either side of the origin

$$a_k = \frac{1}{N} \sum_{n=0}^{N-1} x[n] \exp(-j2\pi kn/N) = \frac{1}{N} \sum_{n=-(N-1)/2}^{(N-1)/2} x[n] \exp(-j2\pi kn/N) \qquad (5.7)$$

Therefore in this case

$$a_k = \frac{1}{N} \sum_{n=-N_1}^{N_1} \exp(-j2\pi kn/N) \qquad (5.8)$$

Writing $(n + N_1)$ as m, equation (5.8) may be recast as

$$a_k = \frac{1}{N} \sum_{m=0}^{2N_1} \exp(-j2\pi k\{m - N_1\}/N)$$

$$\therefore a_k = \frac{1}{N} \exp(j2\pi kN_1/N) \sum_{m=0}^{2N_1} \exp(-j2\pi km/N) \qquad (5.9)$$

The summation on the right-hand side of equation (5.9) may be expressed in closed form, using the following infinite series

$$1 + \alpha + \alpha^2 + \alpha^3 + \ldots = \frac{1}{(1-\alpha)}, \qquad |\alpha| < 1 \qquad (5.10)$$

Hence the finite series

$$\sum_{m=0}^{M} \alpha^m = 1 + \alpha + \alpha^2 + \alpha^3 + \ldots \alpha^M$$

may be written as

$$(1 + \alpha + \alpha^2 + \alpha^3 + \ldots) - \alpha^{M+1}(1 + \alpha + \alpha^2 + \alpha^3 + \ldots)$$

$$= \frac{1}{(1-\alpha)} - \frac{\alpha^{M+1}}{(1-\alpha)} = \frac{(1-\alpha^{M+1})}{(1-\alpha)} \qquad (5.11)$$

Using this result in equation (5.9), we obtain

$$a_k = \frac{1}{N} \exp(j2\pi kN_1/N) \left\{ \frac{1 - \exp(-j2\pi k\{2N_1 + 1\}/N)}{1 - \exp(-j\pi k/N)} \right\}$$

$$\therefore a_k = \frac{1}{N} \left\{ \frac{\exp(j2\pi k\{N_1 + \frac{1}{2}\}/N) - \exp(-j2\pi k\{N_1 + \frac{1}{2}\}/N)}{\exp(j2\pi k/2N) - \exp(-j2\pi k/2N)} \right\}$$

$$\therefore a_k = \frac{1}{N} \frac{\sin(2\pi k\{N_1 + \frac{1}{2}\}/N)}{\sin(2\pi k/2N)}, \qquad \text{when } k \neq 0, \pm N, \pm 2N, \ldots \qquad (5.12)$$

and

$$a_k = \frac{(2N_1 + 1)}{N}, \qquad \text{when } k = 0, \pm N, \pm 2N, \ldots \qquad (5.13)$$

Equation (5.12) is rather hard to interpret as it stands. However, if we write $2\pi k/N$ as Ω, then

$$Na_k = \frac{\sin(\Omega\{2N_1 + 1\}/2)}{\sin(\Omega/2)} \qquad (5.14)$$

This last function represents an *envelope* within which the various coefficients a_k, weighted by the integer N, fall. This is illustrated in figure 5.3(b) and (c). In both cases $(2N_1 + 1) = 7$, giving 7 sample values per pulse. In part (b) of the figure the signal's period N is 14 sampling intervals; in part (c), $N = 28$ (note that neither value corresponds to the top part of the figure, which has been drawn for $N = 11$). Two points need emphasis. Firstly, each spectral diagram represents just one 'period' of a repetitive pattern. Secondly, as the period N increases, the coefficients become more densely packed within the same envelope. Therefore, since we are plotting Na_k, the value of each coefficient a_k reduces.

To derive the equations of the discrete-time Fourier Transform, we next allow the period N to increase towards infinity, leaving a single 'pulse' centred at $n = 0$. This pulse will be assumed to contain $(2N_1 + 1)$ sample values, as before. However, to generalise the argument, we will not assume that they are all unity. Equation (5.7) has already defined the spectral coefficients a_k by summation over a complete signal period

$$a_k = \frac{1}{N} \sum_{n=-(N-1)/2}^{(N-1)/2} x[n] \exp(-j2\pi kn/N)$$

As $N \to \infty$, this may be written as

$$a_k = \frac{1}{N} \sum_{n=-\infty}^{\infty} x[n] \exp(-j2\pi kn/N) \tag{5.15}$$

Denoting $2\pi/N$ as Ω_0, and the spectral envelope Na_k by X, we obtain

$$Na_k = \sum_{n=-\infty}^{\infty} x[n] \exp(-jk\Omega_0 n) = X(k\Omega_0) \tag{5.16}$$

and also

$$a_k = \frac{1}{N} X(k\Omega_0) \tag{5.17}$$

Returning to the synthesis equation for the discrete-time Fourier Series, equation (5.2)

$$x[n] = \sum_{k=0}^{N-1} a_k \exp(j2\pi kn/N)$$

we may now write

$$x[n] = \sum_{k=0}^{N-1} \frac{1}{N} X(k\Omega_0) \exp(jk\Omega_0 n) \tag{5.18}$$

Furthermore, since $1/N = \Omega_0/2\pi$ we have

$$x[n] = \frac{1}{2\pi} \sum_{k=0}^{N-1} X(k\Omega_0) \exp(jk\Omega_0 n)\Omega_0 \tag{5.19}$$

Equations (5.16) and (5.19) contain $k\Omega_0$, which is effectively a discrete frequency variable. However, as $N \to \infty$ and $\Omega_0 \to 0$ this may be replaced by a continuous variable Ω. Hence

$$X(\Omega) = \sum_{n=-\infty}^{\infty} x[n] \exp(-j\Omega n) \tag{5.20}$$

and

$$x[n] = \frac{1}{2\pi} \sum_{k=0}^{N-1} X(\Omega) \exp(j\Omega n) \Omega_0 \tag{5.21}$$

As already mentioned, the spectral envelope of a discrete-time signal is always periodic, repeating at intervals in Ω equal to 2π. This is reflected in the synthesis equations (5.19) and (5.21) by summing over one complete spectral period. As $N \to \infty$ and an increasing number of coefficients bunch within the spectral envelope, we may therefore replace the summation between $k = 0$ and $(N - 1)$ by an integration, taken over one spectral period of 2π. Furthermore, the spacing between adjacent coefficients, which equals Ω_0, becomes vanishingly small, and may be written as $d\Omega$. Finally we obtain

$$x[n] = \frac{1}{2\pi} \int_{2\pi} X(\Omega) \exp(j\Omega n) \, d\Omega \tag{5.22}$$

The above derivation, although rather lengthy, is essentially similar to that used in section 4.2.3.1 to obtain the continuous Fourier Transform as a limiting case of the Fourier Series. For emphasis, we repeat the two key equations (5.20) and (5.22), which form the *discrete-time Fourier Transform* pair

$$X(\Omega) = \sum_{n=-\infty}^{\infty} x[n] \exp(-j\Omega n) \tag{5.20}$$

$$x[n] = \frac{1}{2\pi} \int_{2\pi} X(\Omega) \exp(j\Omega n) \, d\Omega \tag{5.22}$$

The first of these is the *analysis equation*, showing how a discrete aperiodic signal $x[n]$ may be expressed in terms of discrete imaginary exponentials (or sines and cosines). The second shows how $x[n]$ may be *synthesised* from its frequency spectrum $X(\Omega)$. Reference back to equations (4.33) and (4.34) confirms the close parallels between the continuous-time and discrete-time versions of the transform. However, there are two significant differences. Firstly, $X(\Omega)$ is always periodic in form, unlike its continuous counterpart $X(\omega)$. Secondly, the discrete synthesis equation specifies integration over a *finite* interval in Ω. Both distinctions reflect the inherent ambiguity of discrete-time sinusoids and exponentials, and are an inevitable consequence of working with sampled signals.

Example E5.2

Evaluate the discrete-time Fourier Transforms of the aperiodic signals shown in figure E5.2(a) and (b), and sketch their magnitudes in the range $-\pi < \Omega < \pi$.

Solution

(a)

$$X(\Omega) = \sum_{n=-\infty}^{\infty} x[n] \exp(-j\Omega n)$$

$$= \exp(-j3\Omega) + \exp(-j2\Omega) + \exp(-j\Omega) + 1 + \exp(j\Omega) + \exp(j2\Omega) + \exp(j3\Omega)$$

$$= (1 + 2\cos\Omega + 2\cos 2\Omega + 2\cos 3\Omega)$$

This spectrum is purely real since $x[n]$ is even. It is drawn over one complete period in the lower part of figure E5.2(a).

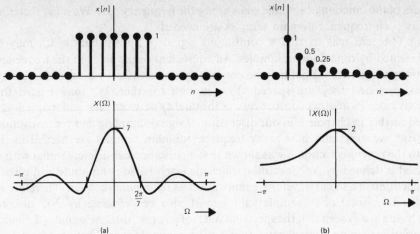

Figure E5.2

Note that the above expression for $X(\Omega)$ is an alternative form for the spectral envelope given in equation (5.14) (with $N_1 = 3$), and already shown in parts (b) and (c) of figure 5.3.

(b)

$$X(\Omega) = \sum_{n=-\infty}^{\infty} x[n] \exp(-j\Omega n)$$

$$= 1 + 0.5 \exp(-j\Omega) + 0.25 \exp(-j2\Omega) + 0.125 \exp(-j3\Omega) + \ldots$$

$$\therefore \ X(\Omega) = \sum_{n=0}^{\infty} \{0.5 \exp(-j\Omega)\}^n = \frac{1}{\{1 - 0.5 \exp(-j\Omega)\}}$$

The magnitude of the spectrum is given by

$$|X(\Omega)| = \frac{1}{\{(1 - 0.5 \cos \Omega)^2 + (0.5 \sin \Omega)^2\}^{1/2}}$$

$$= \frac{1}{(1 - \cos \Omega + 0.25 \cos^2 \Omega + 0.25 \sin^2 \Omega)^{1/2}}$$

$$= \frac{1}{(1.25 - \cos \Omega)^{1/2}}$$

This function is sketched in the lower part of figure E5.2(b). Like the spectrum in part (a) of the figure, $X(\Omega)$ is richest in low frequencies close to $\Omega = 0$, but there are no 'spot' frequencies at which signal energy is completely absent. Remember that $X(\Omega)$ is a complex function of Ω here, so a complete spectral representation would involve phase as well as magnitude.

The signals in the above worked example are simple ones, and their spectra may be expressed in closed analytic form. Practical discrete signals, such as the temperature record shown in figure 3.8, are generally much more complicated. They may contain hundreds, or thousands, of sample values, with little chance of description by analytic functions. So discrete-time Fourier Transforms are commonly estimated by digital computer. This raises an immediate question, because a computer cannot work directly with a continuous frequency function $X(\Omega)$. It can only find sample values of the function at suitable steps along the frequency axis. We must therefore decide how many such frequency-domain samples are needed.

The Sampling Theorem tells us that a continuous signal of known bandwidth may be completely represented by time-domain samples. An equivalent result holds in the frequency-domain. A continuous spectrum $X(\Omega)$ may be completely represented by a set of frequency-domain samples, provided they are spaced close enough together. We may regard this intuitively attractive idea as another consequence of the duality between time and frequency. It will be developed further in chapter 8, in our discussion of signal sampling and reconstitution.

For the moment, we may infer how many frequency-domain samples are needed in the following way. In the previous section it was shown that a periodic, real, discrete signal with N samples per period is defined by $N/2$ spectral coefficients (each having amplitude and phase). Now the mere repetition of a signal waveform cannot affect its *information* content. Therefore an *aperiodic* signal with a total of N sample values must also be definable by $N/2$ discrete frequencies. We have already seen that the spectrum $X(\Omega)$ of any real, discrete signal is definable in terms of its variation over an interval equal to π. So the required interval between frequency samples is $2\pi/N$ radians per second. This is in fact the spacing between adjacent spectral coefficients in the discrete Fourier Series. The argument has come full-circle!

The spectral coefficients a_k of a discrete periodic signal may therefore be regarded as samples of an underlying function $X(\Omega)$, which represents an aperiodic version of the same signal. This important conclusion is illustrated by figure 5.4. Part (a) shows an aperiodic signal $x[n]$ and, on the right-hand side, its spectrum (only the magnitude of $X(\Omega)$ is given, for convenience). The spectrum is continuous and repetitive, with a period of 2π. Since we are dealing with a real time function, the portion of $|X(\Omega)|$ between 0 and π is a mirror image of the portion between π and 2π. So the spectrum is definable in terms of its fluctuations over any frequency interval equal to π. Taking samples of the continuous spectrum—as indicated by the dotted lines—we obtain the set of spectral magnitude coefficients $|a_k|$ shown below. These coefficients represent the Fourier Series of the periodic version of the signal illustrated in part (b) of the figure.

Fourier transformation of an *aperiodic* discrete signal by digital computer therefore reduces

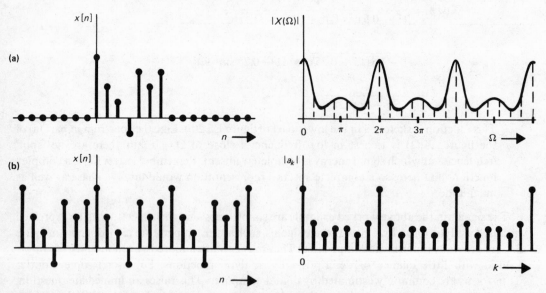

Figure 5.4 Aperiodic and periodic versions of the same discrete signal, and their spectral representations.

to finding the spectral coefficients a_k of the corresponding *periodic* signal. This process is widely referred to as *discrete* Fourier transformation, abbreviated to DFT. In an attempt to avoid confusion, we use the slightly different term *discrete-time* Fourier transformation when deriving the continuous spectrum $X(\Omega)$ of an aperiodic signal. We may always obtain $X(\Omega)$ from the coefficients a_k if we wish—although in practice it is rarely necessary to do so.

Now that we have covered the basic theoretical aspects of discrete-time Fourier transformation, it is time to consider an example with a more practical flavour. The discrete signal at the top of figure 5.5 represents traffic movements in one direction along a highway. Each sample value gives the flow rate in vehicles per hour, averaged over a 6-hour interval. There are 4 samples per day, and the total record represents a fortnight in summer. Days of the week are also indicated (M = Monday, and so on). The first sample value on each day covers midnight to 0600 hours, and shows a low rate of traffic. The next value (0600 to 1200 hours) is much larger, because of commuter traffic into a nearby city. Afternoon flow is lighter; evening flow even more so. There is, in other words, a clear daily pattern of fluctuation. However, this is not strictly periodic, because of statistical variations caused by weather and other factors. Furthermore, Friday evening and Saturday morning flow is rather heavy, because of holiday traffic. Sunday traffic is light. These latter features produce additional, weekly fluctuations in the data.

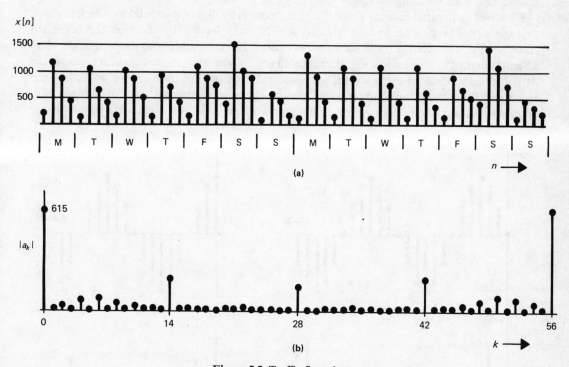

Figure 5.5 Traffic-flow data.

Discrete Fourier transformation produced the traffic-flow spectrum in the lower part of the figure. (The data were processed using computer program no. 4 already described in section 5.1, modified to accept 56 sample values and to calculate the magnitude of each spectral coefficient.) Since $x[n]$ is real, the results display the usual mirror-image pattern. The complete spectrum may be defined by coefficients in the range $0 < k < 28$. We may relate this to the Sampling Theorem as follows. Since there are 4 samples per day, the theorem tells us that underlying signal frequencies up to 2 cycles per day are 'adequately represented'. The record is 14 days long, so the fundamental frequency (corresponding to $k = 1$) is 1 cycle in 14 days. 2 cycles per day corresponds to the 28th harmonic, or $k = 28$. The Sampling Theorem therefore confirms that only harmonics up to the 28th need be taken into account when interpreting the spectrum.

The largest spectral coefficients occur when $k = 0$, 14, and 28. The first of these is the zero-frequency, or DC, term and represents the overall average traffic-flow rate (615 vehicles per hour). $k = 14$ is equivalent to 1 cycle per day, and a_{14} therefore reflects the large daily fluctuations in the record. However these are by no means sinusoidal, and there is a significant component at 2 cycles per day, represented by a_{28}. The other coefficients have small, but finite, values. Most of them represent statistical fluctuations in the data, which may be thought of as a type of random noise. This often has a wide spectral distribution. Note, however, that coefficients a_2, a_4, a_6, a_8 and a_{10} are larger than the rest. a_2 corresponds to energy at 1 cycle per week; so it, and its harmonics, account for the weekly fluctuations in the record to which we have already drawn attention.

Perhaps the most striking feature of this particular transform is the way it highlights the dominant periodicities in the data. This is indeed a principal advantage of discrete Fourier transformation in a wide variety of practical applications—including, of course, those arising in mainstream electronic engineering.

We noted earlier that discrete Fourier transformation by digital computer assumes, in effect, that the signal being transformed is periodic. This may have little effect on the estimated spectrum. For example, the traffic-flow data in figure 5.5 start on a Monday morning and end on a Sunday night. If this aperiodic signal is repeated end-on-end, the inherent cyclical nature of the data is not disturbed. In other words, no unnatural steps or transients are introduced by the repetition. But if such transients *do* occur, they can produce significant spectral changes. This point is well illustrated by the two signals in figure 5.6. Part (a) shows a signal $x[n]$ consisting of

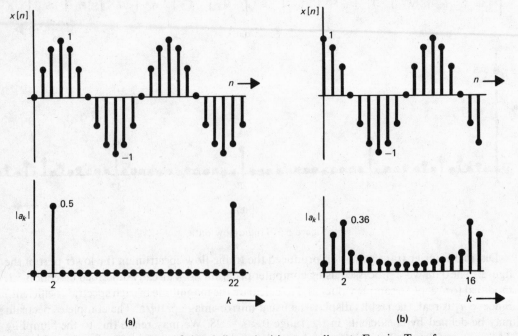

Figure 5.6 The effects of signal discontinuities on a discrete Fourier Transform.

two complete cycles of the sampled sinusoid $\sin(n\pi/6)$. No artificial discontinuities are produced when this signal is repeated. Therefore its DFT, shown below, indicates the presence of a single frequency component. However the signal in part (b) of the figure contains only $1\frac{1}{2}$ cycles. Repetition end-on-end involves sudden jumps in the data. The effect on the computed spectral magnitudes is quite dramatic, with energy 'spreading' away from the nominal frequency of the signal. This is normally considered undesirable, because it tends to mask the required spectral information. Signal processing techniques are fortunately available for reducing the problem, and these will be discussed in chapter 8.

5.3.2 *Properties of the transform*

We have already seen in section 4.2.3.2 that the continuous-time Fourier Transform has a number of important properties. These give valuable insights into the nature of Fourier transformation, and can often simplify the estimation of transforms—or inverse transforms—of practical signals. The reader will hardly be surprised to learn that, with a few minor exceptions and modifications, an equivalent set of properties holds in discrete time. These may be stated equally well for the discrete-time Fourier Series, or the Transform. We choose to focus here on the series, because our main practical interest is evaluating discrete-time transforms by digital computer. As pointed out in the previous section, this involves treating aperiodic signals as periodic for the purposes of numerical computation. Table 5A, at the end of this chapter, summarises the properties of the discrete-time series. For completeness, some of the major ones are also given for the discrete-time transform in table 5B.

We have already mentioned that discrete periodic signals share two properties with their continuous-time counterparts. They obey a form of Parseval's Theorem and, if half-wave symmetrical, they contain no even-order harmonics. In a third respect, however, they are rather different. The Gibbs phenomenon, discussed in section 4.2.2.1, refers to the tendency of a continuous signal to display 'overshoot' at a discontinuity if it is approximated by a limited number of Fourier Series terms. Such effects were seen in our computer simulation of the synthesis of a rectangular pulse in section 4.2.3.1 and figure 4.13. Essentially, the Gibbs phenomenon reflects a *convergence problem* in continuous-time Fourier analysis. However, the situation is rather different in discrete time. A periodic discrete signal having N real sample values per period is *completely* specified by $N/2$ spectral coefficients. No approximation is involved. This explains why the Gibbs phenomenon does not arise with discrete periodic signals.

We now turn to the major group of properties covered in chapter 4 for continuous signals—linearity, time-shifting and scaling, differentiation and integration, and convolution and modulation. Apart from time-scaling, all have direct counterparts in discrete time. For this reason, they will be summarised here, rather than developed in any mathematical detail. The reader who requires practice in the application of these properties will find several relevant problems at the end of the chapter. The following discussion will be simplified by again using a double-headed arrow to signify the relationship between a signal and its spectrum.

The *linearity* property is straightforward, and may be stated as follows

If $\quad x[n] \leftrightarrow a_k \quad$ and $\quad y[n] \leftrightarrow b_k$

then $\quad Ax[n] + By[n] \leftrightarrow Aa_k + Bb_k$ (5.23)

where A and B are constants. The *time-shifting* property is given by

If $\quad x[n] \leftrightarrow a_k$

then $\quad x[n - n_0] \leftrightarrow a_k \exp(-j2\pi kn_0/N)$ (5.24)

The exponential changes the phases of the various spectral coefficients, but not their magnitudes. Note that if we put $n_0 = N$, the signal is shifted by one complete period, and

$$\exp(-j2\pi k n_0/N) = \exp(-j2\pi k) = 1$$

for all integer values of k. Therefore, as expected, the spectrum is unchanged.

In contrast to time-shifting, *time-scaling* is rather an awkward concept in discrete time. The scaling factor must be restricted to an integer (or the reciprocal of an integer), and there is a problem over discarding unwanted sample values, or creating new ones. Such difficulties led us to omit the time-scaling of discrete signals from figure 2.5, which dealt with transformations of the independent variable. For the same reasons, we do not consider it further here.

The *differentiation* property of the discrete-time Fourier Series may be expressed as follows

If $\quad x[n] \leftrightarrow a_k$

then $\quad x[n] - x[n-1] \leftrightarrow a_k\{1 - \exp(-j2\pi k/N)\}$ $\hspace{2cm}$ (5.25)

Note that we interpret 'differentiation' as forming the *first-order difference*—in other words, finding the difference between two adjacent sample values. This gives a measure of the *slope* of the signal in the region of $x[n]$. The above result then follows directly from the linearity and time-shifting properties already defined.

Provided the coefficient a_0 of a discrete periodic signal is zero, the following *integration* property may be stated

If $\quad x[n] \leftrightarrow a_k$

then $\quad \displaystyle\sum_{k=-\infty}^{n} x[k] \leftrightarrow a_k\{1 - \exp(-j2\pi k/N\}^{-1}$ $\hspace{2cm}$ (5.26)

Integration is defined here as a *running summation*. This gives only a periodic result if $x[n]$ has zero average, or DC, value—in other words, if $a_0 = 0$. Otherwise, the summation grows or reduces without limit, and invalidates expression (5.26). It is interesting to recall a comparable difficulty with the integration property of the continuous-time Fourier Transform (see expression (4.57)). In that case, the presence of a DC term in the signal could only be catered for by the rather awkward expedient of adding a spectral impulse at $\omega = 0$.

We next consider the *convolution* property. If the discrete periodic signals $x[n]$ and $y[n]$ share the same period, and

If $\quad x[n] \leftrightarrow a_k \quad$ and $\quad y[n] \leftrightarrow b_k$

then $\quad \displaystyle\sum_{m=0}^{N-1} x[m]y[n-m] \leftrightarrow Na_k b_k$ $\hspace{2cm}$ (5.27)

The left-hand side of this expression represents a convolution over one period. This ensures convergence of the summation. The operation is referred to as *periodic convolution*, or *circular convolution* and is often denoted by the symbol ⊛. It may be visualised as placing the N samples of $x[n]$ around the circumference of a cylinder, and the N samples of $y[n]$ in *reverse order* on another, concentric cylinder. One cylinder is rotated, and coincident sample values in $x[n]$ and $y[n]$ are multiplied and summed. As expression (5.27) shows, this time-domain convolution is equivalent to frequency-domain multiplication.

The converse proposition, that time-domain multiplication is equivalent to frequency-domain convolution, is summarised by the following *modulation* property

If $\quad x[n] \leftrightarrow a_k \quad$ and $\quad y[n] \leftrightarrow b_k$

then $\quad x[n]y[n] \leftrightarrow \sum_{m=0}^{N-1} a_m b_{k-m}$ (5.28)

Note the similarity between expressions (5.27) and (5.28). This underlines, once again, the duality between time and frequency domains, and the essential symmetry of Fourier transformation.

5.3.3 *The fast Fourier Transform (FFT)*

The time taken to estimate a discrete Fourier Transform (DFT) on a digital computer depends largely on the number of multiplications involved, since these are relatively slow operations. Using the DFT equations (5.1) or (5.2), this number is directly related to N^2, where N is the length of the transform. The longest transform so far considered in this chapter was for a signal with 56 sample values (see figure 5.5). However, hundreds or even thousands of samples are quite common in practice. In such cases, computation speed may become a major consideration.

Highly efficient computer algorithms for estimating DFTs have been developed since the middle of the 1960s. Collectively known as fast Fourier Transforms (FFTs), they all rely upon the fact that standard discrete Fourier transformation involves a lot of redundant calculation. To explain this, we may focus on equation (5.1), writing it as

$$a_k = \frac{1}{N} \sum_{n=0}^{N-1} x[n] \exp(-j2\pi kn/N) = \frac{1}{N} \sum_{n=0}^{N-1} x[n] W_N^{kn}$$ (5.29)

where

$$W_N = \exp(-j2\pi/N)$$ (5.30)

The same values of W_N^{kn} are calculated many times as the computation proceeds, for two reasons. Firstly, the integer product kn repeats for different combinations of n and k, and secondly, W_N^{kn} is a periodic function with only N distinct values. For example, suppose we wish to compute an 8-point transform ($N = 8$), so that

$$a_k = \frac{1}{8} \sum_{n=0}^{7} x[n] W_8^{kn}$$ (5.31)

where

$$W_8 = \exp(-j\pi/4)$$ (5.32)

Regardless of the value of kn, W_8^{kn} has only 8 possible values, as follows

$$W_8^0 = 1 \qquad\qquad W_8^1 = \exp(-j\pi/4) = \frac{(1-j)}{\sqrt{2}}$$

$$W_8^2 = \exp(-j\pi/2) = -j \qquad W_8^3 = W_8^1 W_8^2 = -\frac{(1+j)}{\sqrt{2}}$$

$$W_8^4 = (W_8^2)^2 = -1 \qquad W_8^5 = W_8^4 W_8^1 = -\frac{(1-j)}{\sqrt{2}}$$

$$W_8^6 = W_8^4 W_8^2 = j \qquad W_8^7 = W_8^6 W_8^1 = \frac{(1+j)}{\sqrt{2}}$$

If kn falls outside the range 0–7, we still get one of the above values. For example, $kn = 35$ gives

$$W_8^{35} = (W_8^4)^8 W_8^3 = -\frac{(1+j)}{\sqrt{2}}$$

which is the same as W_8^3. Computation of the complete transform involves varying both k and n over the range 0–7 inclusive. (It might be objected that when the signal $x[n]$ is real, the coefficients a_k show a mirror-image pattern within this range. However, FFT algorithms generally cater for complex signals, in which case all the coefficients are needed.)

The values of W_8^{kn} for all 64 possible combinations of k and n are tabulated in figure 5.7. Note that the value ± 1 occurs 32 times; $\pm j$, 16 times; $\pm(1+j)/\sqrt{2}$, 8 times; and $\pm(1-j)/\sqrt{2}$, 8 times. Furthermore, there is a definite structure within the table, which forms a matrix with diagonal symmetry. It is therefore clear that the DFT, as it stands, involves many repeated calculations.

Value of k \ Value of n	0	1	2	3	4	5	6	7
0	1	1	1	1	1	1	1	1
1	1	$\left(\frac{1-j}{\sqrt{2}}\right)$	$-j$	$-\left(\frac{1+j}{\sqrt{2}}\right)$	-1	$-\left(\frac{1-j}{\sqrt{2}}\right)$	j	$\left(\frac{1+j}{\sqrt{2}}\right)$
2	1	$-j$	-1	j	1	$-j$	-1	j
3	1	$-\left(\frac{1+j}{\sqrt{2}}\right)$	j	$\left(\frac{1-j}{\sqrt{2}}\right)$	-1	$\left(\frac{1+j}{\sqrt{2}}\right)$	$-j$	$-\left(\frac{1-j}{\sqrt{2}}\right)$
4	1	-1	1	-1	1	-1	1	-1
5	1	$-\left(\frac{1-j}{\sqrt{2}}\right)$	$-j$	$\left(\frac{1+j}{\sqrt{2}}\right)$	-1	$\left(\frac{1-j}{\sqrt{2}}\right)$	j	$-\left(\frac{1+j}{\sqrt{2}}\right)$
6	1	j	-1	$-j$	1	j	-1	$-j$
7	1	$\left(\frac{1+j}{\sqrt{2}}\right)$	j	$-\left(\frac{1-j}{\sqrt{2}}\right)$	-1	$-\left(\frac{1+j}{\sqrt{2}}\right)$	$-j$	$\left(\frac{1-j}{\sqrt{2}}\right)$

Figure 5.7 Values of the exponential multiplier W_N for an 8-point DFT.

By careful ordering and structuring of the required numerical computations, FFT algorithms aim to eliminate the redundancy in the DFT. Basically this is done by dividing up, or *decimating*, the sample sequence $x[n]$ into subsequences whose transforms are easier to compute. The process of decimation may be repeated until only two-point transforms remain. In this way the overall transform may be reduced to a succession of simple weightings and additions of carefully ordered sample values. Decimation may also be performed in the frequency-domain, rather than the time-domain. The development of FFT algorithms is a specialist matter, and we will not attempt to cover it in detail here. We should note, however, that FFTs are most efficient when written in machine code, and designed to transform signals of length 2^m, where m is an integer. Specialised FFT hardware is also availabe. It is fast, but expensive.

Based on the number of multiplications involved, the speed advantage of the FFT over a standard DFT is of the order $N/\log_2 N$. As the length of the transform increases, this becomes quite dramatic. The FFT program given in program no. 5, which is written in BASIC, may be used for a practical demonstration. Before we begin, it must be stressed that the program is not optimised for speed on a particular machine, and that BASIC is a rather slow high-level language. However, it should be suitable for a wide range of digital computers, including personal microcomputers.

```
100 REM ******* PROGRAM NO.5        FAST FOURIER TRANSFORM *****
110 REM
120 REM ******************* ENTER INPUT DATA *****************
130 DIM AR(128),AI(128):N=128:N1=7
140 FOR Z=1 TO N:AR(Z)=Z:AI(Z)=0:NEXT Z
150 REM
160 PRINT "CHOOSE TRANSFORM OR INVERSE TRANSFORM ( +1/-1 )"
170 INPUT N2:A=N:B=2*PI/N:FOR C=1 TO N1:D=A:A=A/2:E=0
180 FOR F=1 TO A:CO=COS(E):SI=SIN(E)*N2:E=E+B:FOR G=D TO N STEP D
190 H=G-D+F:J=H+A:K=AR(H)-AR(J):L=AI(H)-AI(J)
200 AR(H)=AR(H)+AR(J):AI(H)=AI(H)+AI(J)
210 AR(J)=CO*K+SI*L:AI(J)=CO*L-SI*K:NEXT G:NEXT F
220 B=2*B:NEXT C:M=1:P=N/2:Q=N-1
230 FOR R=1 TO Q:IF R>(M-0.1) GOTO 250
240 K=AR(M):L=AI(M):AR(M)=AR(R):AI(M)=AI(R):AR(R)=K:AI(R)=L
250 S=P
260 IF S>(M-0.1) GOTO 280
270 M=M-S:S=S/2:GOTO 260
280 M=M+S:NEXT R:IF N2<0 GOTO 320
290 FOR T=1 TO N:AR(T)=AR(T)/N:AI(T)=AI(T)/N:NEXT T
300 REM
310 REM ******* PRINT REAL AND IMAGINARY PARTS OF OUTPUT ******
320 FOR W=1 TO N:PRINT AR(W),AI(W):NEXT W
330 GOTO 160
340 REM ****************************************************
```

A detailed explanation of program no. 5 is beyond the scope of this chapter, so we confine ourselves to a few comments to help the reader who wishes to use it. Line 130 sets up real and imaginary storage arrays AR and AI, specifies the length of the transform (N), and the logarithm of N to base 2 (N1). This line must be altered according to the length of transform required. When transforming a real signal, the sample values must be loaded into array AR, with array AI cleared. This is done for a typical example—a unit ramp signal—in line 140. Line 160 allows a transform or an inverse transform to be selected. For an inverse transform, the sign of the sine term is altered in line 180, and division by N in line 290 is avoided. In effect, these two simple changes convert the analysis equation of the DFT (equation (5.1)) into the synthesis equation (equation (5.2)). An interesting feature of the program is that the results are entered into arrays AR and AI, overwriting the input data. This reduces the program's storage requirements. It also means that inclusion of line 330 (which is optional) allows an estimated transform to be inverse-transformed to check that the original signal is recovered! The ease with which the program handles transforms and inverse transforms vividly demonstrates the symmetry of Fourier transformation.

The results of some speed tests on a personal microcomputer are shown in figure 5.8. This offers a comparison between the times taken to estimate various lengths of transform, for the FFT program and for a DFT program of the type listed previously in section 5.2. Much less emphasis should be placed on the *absolute* times given, than on their *relative* values. This is

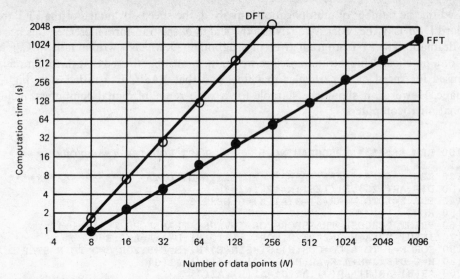

Figure 5.8 A comparison of DFT and FFT computation times on a microcomputer.

because the operating speeds of digital computers vary widely, and improve year by year. But the results confirm an increasing advantage for the FFT as the transform length increases. For example, a 128-point transform took about 25 seconds using the FFT, but about 10 minutes with the DFT. A very lengthy 4096-point transform was tackled in about 20 minutes with the FFT; but, had patience held out, it would have needed around 6 days with the DFT!

The value of discrete Fourier transformation may be illustrated by a further example. Figure 5.9(a) shows a 512-point signal severely contaminated by random noise. The signal has two discrete frequency components and is given by

$$0.75 \sin(2\pi n/4) + \cos(2\pi n/12)$$

The noise, added to the signal, has values equally distributed over the range ± 2.5. This level of

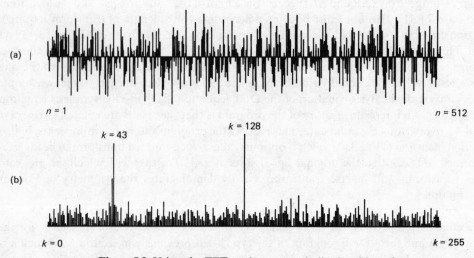

Figure 5.9 Using the FFT to detect a periodic signal in noise.

noise makes it almost impossible to detect the periodic signal fluctuations by eye. However, the spectrum in part (b) of the figure, which was estimated using the FFT program just described, clearly reveals the signal components. Essentially, this is possible because the signal is narrowband, whereas the noise is distributed widely in the frequency-domain. Note that since the signal is real, we have indicated only the first 256 spectral coefficients—and have omitted phase information. (Also, the sample values are too close together to have 'blobs' on them!) Recalling that the 256th harmonic of a 512-point transform represents a sinusoid with 2 samples per cycle, we expect to see the term $0.75 \sin(2\pi n/4)$ appearing at $k = 128$. This is confirmed by the figure. It is interesting to note that the term $\cos(2\pi n/12)$, which has 12 samples per cycle, represents a frequency *between* $k = 42$ and 43. Accordingly, the transform shows signal energy at both values of k. Of course, all signal components are corrupted to some degree by the presence of the noise.

This type of problem has important practical implications. For example, we might be interested in the natural vibration frequencies, or *modes*, of a structure—a building or bridge buffeted by the wind, or an aircraft flying through turbulence. Signals carrying such information are generally contaminated by unwanted noise or interference. Fortunately, the noise is often wideband, whereas vibrations in lightly damped structures are relatively narrowband. This is the key to separating them by spectral analysis.

We have already noted that the FFT is most efficient when the number of samples is an integer power of 2. Of course, a practical signal often fails to meet this criterion, so a widely used approach is to choose a transform length greater than that of the signal, and fill the unused storage locations with zeros. This is referred to as *zero-padding*. We will meet an example of the technique towards the end of the next section.

5.4 Discrete LTI systems

In our discussion of Fourier analysis applied to continuous LTI systems in section 4.3.1, we saw that the impulse response $h(t)$ and the frequency response $H(\omega)$ of such a system are a Fourier Transform pair. We may find the system's output by *convolving* the input signal with the impulse response, or by *multipying* the input spectrum by the frequency response. This was summarised by figure 4.17. The equivalent processes in discrete time are illustrated in figure 5.10. Once again, we may define the system in terms of a frequency response $H(\Omega)$, and multiply this by the input spectrum $X(\Omega)$ to produce the output spectrum $Y(\Omega)$. Furthermore, $H(\Omega)$ is the discrete-time Fourier Transform of the impulse response $h[n]$.

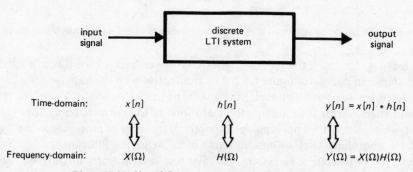

Figure 5.10 Signal flow through a discrete LTI system.

These ideas allow us to explore the frequency-domain characteristics of some discrete LTI systems encountered in earlier chapters. In section 3.4 on discrete-time convolution, and figure 3.8, a simple 5-point moving-average filter was used to smooth temperature data. (A causal hardware realisation of this type of filter was also shown in figure 3.10.) We saw that such smoothing is equivalent to low-pass filtering, and that a filter's weighting function is the same as its impulse response. In this case, the impulse response is

$$h[n] = 0.2(\delta[n+2] + \delta[n+1] + \delta[n] + \delta[n-1] + \delta[n-2]) \tag{5.33}$$

Let us now use the discrete-time Fourier Transform, equation (5.20), to find the filter's frequency response

$$H(\Omega) = \sum_{n=-\infty}^{\infty} h[n] \exp(-j\Omega n) \tag{5.34}$$

Recalling the sifting property of the discrete impulse function, we obtain directly

$$H(\Omega) = 0.2\{\exp(-j2\Omega) + \exp(-j\Omega) + 1 + \exp(j\Omega) + \exp(j2\Omega)\}$$

$$\therefore \ H(\Omega) = 0.2(1 + 2\cos\Omega + 2\cos 2\Omega) \tag{5.35}$$

The impulse and frequency responses are shown in figure 5.11. Both are even functions, and $H(\Omega)$ is real (this is possible when we are filtering *pre-recorded* data, because the filter need not be causal). $H(\Omega)$ is also periodic in Ω, since it is the transform of an aperiodic, discrete, impulse response. This need not cause confusion if we remember that, according to the Sampling Theorem, the filter's performance over the range $0 < \Omega < \pi$ defines its action on any *adequately sampled* signal. We therefore see that the 5-point smoothing filter does indeed possess low-pass characteristics, with a peak response of unity at zero frequency. The cut-off is not very sharp or well-defined, and there are substantial sidelobes. Nevertheless, moving-average low-pass filters are widely used for smoothing data because of their simplicity.

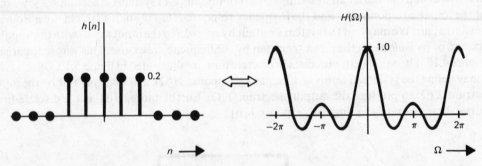

Figure 5.11 The impulse response and frequency response of a 5-point moving-average filter.

Before leaving this topic, the reader might like to refer back to the discrete signal and its transform shown in part (a) of figure E5.2. The similarities with the impulse response we have just considered are obvious—although the signal $x[n]$ has 7 equal-valued samples, rather than 5. The main effect of this is to narrow the main lobe of the corresponding spectral function somewhat. This ties up with a point made in chapter 3: that a more pronounced low-pass action is given by a smoothing filter with more terms in its weighting function.

Another type of discrete LTI system we have met several times already has an impulse response of decaying exponential form (see, for example, worked example E3.1, and worked example E3.3 on the measurement of oven temperature using a microcomputer). We may get a general idea of the frequency responses of such systems from part (b) of worked example E5.2, in which we found that a decaying exponential signal $x[n]$ has a spectrum $X(\Omega)$ which peaks at $\Omega = 0$. Since a function $x[n]$ may, in principle, represent a system's impulse response as well as a signal, it is clear that systems of this type must possess low-pass properties. We shall explore such matters more carefully a little later, in our review of first and second-order discrete systems.

In previous sections of this chapter we have emphasised the Fourier Series representation of discrete signals, because it relates directly to digital computation and the FFT. But so far in this section we have concentrated on the discrete-time Fourier Transform, expressing frequency responses as continuous functions of the variable Ω. The reason for this is that most discrete LTI systems are amenable to analysis using the Fourier Transform equations; whereas practical discrete signals are often rather 'ill-behaved', and need a computer to handle them. However, there is no fundamental difference between the two approaches. They give the same basic information about a signal or system, albeit in a slightly different form.

An alternative way of finding the frequency response of a discrete system makes use of its difference equation. This is equivalent to using the differential equation in the case of a continuous system (a method described in section 4.3.1). In our earlier discussion of difference equations in section 3.6, it was pointed out that discrete LTI systems are characterised by an equation of the general form

$$\sum_{k=0}^{N} a_k y[n-k] = \sum_{k=0}^{M} b_k x[n-k] \tag{5.36}$$

We may write the discrete-time Fourier Transforms of both sides of this equation as follows

$$\sum_{k=0}^{N} a_k \exp(-jk\Omega) Y(\Omega) = \sum_{k=0}^{M} b_k \exp(-jk\Omega) X(\Omega) \tag{5.37}$$

where

$$y[n] \leftrightarrow Y(\Omega) \quad \text{and} \quad x[n] \leftrightarrow X(\Omega) \tag{5.38}$$

This result relies upon the linearity and time-shifting properties of the transform. These are directly comparable to the equivalent properties of the discrete Fourier Series given in table 5A and, in a similar way, appear in table 5B at the end of the chapter. Writing the frequency response $H(\Omega)$ as the ratio of output and input signal transforms, we obtain

$$H(\Omega) = \frac{Y(\Omega)}{X(\Omega)} = \frac{\displaystyle\sum_{k=0}^{M} b_k \exp(-jk\Omega)}{\displaystyle\sum_{k=0}^{N} a_k \exp(-jk\Omega)} \tag{5.39}$$

When interpreting this result, we must be careful to remember that the terms a_k here represent recursive *multiplier coefficients* of the system. We have also used the symbol a_k in this chapter to denote the spectral coefficients, or harmonics, of a discrete-time Fourier Series. Such are the difficulties of finding enough symbols for a book on electronic signals and systems!

Example E5.3

The block diagram in figure E5.3(a) shows a digital high-pass filter. Find the difference equation relating input and output signals, and hence the filter's frequency response $H(\Omega)$. Sketch the magnitude and phase of $H(\Omega)$ over the range $0 < \Omega < \pi$. What is the gain of the filter at $\Omega = \pi$? Find the impulse response of the filter, and check this gain value by convolving the impulse response with a sampled sinusoid at the appropriate frequency. Finally, comment on the contribution of the input term $-x[n-1]$ to the filter's frequency response.

Solution

By inspection, we may write down the following recurrence formula relating input and output signals

$$y[n] = -0.8y[n-1] + x[n] - x[n-1]$$

$$\therefore \ y[n] + 0.8y[n-1] = x[n] - x[n-1]$$

Referring back to equation (5.36), we see that the only nonzero filter coefficients are

$$a_0 = 1, \qquad a_1 = 0.8, \qquad b_0 = 1, \qquad b_1 = -1$$

Therefore equation (5.39) becomes

$$H(\Omega) = \frac{\{1 \exp(-j0)\} + \{-1 \exp(-j\Omega)\}}{\{1 \exp(-j0)\} + \{0.8 \exp(-j\Omega)\}} = \frac{1 - \exp(-j\Omega)}{1 + 0.8 \exp(-j\Omega)}$$

$$\therefore \ H(\Omega) = \frac{1 - \cos \Omega + j \sin \Omega}{1 + 0.8 \cos \Omega - 0.8j \sin \Omega}$$

Hence

$$|H(\Omega)| = \frac{\{(1 - \cos \Omega)^2 + \sin^2 \Omega\}^{1/2}}{\{(1 + 0.8 \cos \Omega)^2 + 0.64 \sin^2 \Omega\}^{1/2}} = \left\{ \frac{2 - 2 \cos \Omega}{1.64 - 1.6 \cos \Omega} \right\}^{1/2}$$

and the associated phase function is

$$\Phi_H(\Omega) = \tan^{-1} \left(\frac{\sin \Omega}{1 - \cos \Omega} \right) - \tan^{-1} \left(\frac{-0.8 \sin \Omega}{1 + 0.8 \cos \Omega} \right)$$

These are plotted over the range $0 < \Omega < \pi$ in part (b) of figure E5.3. We should remember that both functions are periodic in Ω, but that their behaviour over the range shown defines the filter's action on any adequately sampled signal. Note that the filter is high-pass, with a peak gain at $\Omega = \pi$ equal to 10.

The impulse response is easily found from the recurrence formula, by delivering a unit impulse $\delta[n]$ at the input and evaluating the output term by term. Thus

$$h[0] = 1 \qquad\qquad\qquad h[1] = -0.8(1) - 1 = -1.8$$

$$h[2] = -0.8(-1.8) = 0.8(1.8) \qquad h[3] = -0.8^2(1.8)$$

$$h[4] = 0.8^3(1.8) \qquad\qquad\qquad h[5] = -0.8^4(1.8)$$

and so on. A discrete sinusoid input signal at the frequency $\Omega = \pi$ has 2 samples per cycle. Therefore at this frequency successive input samples are equal but opposite. For convenience, let us assume them to be ± 1. The graphical interpretation of discrete-time convolution involves laying the impulse response $h[n]$ out backwards beneath the input signal, cross-multiplying and summing all finite products. In this case, it is clear that this is equivalent to summing all impulse response terms, but with alternate ones inverted. When the impulse response is moved along by one sampling interval, and the process repeated, we

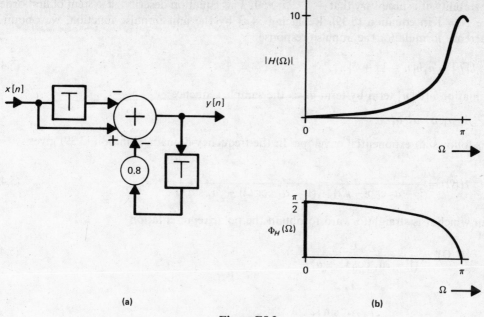

Figure E5.3

get an equal but opposite result. Hence successive output samples from the filter must be $\pm G$, where

$$G = 1 + 1.8 + 0.8(1.8) + 0.8^2(1.8) + 0.8^3(1.8) + \ldots$$

$$\therefore\ G = 1 + 1.8(1 + 0.8 + 0.8^2 + 0.8^3 + \ldots) = 1 + \frac{1.8}{(1 - 0.8)} = 10$$

But we have assumed input samples to be ± 1. Therefore G is the gain of the filter for a steady-state discrete sinusoid of frequency $\Omega = \pi$. This derivation neatly confirms that the peak gain of the filter is 10, and ties up its frequency and time domain performances. Note, however, that the gain refers to steady-state inputs and does not describe the transients which occur when an input signal is first applied, or removed.

The inclusion of the input term $-x[n - 1]$ provides a true zero in the frequency response at $\Omega = 0$. This may be desirable if an input signal contains a DC level which must be suppressed. There are at least two possible explanations. Referring to the frequency response $H(\Omega)$, we see that the nonrecursive input term produces a numerator equal to $\{1 - \exp(-j\Omega)\}$, which equals zero at $\Omega = 0$. In the time-domain, we recall that forming the first-order difference $\{x[n] - x[n - 1]\}$ is equivalent to differentiation—see expression (5.25) in the main text. This gives zero response at $\Omega = 0$, because a DC level has zero slope.

We next consider first and second-order discrete LTI systems in some detail. These have a number of similarities with the continuous systems covered in section 4.3.1. It has already been mentioned several times that a discrete system with a decaying exponential impulse response possesses simple low-pass properties. To develop this idea, let us consider the system difference equation

$$y[n] = a_1 y[n - 1] + x[n] \tag{5.40}$$

For stability, it is necessary that $-1 < a_1 < 1$. This equation describes a system of first order, since $N = 1$ in equation (5.39). Replacing $x[n]$ by the unit impulse function, we obtain a recurrence formula for the impulse response

$$h[n] = a_1 h[n-1] + \delta[n] \tag{5.41}$$

Evaluation of $h[n]$ term by term gives the sample sequence

$$1, a_1, a_1^2, a_1^3, a_1^4 \ldots$$

This follows an exponential envelope. In the frequency-domain, equation (5.39) gives

$$H(\Omega) = \frac{1}{1 - a_1 \exp(-j\Omega)} = \frac{1}{(1 - a_1 \cos \Omega) + j a_1 \sin \Omega} \tag{5.42}$$

from which it is straightforward to obtain the polar representation

$$|H(\Omega)| = \frac{1}{(1 - 2a_1 \cos \Omega + a_1^2)^{1/2}} \tag{5.43}$$

and

$$\Phi_H(\Omega) = -\tan^{-1}\left(\frac{a_1 \sin \Omega}{1 - a_1 \cos \Omega}\right) \tag{5.44}$$

If a_1 is positive, $|H(\Omega)|$ peaks at $\Omega = 0$ giving a low-pass performance. If a_1 is negative, $|H(\Omega)|$ peaks at $\Omega = \pm\pi$ giving high-pass properties.

These results are illustrated in figure 5.12. The impulse responses shown in parts (a) and (b) are for $a_1 = 0.9$ and 0.6 respectively. The value of a_1 controls the rate of decay of the exponential envelope, and has a role similar to that of the time constant in a first-order continuous system. $|H(\Omega)|$ and $\Phi_H(\Omega)$ for both these cases are shown at the top right of the figure. Note that $|H(\Omega)|$ is plotted on a logarithmic (decibel) scale. When $a_1 = 0.9$, $|H(\Omega)|$ is sharper and higher, giving a more selective filtering action—but $h[n]$ is more prolonged. This underlines the general point that limitation in the frequency-domain implies spreading in the time-domain—and vice versa.

Parts (c) and (d) of the figure show high-pass impulse responses for $a_1 = -0.9$ and -0.6 respectively. Successive impulse response terms are now inverted. The frequency response functions, shown below right, are unaltered in shape but displaced by π compared with their low-pass counterparts. Although these characteristics show some similarities with first-order continuous systems, there are two substantial differences. Firstly, the frequency responses of discrete systems are periodic, and do not display a progressive cut-off. Secondly, high-pass discrete systems have impulse responses which are oscillatory in form. This arises because the term 'high-pass', in the context of discrete systems, implies strong transmission of frequencies in the neighbourhood of $\Omega = \pi$. A discrete sinusoid at this frequency has 2 samples per cycle, with successive samples inverted. Such first-order systems are widely used in applications requiring basic low-pass or high-pass filters. Equation (5.40) shows that they may be implemented in hardware with a single summing unit, delay unit, and multiplier—or by a simple software routine.

Figure 5.13 illustrates the action of the first-order high-pass filter

$$y[n] = -0.6y[n-1] + 0.4x[n] \tag{5.45}$$

The multiplier 0.4 is included to make the peak gain of the filter equal to unity. This may be seen

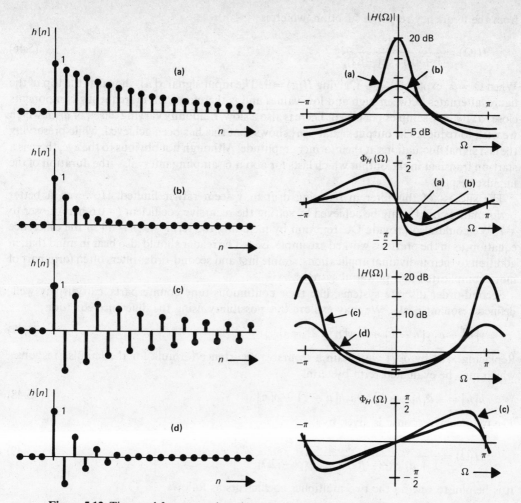

Figure 5.12 Time and frequency domain properties of first-order discrete LTI systems.

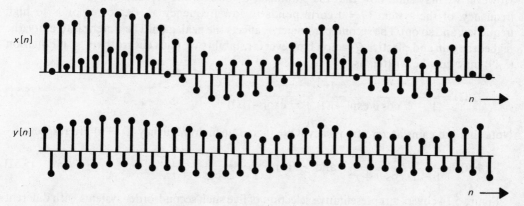

Figure 5.13 The filtering action of a first-order discrete system with high-pass properties.

from the frequency response function, which is

$$H(\Omega) = \frac{0.4}{1 + 0.6 \exp(-j\Omega)} \tag{5.46}$$

When $\Omega = \pi$, $\exp(-j\Omega) = -1$, giving $H(\pi) = 1$. The input signal $x[n]$, shown at the top of the figure, alternates between high and low values and is therefore rich in frequency components close to $\Omega = \pi$ (2 samples per cycle). There is also a slow, randomly varying offset, or *drift*, which we wish to reduce. The output signal $y[n]$ shows that this has been achieved, while preserving the fast signal fluctuations at their former amplitude. Although not obvious to the eye, there is a start-up transient in the output which lasts for about 6 sampling intervals—the duration of the impulse response.

The success of this filter in reducing drift may seem rather limited. However, a better performance could easily be achieved by setting the recursive coefficient (-0.6 here) closer to -1. We could also provide DC rejection by including the term $-x[n-1]$ in the difference equation, as in the previous worked excample, E5.3. The reader should also bear in mind that, in addition to their individual applications, simple first and second-order filters often form part of more complicated and powerful systems.

Second-order discrete systems, like their continuous-time counterparts, can display well-defined resonant peaks. We may explore this possibility using the difference equation

$$y[n] + a_1 y[n-1] + a_2 y[n-2] = x[n] \tag{5.47}$$

Replacing $x[n]$ by $\delta[n]$ we obtain a recursive recurrence formula for the impulse response, which may be evaluated term by term

$$h[n] = -a_1 h[n-1] - a_2 h[n-2] + \delta[n] \tag{5.48}$$

The frequency response is given by

$$H(\Omega) = \frac{1}{1 + a_1 \exp(-j\Omega) + a_2 \exp(-j2\Omega)} \tag{5.49}$$

It is helpful to rewrite the two multiplier coefficients as follows

$$a_1 = -2r \cos \theta \quad \text{and} \quad a_2 = r^2 \tag{5.50}$$

The reasons for this will become clear in our discussion of the z-transform in the next chapter. However we may state now that the parameter θ controls the resonant frequency, or centre frequency, of the system ($\theta = 0$ corresponds to low frequency, $\theta = \pi$ corresponds to high frequency, and so on). The second parameter, r, affects the peak gain. The closer r is to unity, the higher the gain and effective Q-factor. However for stability we must ensure that $r < 1$. Equation (5.49) may now be written as

$$H(\Omega) = \frac{1}{1 - 2r \cos \theta \exp(-j\Omega) + r^2 \exp(-j2\Omega)} \tag{5.51}$$

Note that the gains at zero frequency ($\Omega = 0$) and at high frequency ($\Omega = \pi$) are respectively

$$H(0) = \frac{1}{1 - 2r \cos \theta + r^2} \quad \text{and} \quad H(\pi) = \frac{1}{1 + 2r \cos \theta + r^2} \tag{5.52}$$

Figure 5.14 covers a representative selection of five such second-order systems with different values of θ and r. Parts (a) and (b) show impulse responses for low-pass systems ($\theta = 0$). When

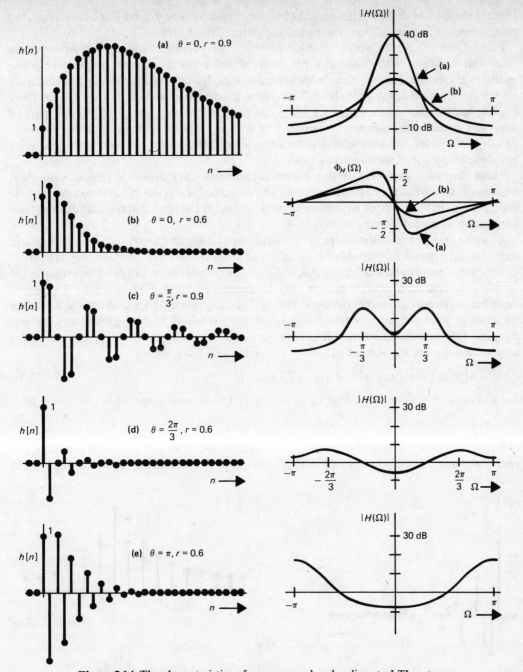

Figure 5.14 The characteristics of some second-order discrete LTI systems.

$r = 0.9$, the response is prolonged (only part of it is included on the diagram). When $r = 0.6$ it is shorter in duration and smaller in amplitude. On the top right-hand side are shown the magnitude and phase characteristics of these two systems. System (a) is much more sharply tuned, with a variation of more than 50 dB between its maximum and minimum responses.

There is also a rapid change of phase as the frequency passes through zero. For convenience, the phase response is omitted from the remaining parts of the figure.

Part (c) refers to a bandpass system with $\theta = \pi/3$. This centre frequency corresponds to a sinusoidal variation with 6 samples per cycle, which explains why the impulse response oscillates at this rate. The frequency response magnitude displays peaks at $\Omega = \pm\pi/3$, and since $r = 0.9$ the tuning is again quite sharp. The system illustrated in part (d), having $\theta = 2\pi/3$ and $r = 0.6$, has a higher centre frequency but a less pronounced resonant peak. Finally, part (e) refers to a system with high-pass properties. The impulse response is identical to that shown in part (b) of the figure, but with successive terms inverted. Its frequency response is also the same, but shifted by π along the frequency axis.

These diagrams are worth studying carefully, because they illustrate various important relationships between the impulse responses and frequency responses of second-order discrete systems. We shall have more to say about such systems in the next chapter, and explore their application to digital filtering in chapter 8.

As we have seen, the relationships between the impulse and frequency responses of first and second-order systems may readily be investigated using the discrete-time Fourier Transform In the case of more complicated systems, a digital computer is often helpful. For example, the impulse response of a discrete system may be entered as input data in the FFT program described in the previous section (program no. 5). The computer will then estimate the frequency response as a set of spectral coefficients. As already explained, these are frequency-domain samples of the underlying function $H(\Omega)$. We may illustrate the approach using a second-order difference equation. Combining equations (5.47) and (5.50), we obtain

$$y[n] = 2r \cos \theta y[n-1] - r^2 y[n-2] + x[n] \tag{5.53}$$

Let us choose $r = 0.8$ and $\theta = 0.6\pi$ as an example. The impulse response is then given by

$$h[n] = -0.4944h[n-1] - 0.64h[n-2] + \delta[n] \tag{5.54}$$

It is quite easy to evaluate $h[n]$ term-by-term, using a calculator or a computer program. The result is shown in part (a) of figure 5.15. Although $h[n]$ theoretically continues forever, in

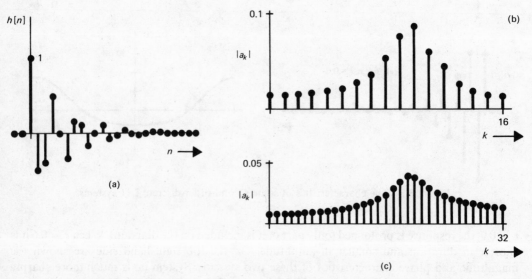

Figure 5.15 The frequency-domain properties of a system, estimated using a zero-padded FFT.

practice its sample values become negligible beyond $n = 20$. The corresponding frequency response could therefore be obtained by performing a DFT on the sequence $h[0]$ to $h[20]$. However, we normally use an FFT program for this purpose, and such programs often only accept a number of samples (N) equal to an integer power of 2. In this case we must choose $N \geqslant 32$, and fill the spare locations with zeros. This technique, known as *zero-padding*, was mentioned at the end of the previous section. Part (b) of the figure gives the magnitudes of the computed spectral coefficients for $N = 32$, plotted on a linear scale. Only half of them are shown because, as always, the other half form a mirror-image set. The 16th harmonic corresponds to the frequency $\Omega = \pi$. Since the parameter θ in the filter's difference equation has been chosen as 0.6π, a response peak is expected between the 9th and 10th harmonics. This is confirmed by the figure.

The spectral effects of zero-padding may be summarised as follows. The function $h[n]$ is real and has only 20 significant sample values, so it *could* be adequately represented in the frequency-domain by just 10 harmonics. Since we have used 16, they must be more closely spaced than necessary. In other words, we have *oversampled* in the frequency-domain. This does not matter, because the computed values are true samples of the underlying frequency response magnitude function $|H(\Omega)|$ — apart from a simple scale factor.

The situation may be clarified by performing a longer FFT on the same data, with more zero-padding. Figure 5.15(c) shows the results for a 64-point transform. There are twice as many spectral coefficients as before, of half the size. But they, too, follow an envelope which has the same shape as $H(\Omega)$. We therefore see that a zero-padded transform gives a valid result, provided we remember that the spectral coefficients are spaced and scaled in inverse proportion to the length of the transform.

Problems to chapter 5

Section 5.2

Q5.1. Find the spectral coefficients a_k for the following discrete periodic signals

    (a) $x[n] = 3 + \sin(2\pi n/4) + \cos(2\pi n/8)$
    (b) $x[n] = \cos(2\pi n/4 - \pi/4)$
    (c) $x[n] = n, \qquad 0 \leqslant n \leqslant 3$, and repeats.

Q5.2. Use the BASIC program given in section 5.2 (program no. 4) to find the real and imaginary parts of spectral coefficients a_0 to a_6, for a periodic signal $x[n]$ having one period as follows

$$x[0] = 1 \qquad x[1] = -2 \qquad x[2] = 2$$

$$x[3] = -1 \qquad x[4] = 1 \qquad x[5] = -2$$

$$x[6] = 1$$

Why is a_0 equal to zero? Also, why are the magnitudes of a_3 and a_4 relatively large? If the signal is sampled at 1 kHz, what frequency is represented by the coefficient a_2?

Section 5.3.1

Q5.3.   Find the discrete-time Fourier Transforms of the aperiodic signals shown in figure Q5.3. Sketch the magnitude of both functions over the range $-\pi < \Omega < \pi$. Why does the signal in part (a) contain much low-frequency energy, unlike the signal in part (b)?

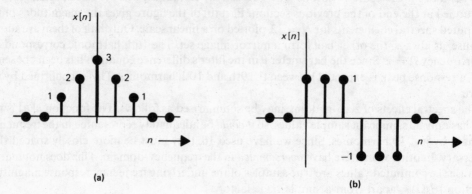

Figure Q5.3

Q5.4.   Find the discrete-time Fourier Transforms of the following signals

(a) $x[n] = 2^{-n}u[n]$
(b) $x[n] = \delta[n] + \delta[n - 4]$

Section 5.3.2

Q5.5.   Sketch the discrete periodic signal $x[n] = \sin 2\pi n/12$ in the range $0 \leqslant n \leqslant 18$. Use the differentiation property of the discrete Fourier Series to find the relative magnitude and phase of the first-order difference signal $\{x[n] - x[n-1]\}$. Confirm your results by sketching the latter signal.

Q5.6.   Two periodic signals, $x[n]$ and $y[n]$, repeat every 7 sample values. One period of each signal is as follows

$$x[0] = 1 \qquad x[1] = 0 \qquad x[2] = 0.5 \qquad x[3] = 0$$
$$x[4] = 0 \qquad x[5] = 0.5 \qquad x[6] = 0$$
$$y[0] = 0 \qquad y[1] = 1 \qquad y[2] = 0 \qquad y[3] = 0$$
$$y[4] = 0 \qquad y[5] = 0 \qquad y[6] = 1$$

Perform a periodic convolution of the two signals, defining the result $x[n] \circledast y[n]$ over the period $0 \leqslant n \leqslant 6$. Using the DFT program listed in section 5.2 (program no. 4), or by analysis, find the spectral coefficients of $x[n]$, $y[n]$, and $x[n] \circledast y[n]$. Check that they obey the convolution property of the discrete-time Fourier Series (see equation (5.27) in the main text).

Q5.7.   The product of the two signals $x[n]$ and $y[n]$ in Q5.6 is zero for all values of n. Use the modulation property of the discrete-time Fourier Series (see equation (5.28)) to confirm that all the spectral coefficients of the product $x[n]\,y[n]$ are also zero.

Section 5.3.3

Q5.8. Assuming you have access to a suitable digital computer, enter the BASIC fast Fourier Transform program listed in section 5.3.3 (program no. 5). Edit the program to perform 16-point transforms, and so that it can inverse-transform data for which it has already computed the transform. Check that a given signal can be transformed, and then recovered by inverse transformation. Finally, enter a 'rectangular pulse' consisting of 5 consecutive samples of value 100, followed by 11 zeros, and compute the magnitudes of the various spectral coefficients. Confirm that these magnitudes are unaltered by time-shifting the 'pulse'.

Q5.9. Use the FFT program listed in section 5.3.3 (program no. 5) to investigate the spreading of spectral energy as a result of sudden discontinuities at the beginning and end of a signal, as illustrated in figure 5.6 of the main text.

Section 5.4

Q5.10. Worked example E3.3 in the main text describes the use of a digital filter for reducing high-frequency noise in a thermocouple signal. The signal is sampled every 10 seconds. Find an expression for the frequency response $H(\Omega)$ of the filter. Estimate its gain (in decibels) to noise components at (a) 0.03 Hz and (b) 0.05 Hz.

Q5.11. Find an expression for the frequency response $H(\Omega)$ of the nonrecursive digital filter described in problem Q3.7 at the end of chapter 3. The maximum gain of the filter occurs at $\Omega = \pi$. What is its value in decibels?

Q5.12. Estimate the peak gain in decibels of the first-order discrete filters defined by the following difference equations

(a) $y[n] = 0.98y[n - 1] + x[n]$
(b) $y[n] = -0.7y[n - 1] + 0.6x[n]$

Q5.13. Worked example E4.7 in chapter 4 showed that a simple continuous bandpass filter could be made by joining a first-order low-pass filter and a first-order high-pass filter. Find the impulse response $h[n]$ of a discrete system formed by cascading a low-pass filter having the difference equation

$$y[n] = \alpha y[n - 1] + x[n]$$

and a high-pass filter having the difference equation

$$y[n] = -\alpha y[n - 1] + x[n]$$

where $0 < \alpha < 1$.

    Does this represent a bandpass function? If not, can you explain the reason? At what frequency, or frequencies, does the discrete system display its peak gain, and what is the value of this gain?

Q5.14. The block diagram of a hardware version of a digital bandpass filter is shown in figure Q5.14. The system sampling rate is 100 kHz.

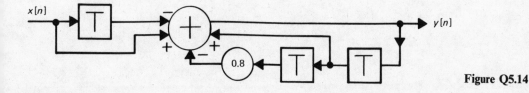

Figure Q5.14

(a) Show that the delay and subtraction on the input side of the filter cause rejection of any steady (zero-frequency) component in the input signal.

(b) Find the centre frequency of the filter.

(c) Estimate the filter's gain (in dB) at the centre frequency, and also at 50 kHz.

(d) If the centre frequency is required to be 16 kHz, by what percentage must the sampling frequency be changed?

Q5.15. A discrete bandpass filter has the difference equation

$$y[n] + 0.9y[n - 2] = x[n]$$

By examining the form of its frequency response $H(\Omega)$, satisfy yourself that its peak gain occurs at $\Omega = \pi/2$. What is the magnitude and phase of $H(\Omega)$ at this frequency?

Q5.16. Towards the end of section 4.3.2, we discussed the problem of phase distortion produced by LTI systems, and mentioned the use of *phase equalisers*. A phase equaliser (which is itself an LTI system) provides phase adjustments to the various frequency components in an input signal without altering their relative magnitudes. This possibility is quite easily demonstrated using a discrete system.

Consider a discrete LTI system with the difference equation

$$y[n] = ay[n - 1] + bx[n] + x[n - 1]$$

where $|a| < 1$. Derive an expression for the magnitude of its frequency response, and find the value of the coefficient b which makes $|H(\Omega)| = 1$ for *all values* of Ω. Calculate and sketch the first few values of the system's impulse response, $h[n]$. (If you find it hard to believe that the system only affects the *phase* of an input signal, try a Fourier Transform of $h[n]$ using the FFT program listed in section 5.3.3 (program no. 5).)

Table 5A The discrete-time Fourier Series: properties

Property or operation	Periodic signal	Discrete Fourier Series
transformation	$x[n]$	$a_k = \dfrac{1}{N} \displaystyle\sum_{n=0}^{N-1} x[n] \, \exp(-j2\pi kn/N)$
inverse transformation	$x[n] = \displaystyle\sum_{k=0}^{N-1} a_k \, \exp(j2\pi kn/N)$	a_k
linearity	$A\,x[n] + B\,y[n]$	$A\,a_k + B\,b_k$
time-reversal	$x[-n]$	a_{-k} $= a_k^*, x[n]$ real
time-shifting	$x[n - n_0]$	$a_k \, \exp(-j2\pi kn_0/N)$
time-differentiation	$x[n] - x[n-1]$	$a_k \left\{ 1 - \exp(-j2k/N) \right\}$
time-integration	$\displaystyle\sum_{k=-\infty}^{n} x[k], a_0 = 0$	$a_k \left\{ 1 - \exp(-j2\pi k/N) \right\}^{-1}$
convolution	$\displaystyle\sum_{m=0}^{N-1} x[m]\, y[n-m]$	$N a_k b_k$
modulation	$x[n]\, y[n]$	$\displaystyle\sum_{m=0}^{N-1} a_m \, b_{k-m}$
real time-function	$x[n]$	$a_k = a_{-k}^*$ $Re(a_k) = Re(a_{-k})$ $Im(a_k) = -Im(a_{-k})$

Table 5B The discrete-time Fourier Transform: properties and pairs

Property or operation	*Aperiodic signal*	*Discrete-time Fourier Transform*
transformation	$x[n]$	$X(\Omega) = \displaystyle\sum_{n=-\infty}^{\infty} x[n]\exp(-j\Omega n)$
inverse transformation	$x[n] = \dfrac{1}{2\pi}\displaystyle\int_{2\pi} X(\Omega)\exp(j\Omega n)\,d\Omega$	$X(\Omega)$
linearity	$a\,x[n] + b\,y[n]$	$a\,X(\Omega) + b\,Y(\Omega)$
time-shifting	$x[n-n_0]$	$X(\Omega)\,\exp(-j\Omega n_0)$
time-differentiation	$x[n]-x[n-1]$	$X(\Omega)\{1-\exp(-j\Omega)\}$
time-integration	$\displaystyle\sum_{k=-\infty}^{n} x[k]$	$X(\Omega)\{1-\exp(-j\Omega)\}^{-1}$ $+\pi X(0)\displaystyle\sum_{k=-\infty}^{\infty}\delta(\Omega-2\pi k)$
convolution	$x[n]*y[n]$	$X(\Omega)\,Y(\Omega)$
modulation	$x[n]\,y[n]$	$\dfrac{1}{2\pi}\displaystyle\int_{2\pi} X(\lambda)\,Y(\Omega-\lambda)\,d\lambda$
waveform	**aperiodic signal $x[n]$**	**spectrum $X(\Omega)$**
unit impulse	$\delta[n]$	1
shifted unit impulse	$\delta[n-n_0]$	$\exp(-j\Omega n_0)$
unit step	$u[n]$	$\{1-\exp(-j\Omega)\}^{-1}$ $+\displaystyle\sum_{k=-\infty}^{\infty}\pi\,\delta(\Omega-2\pi k)$
exponential	$a^n\,u[n],\ \lvert a\rvert<1$	$\{1-a\exp(-j\Omega)\}^{-1}$
rectangular pulse	$x[n]=1,\ \lvert n\rvert\leqslant m$ $x[n]=0,\ \lvert n\rvert> m$	$\dfrac{\sin\left\{\left(m+\dfrac{1}{2}\right)\Omega\right\}}{\sin\left(\dfrac{\Omega}{2}\right)}$

6 The Laplace Transform and the z-transform

"I have a little shadow
That goes in and out with me,
And what can be the use of him
Is more than I can see."

Robert Louis Stevenson (1850–1894)

"Keeping time, time, time,
In a sort of Runic rhyme,
To the tintinabulation that so musically wells
From the bells, bells, bells, bells."

Edgar Allen Poe (1809–1849)

6.1 Introduction

The Laplace Transform and the z-transform are closely related to the Fourier Transform, and to our work in the two preceding chapters. There are several good reasons for covering these additional transforms in a book on electronic signals and systems. The Laplace Transform is somewhat more general in scope than the Fourier Transform, and is widely used by engineers for describing continuous circuits and systems, including automatic control systems. It is particularly valuable for analysing signal flow through causal LTI systems with nonzero initial conditions. The Laplace Transform also overcomes some of the convergence problems associated with the continuous-time Fourier Transform, and can handle a broader class of signal waveforms. The z-transform, on the other hand, is especially suitable for dealing with discrete signals and systems. It offers a more compact and convenient notation than the discrete-time Fourier Transform. The Laplace Transform and the z-transform should be viewed as complementary to the Fourier Transform, rather than essentially different. Since we have already covered much of the relevant conceptual framework, we will concentrate on those features of the transforms which shed additional light on electronic systems.

6.2 Response of LTI systems to complex exponential signals

Before involving ourselves in detail, it is worth considering the special role played by complex exponential signals in the theory of LTI systems. Indeed, some books on signals and systems emphasise this aspect from the beginning, because it is fundamental to frequency-domain analysis. Our own approach so far has been to concentrate on sines and cosines and the techniques of Fourier analysis, because most readers find them simpler to visualise. Of course, we have already seen that any sinusoidal signal may be expressed in exponential form. Furthermore, the Fourier Transform equations themselves involve imaginary exponential functions. So it is hardly a major hurdle to extend the discussion to complex exponentials.

In our treatment of exponential, sine, and cosine signals in section 2.2.3, we considered continuous signals of the form

$$x(t) = A \exp(\alpha t)$$

where A and α are constants. Fourier analysis, which deals with sines and cosines and the frequency responses of systems, effectively limits itself to imaginary values of α (that is, $\alpha = j\omega$). We shall see that the Laplace Transform takes a more general approach, allowing α to be complex. The symbol α is normally replaced by s in Laplace notation. We shall therefore be dealing with signals of the form

$$x(t) = A \exp(st) = A \exp(\{\sigma + j\omega\}t)$$
$$= A \exp(\sigma t) \exp(j\omega t) \tag{6.1}$$

where α and $j\omega$ are the real and imaginary parts of s respectively.

Why are complex exponentials so important in the theory of linear circuits and systems? The reason relates to the form of differential equation describing the operation of continuous LTI systems. This is known as a linear differential equation with constant coefficients, and was first given in section 3.6 and equation (3.43)

$$\sum_{k=0}^{N} a_k \frac{\mathrm{d}^k y(t)}{\mathrm{d}t^k} = \sum_{k=0}^{M} b_k \frac{\mathrm{d}^k x(t)}{\mathrm{d}t^k} \tag{6.2}$$

If the input signal $x(t)$ is exponential, then so are all its derivatives, with the *same exponential index*. This in turn implies that the output signal $y(t)$, and all *its* derivatives, must take the same exponential form as the input. (In terms of sines and cosines, it means that an LTI system cannot generate new frequencies—the important frequency-preservation property already mentioned in section 2.3.1.) To summarise, exponential signals have the rather special property that, when applied to the input of an LTI system, the same *form* of signal appears at the output. This is true whether the exponential is real, imaginary, or complex.

When an input signal produces an output of the same form (apart from a constant, or gain, factor—which may be complex) then the input is said to be an *eigenfunction* of the system. We may use the convolution integral derived in section 3.5 to show that complex exponentials are indeed eigenfunctions of continuous LTI systems. Equation (3.19) gave

$$y(t) = \int_{-\infty}^{\infty} h(\tau)x(t - \tau)\,\mathrm{d}\tau \tag{6.3}$$

where $h(t)$ is the system's impulse response. If $x(t) = A \exp(st)$ we have

$$y(t) = \int_{-\infty}^{\infty} h(\tau)A \exp(s\{t - \tau\})\,d\tau$$

$$= A \exp(st) \int_{-\infty}^{\infty} h(\tau) \exp(-s\tau)\,d\tau \tag{6.4}$$

Noting that the integral is not a function of t, but only of the exponential index s, we may substitute

$$H(s) = \int_{-\infty}^{\infty} h(\tau) \exp(-s\tau)\,d\tau \tag{6.5}$$

giving

$$y(t) = H(s)A \exp(st) \tag{6.6}$$

Hence the output signal takes the same form as the input, multiplied by a complex constant $H(s)$. The value of $H(s)$ depends on the characteristics of the system, and on the value of the exponent s.

The foregoing discussion summarises the importance of complex exponentials in linear system analysis. Although presented in terms of continuous signals and systems, essentially similar ideas apply to the discrete case. Of course, practical input signals are not often exponential, but we may generally decompose them into a set of exponential components. As in Fourier analysis, the linearity property of LTI systems may then be used to find the overall output signal by superposition.

6.3 The Laplace Transform

Pierre Simon, Marquis de Laplace, was born some twenty years before Fourier, and became perhaps the greatest theoretical astronomer since Newton. He was one of the distinguished group of mathematicians appointed to examine Fourier's work on heat diffusion, submitted to the Institut de France in 1807. Laplace contributed widely to mathematics and astronomy, but is perhaps best known for his *Celestial Mechanics*. In this work he proposed that the solar system had condensed out of a vast gaseous nebula. The transform which bears his name has found many applications in engineering and applied science, and is of major importance in electronic engineering.

6.3.1 *Definition and properties*

The Laplace Transform of a signal $x(t)$ is defined as

$$X(s) = \int_{0}^{\infty} x(t) \exp(-st)\,dt \tag{6.7}$$

where s may be thought of as a *complex frequency*. We should note at once that this form of the transform is referred to as single-sided, or *unilateral*, because it does not depend on the history of $x(t)$ prior to $t = 0$. Another form, known as the double-sided or *bilateral* Laplace Transform, specifies the lower limit of integration as $t = -\infty$. It therefore takes account of $x(t)$ over all time. We shall have more to say about bilateral transforms in section 6.5. Although restriction of the unilateral transform to positive time may at first seem rather a disadvantage, in practice it is rarely a problem when dealing with electronic signals and systems. This is because we may generally consider an input signal to be 'switched on' at some instant, before which it is zero. The instant is normally taken as $t = 0$. As we shall see, any energy storage in a system (as a result, for example, of charge storage on a capacitor) caused by input signals applied *before* $t = 0$ may be accounted for in terms of initial conditions.

There are obvious similarities between the Laplace Transform, defined in equation (6.7), and the continuous-time Fourier Transform which we met in chapter 4 (see equation (4.33)). As already noted, the Laplace variable s may in general be real, imaginary, or complex. If we make it imaginary, replacing s by $j\omega$, we obtain

$$X(j\omega) = \int_0^\infty x(t) \exp(-j\omega t)\, dt \tag{6.8}$$

Apart from a change in the lower limit of integration, this is identical to the Fourier Transform. Just as the Fourier Transform in effect analyses a signal $x(t)$ into a set of imaginary exponentials (which, in pairs, constitute sines and cosines), so the Laplace Transform uses complex exponentials. There tends to be some conceptual difficulty here, because generalised exponentials are harder to visualise than sinusoids. Figure 6.1 may help. It shows a number of real signals, zero before $t = 0$. Since they may readily be expressed in exponential form, all are members of the family of functions encompassed by the unilateral Laplace Transform.

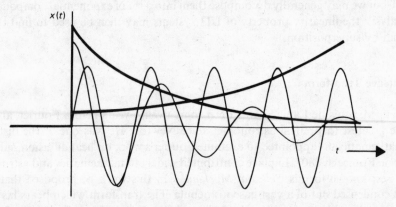

Figure 6.1 Typical members of the family of signals defined by $x(t) = \exp(st)\,u(t)$, where s is complex.

Example E6.1

We have already noted that the Laplace Transform overcomes some of the convergence problems associated with the continuous-time Fourier Transform. These were mentioned in section 4.2.3.1. We may demonstrate this advantage—and obtain some practice in Laplace transformation—by finding the transforms of 'awkward' signals which fail to meet the criterion of *absolute integrability* (see equation (4.46)). Two such signals are

(a) $x(t) = r(t) = t\,u(t)$

and

(b) $x(t) = \exp(2t) \cos t\, u(t)$

Solution

(a) The Laplace Transform of the unit ramp function $r(t)$ is given by

$$X(s) = \int_0^\infty x(t)\exp(-st)\,dt = \int_0^\infty t\exp(-st)\,dt$$

Integrating by parts, we obtain

$$X(s) = \left[\frac{t\exp(-st)}{-s}\right]_0^\infty - \int_0^\infty \frac{1\exp(-st)}{-s}\,dt$$

$$= \frac{(0-0)}{-s} - \left[\frac{\exp(-st)}{s^2}\right]_0^\infty = \frac{1}{s^2}$$

Note that we have assumed that $t\exp(-st)$ becomes zero as $t \to \infty$. While it is generally true that a decaying exponential 'overcomes' a term of the form t^n at sufficiently large values of t, our assumption only holds good for appropriate values of s. This is essentially a convergence problem, and we will discuss it further after completing the worked example.

(b) The Laplace Transform is given by

$$X(s) = \int_0^\infty x(t)\exp(-st)\,dt = \int_0^\infty \cos t\exp(2t - st)\,dt$$

$$\therefore\; X(s) = \frac{1}{2}\int_0^\infty \{\exp(jt) + \exp(-jt)\}\exp(2t - st)\,dt$$

$$= \frac{1}{2}\left[\frac{\exp(jt + 2t - st)}{(j + 2 - s)}\right]_0^\infty + \frac{1}{2}\left[\frac{\exp(-jt + 2t - st)}{(-j + 2 - s)}\right]_0^\infty$$

$$= \frac{1}{2}\left\{\frac{(0-1)}{(j + 2 - s)} + \frac{(0-1)}{(-j + 2 - s)}\right\}$$

$$= \frac{1}{2}\left\{\frac{j - 2 + s - j - 2 + s}{(2 - s + j)(2 - s - j)}\right\} = \frac{(s - 2)}{(s^2 - 4s + 5)}$$

Although we have again evaluated this transform without difficulty, it has been assumed that a term of the form $\exp(jt + 2t - st)$ becomes zero as $t \to \infty$. Once again, this is only true for appropriate values of s.

In the worked example just completed, we have seen that the validity of a Laplace Transform depends upon a suitable choice of the complex frequency s. This gives rise to the notion of a *region of convergence*. If s is plotted in the complex plane (Argand diagram), then convergence of the transform is assured only for values of s lying within a certain region of the plane. We may see this more clearly by replacing s by $(\sigma + j\omega)$ in equation (6.7)

$$X(s) = \int_0^\infty x(t)\exp(-st)\,dt = \int_0^\infty \{x(t)\exp(-\sigma t)\}\exp(-j\omega t)\,dt \tag{6.9}$$

If $x(t)$ is an 'awkward' function which is not absolutely integrable over the range $0 < t < \infty$, convergence is produced by multiplying it by the real exponential, or *convergence factor*, $\exp(-\sigma t)$. (The term $\exp(-j\omega t)$ is not helpful in this respect, since it is strictly periodic and does not decay as $t \to \infty$.) We therefore see that, for the Laplace Transform to exist, the *real part* of s must be adequate to counteract any tendency of the signal $x(t)$ to continue forever—or to grow without limit. Fortunately, we normally deal with well-behaved signals and causal, stable LTI systems. The convergence conditions of the unilateral Laplace Transform therefore rarely cause difficulty in practice.

So far, we have discussed Laplace Transforms of signals. However, a major interest of this book is signal flow through linear systems. This topic will be covered more fully in section 6.3.3, but a brief outline of the approach is perhaps helpful here. In essence it is the same as that used with the Fourier Transform in the two previous chapters. We find the Laplace Transform $X(s)$ of the input signal, and multiply it by a function $H(s)$ representing the system. This gives the Laplace Transform $Y(s)$ of the output signal. Thus

$$Y(s) = X(s)H(s) \quad \text{or} \quad H(s) = \frac{Y(s)}{X(s)} \tag{6.10}$$

The function $H(s)$ is called the *transfer function* of the LTI system, and is strictly analogous to the frequency response used in Fourier analysis. Not surprisingly, $H(s)$ turns out to be the Laplace Transform of the system's impulse response. Once again, a major advantage of working with transformed functions is that time-domain convolution is replaced by frequency-domain multiplication.

Having found the Laplace Transform $Y(s)$ of the output signal, we convert back to an equivalent time function by inverse transformation. The inverse Laplace Transform equation is

$$x(t) = \frac{1}{2\pi j} \int_{\sigma - j\infty}^{\sigma + j\infty} X(s) \exp(st) \, ds \tag{6.11}$$

This integral is generally difficult to evaluate, requiring *contour integration* in the complex plane—a technique which is beyond the scope of this book. However, we may adopt one of two alternatives. The first, widely used, approach is to consult a table of Laplace Transform pairs. Such a table is included at the end of this chapter (table 6B). But if the transform we require is not given, we may often reduce it to a sum of simpler transforms using the *method of partial fractions*. This was first described in worked example E4.7 and we shall discuss it more fully in section 6.3.3.

Let us now illustrate these ideas with a simple circuit problem. A unit step of voltage is applied to a first-order low-pass filter, as shown in figure 6.2. The capacitor is initially discharged, and we need to find the output signal $v_2(t)$. The Laplace Transform of a unit step function is easily evaluated—or looked up in table 6B at the end of the chapter. It is

$$X(s) = V_1(s) = \frac{1}{s} \tag{6.12}$$

The fundamental way of finding the transfer function of the circuit is to use its differential

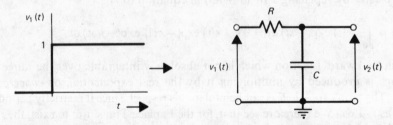

Figure 6.2 A simple circuit problem for solution by Laplace transformation.

equation. We will explain this method in section 6.3.3, when we have covered the properties of the Laplace Transform. An attractive and straightforward alternative is to use the normal rules of circuit analysis, writing the impedance of a capacitor as $1/sC$ and the impedance of an inductor as sL. This is precisely analogous to using the j-notation for finding a frequency response, as discussed in section 4.3.1. Since we are now dealing with complex exponentials rather than imaginary ones, $j\omega$ is replaced by s. The present circuit is a very simple one, and its output terminals are assumed to be open-circuit. We may therefore use the 'potential-divider' principle, obtaining directly

$$H(s) = \frac{Y(s)}{X(s)} = \frac{V_2(s)}{V_1(s)} = \frac{1/sC}{R + (1/sC)} = \frac{1/CR}{s + (1/CR)} \tag{6.13}$$

The Laplace Transform of the output signal is therefore

$$V_2(s) = \frac{1/CR}{s\{s + (1/CR)\}}$$

Consulting table 6B at the end of the chapter, we find that

$$\{1 - \exp(-\alpha t)\}u(t) \leftrightarrow \frac{\alpha}{s(s + \alpha)}$$

Therefore the output signal is

$$v_2(t) = 1 - \exp(-t/CR), \qquad t > 0 \tag{6.14}$$

This is, of course, the circuit's step response, and is (fortunately!) the result previously obtained in section 3.5.

We next turn our attention to the *properties* of the Laplace Transform. Broadly speaking, these parallel the properties of the continuous-time Fourier Transform derived in section 4.2.3.2. We have already noted that the unilateral Laplace Transform is very similar to the Fourier Transform, if s is replaced by $j\omega$. So we may expect that many of the properties will also prove similar, if the same substitution is made. This may be confirmed by comparing the table 6A at the end of this chapter with table 4A at the end of chapter 4. Thus the properties of *linearity, time-shifting, time-scaling, integration* and *convolution* are straightforward and need no further explanation here. Time-reversal is not applicable to the unilateral transform, since signals are assumed zero before $t = 0$. Time-domain modulation is a little awkward. The property holds good in principle, but the equivalent frequency-domain convolution is mathematically rather complicated. So it is omitted from the table. Apart from these, the only major property remaining is *time-differentiation*. Since we need this property later in the chapter, we should discuss it a little more carefully.

Time-differentiation of a function or signal is equivalent to multiplying its transform by s, with an added constant. If we denote Laplace transformation by the symbol $\mathscr{L}$, the property may be summarised as follows

If $\mathscr{L}\{x(t)\} = X(s)$

then $\mathscr{L}\left\{\dfrac{\mathrm{d}x(t)}{\mathrm{d}t}\right\} = sX(s) - x(0_+)$ \hfill (6.15)

Here $x(0_+)$ means the value of $x(t)$ when $t = 0$, and the plus sign indicates that if there is a discontinuity in $x(t)$ at $t = 0$, then $x(0_+)$ is the limit of $x(t)$ as t approaches zero from the positive side. We may prove this result in the following way. Firstly, we have

$$X(s) = \int_0^\infty x(t) \exp(-st)\, dt$$

Integrating the right-hand side of the equation by parts, and denoting the first derivative of $x(t)$ by $x'(t)$, we obtain

$$X(s) = -\left[x(t) \frac{1}{s} \exp(-st) \right]_0^\infty + \int_0^\infty \frac{1}{s} \exp(-st) x'(t)\, dt \tag{6.16}$$

It is assumed that the real part of s is such as to make the first term zero when $t = \infty$. When $t = 0$, $\exp(-st) = 1$ and $x(t) = x(0_+)$. Hence

$$X(s) = \frac{1}{s} x(0_+) + \frac{1}{s} \int_0^\infty x'(t) \exp(-st)\, dt$$

$$\therefore \int_0^\infty x'(t) \exp(-st)\, dt = sX(s) - x(0_+) \tag{6.17}$$

Since the left-hand side is the Laplace Transform of the derivative of $x(t)$, equation (6.15) is confirmed. By an extension of the above arguments, it is possible to find the Laplace Transform of higher derivatives of $x(t)$. For example, it may be shown that

$$\mathscr{L}\left\{ \frac{d^2 x(t)}{dt^2} \right\} = s^2 X(s) - sx(0_+) - x'(0_+) \tag{6.18}$$

where $x'(0_+)$ is the value of the first derivative as $t = 0$ is approached from the positive side.

Two further valuable features of the Laplace Transform are summarised in the *initial and final value theorems*. Quite often, we have an expression for the transform $X(s)$ of a signal, but not for the signal $x(t)$ itself. These two theorems allow us to determine the initial and final values of $x(t)$ without having to evaluate the inverse transform of $X(s)$. The proofs are not difficult, and are given in most books on transform theory. The theorems may be stated as follows

If $x(t)$ and its first derivative are Laplace-transformable, then the initial value of $x(t)$ is given by

$$x(0_+) = \underset{s \to \infty}{\text{limit}}\{sX(s)\} \tag{6.19}$$

and its final value by

$$x(\infty) = \underset{s \to 0}{\text{limit}}\{sX(s)\} \tag{6.20}$$

Most aspects of the Laplace Transform examined in this section parallel closely those of the continuous-time Fourier Transform. In the next section, however, we look at a new aspect of frequency-domain analysis. This proves to be of great value in visualising the properties of signals and the performance of systems.

6.3.2 s-*plane poles and zeros*

Laplace Transforms encountered in the analysis of signals and continuous LTI systems are always *rational functions* of the complex frequency variable. In other words, they may always be written as the ratio of a numerator and denominator polynomial in s

$$X(s) = \frac{N(s)}{D(s)} \tag{6.21}$$

This is true whether the transform represents an input or output signal, or the transfer function of a system. Apart from a constant, or gain, factor it follows that the transform may be completely specified by the *roots* of these two polynomials. Thus, in general, we may express equation (6.21) in the form

$$X(s) = \frac{N(s)}{D(s)} = K \frac{(s - z_1)(s - z_2)(s - z_3)\dots}{(s - p_1)(s - p_2)(s - p_3)\dots} \tag{6.22}$$

The constants $z_1, z_2, z_3 \dots$ are known as the *zeros* of $X(s)$, because they are values of s for which $X(s)$ is zero. Conversely, $p_1, p_2, p_3 \dots$ are referred to as the *poles* of $X(s)$, and give values of s for which $X(s)$ tends to infinity. It is found that whenever the corresponding time function is real, the poles and zeros are themselves either real, or occur in complex-conjugate pairs.

A very useful representation of a Laplace Transform is obtained by plotting its poles and zeros in the complex plane (Argand diagram). The plane is then referred to as the *s-plane*. As we shall see a little later, it is quite easy to visualise the frequency spectrum of a signal, or the frequency response of a system, from such a diagram. It also gives a good indication of the degree of stability of a system.

As well as listing some useful transform pairs, table 6B at the end of this chapter shows the corresponding s-plane poles and zeros. For example, the transform

$$\exp(-\alpha t)u(t) \leftrightarrow \frac{1}{(s + \alpha)} \tag{6.23}$$

is characterised by a single real pole at $s = -\alpha$. The cosine signal and its transform

$$\cos \omega_0 t \, u(t) \leftrightarrow \frac{s}{s^2 + \omega_0^2} \tag{6.24}$$

give rise to a zero at the origin of the s-plane, together with an imaginary pole pair at $s = \pm j\omega_0$. When we deal with an electric or electronic circuit, the poles and zeros of its transfer function are related to the values of the circuit components. We demonstrate this in the following worked example.

Example E6.2

Find the s-plane poles and zeros of the two circuits shown in figure E6.2(a). Plot their locations in the s-plane for the following circuit component values: $R = 100\,\Omega$, $C = 1\,\mu F$, $L = 1.54\,mH$.

Solution

The RC circuit is a simple high-pass filter. Assuming its output terminals are open-circuit, we may use the 'potential-divider' principle to write its voltage transfer function directly

$$H(s) = \frac{V_2(s)}{V_1(s)} = \frac{R}{R + (1/sC)} = \frac{s}{s + (1/CR)}$$

where $1/sC$ represents the impedance of the capacitor at the complex frequency s. $H(s)$ has a zero at $s = 0$, and a real pole at $s = -1/CR$. These are plotted in part (b) of the figure for $R = 100\,\Omega$ and $C = 1\,\mu\text{F}$. Note that the real part of s is plotted along the horizontal axis, the imaginary part along the vertical axis. An open circular symbol is used for the zero, and a cross for the pole. The frequency response of this circuit has already been derived in section 4.3.1 (see equation (4.80)), and is the same as $H(s)$ if $j\omega$ is substituted for s.

The second circuit has also previously been discussed in section 4.3.1. To obtain its voltage transfer function, we write the complex impedances of the capacitor and inductor as $1/sC$ and sL respectively. Denoting the impedance of the paralleled resistor and capacitor by $Z(s)$, and assuming the output terminals are open-circuit, we have

$$H(s) = \frac{V_2(s)}{V_1(s)} = \frac{Z(s)}{sL + Z(s)}$$

where

$$Z(s) = \frac{R/sC}{R + (1/sC)} = \frac{R}{1 + sCR}$$

Hence

$$H(s) = \frac{R}{R + sL(1 + sCR)} = \frac{1}{LC} \times \frac{1}{s^2 + (s/CR) + (1/LC)}$$

The same result could be obtained by replacing $j\omega$ by s in the frequency response expression, equation (4.90). We see that $H(s)$ has two s-plane poles, but no zeros. The poles are given by

$$s = \frac{-(1/CR) \pm \{(1/CR)^2 - (4/LC)\}^{1/2}}{2}$$

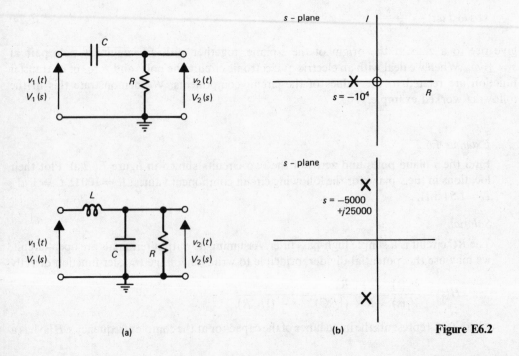

(a)   (b)   **Figure E6.2**

For the circuit values given, these are

$$s = \frac{-10^4 \pm \{-25 \times 10^8\}^{1/2}}{2} = -5000 \pm j\,25\,000 \text{ radians/s}$$

They form a complex conjugate pair, and are also plotted in part (b) of the figure.

As already mentioned, it is straightforward to infer the spectrum of a signal—or the frequency response of a system—from a plot of its s-plane poles and zeros. This technique is sometimes called the *geometric evaluation of the Fourier Transform in the s-plane*. We recall that whereas in general $s = (\sigma + j\omega)$, for Fourier analysis s is restricted to purely imaginary values. So if we replace s by $j\omega$ in the Laplace Transform equation (6.22), we obtain the corresponding Fourier Transform

$$X(s)|_{s=j\omega} = X(j\omega) = \frac{N(j\omega)}{D(j\omega)} = \frac{K(j\omega - z_1)(j\omega - z_2)(j\omega - z_3)\dots}{(j\omega - p_1)(j\omega - p_2)(j\omega - p_3)\dots} \qquad (6.25)$$

(We have denoted the spectral function by $X(j\omega)$ rather than $X(\omega)$, as previously. This has no significance beyond showing that we have replaced s by $j\omega$ in a Laplace Transform expression. It also serves as a reminder that spectral functions are generally complex functions of ω. Both notations are commonly used.) At a particular sinusoidal frequency such as $\omega = \omega_1$, we may write

$$X(j\omega_1) = \frac{K(j\omega_1 - z_1)(j\omega_1 - z_2)(j\omega_1 - z_3)\dots}{(j\omega_1 - p_1)(j\omega_1 - p_2)(j\omega_1 - p_3)\dots} \qquad (6.26)$$

Now each term in brackets may be represented by a vector in the s-plane, drawn from the relevant pole or zero to the point $s = j\omega_1$ on the imaginary axis. By considering changes in the lengths and directions of these vectors as ω_1 varies, we may readily visualise the form of the spectral function.

These ideas will now be related to the two circuits covered in worked example E6.2. Since we are dealing with *systems* rather than signals, the spectral functions we visualise will be *frequency responses*. Substituting $s = j\omega_1$ in the transfer function of the first-order high-pass filter, we obtain

$$H(s)|_{s=j\omega_1} = H(j\omega_1) = \frac{j\omega_1}{j\omega_1 + (1/CR)} \qquad (6.27)$$

The numerator term $j\omega_1$ may be represented by a *zero vector* drawn from the s-plane zero to the point $s = j\omega_1$; and the denominator term $\{j\omega_1 + (1/CR)\}$ by a *pole vector* drawn from the pole at $s = -1/CR$ to the same point. The two vectors, labelled Z_1 and P_1 respectively, are shown in part (a) of figure 6.3.

We may visualise the *magnitude* of the filter's frequency response by considering changes in the *lengths* of the vectors as ω_1 varies. Clearly, if $\omega_1 = 0$ the zero vector vanishes but the pole vector is finite. Since the zero vector represents a term in the numerator, the filter's response magnitude must be zero at DC. As ω_1 increases, the point $s = j\omega_1$ moves out along the imaginary axis, and the zero vector grows in length. When $\omega_1 = 1/CR$ it is $1/\sqrt{2}$ times the pole vector length, equivalent to a response magnitude of -3 dB. As ω_1 increases further, the two vectors tend to the same length, and the filter gain approaches unity. The reader may relate these conclusions to the frequency response magnitude characteristic of this circuit previously shown in figure 4.18(b). We therefore see that whenever the zero vector is short, or the pole vector is long, the response magnitude tends to be small—and vice versa.

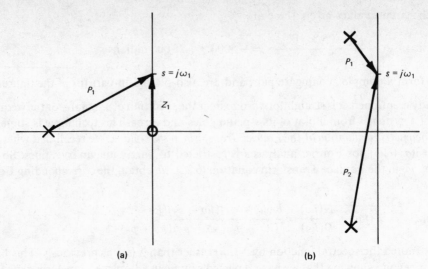

Figure 6.3 Pole and zero vectors in the s-plane.

As far as phase response is concerned, we may find the net phase shift of the circuit by subtracting the phase angle of the pole vector from that of the zero vector. Both angles are measured with respect to the positive real axis.

If the system is a complicated one, there may be many poles and zeros. In this case, the response magnitude at a particular frequency is found by taking the product of the lengths of the various zero vectors, and dividing this by the product of the lengths of the various pole vectors. The net phase term is found as the sum of the phases contributed by the various zero vectors, minus the sum of phases due to the pole vectors. With these rules in mind, it is not hard to see that a pole close to the imaginary axis in the s-plane produces a hump in the frequency response as ω approaches a value equal to the pole's imaginary part (that is, a pole at $s = (\sigma_1 + j\omega_1)$ produces a hump in the region of $\omega = \omega_1$, if σ_1 is sufficiently small). A zero in a similar location gives rise to a trough, or minimum.

The s-plane poles and zeros of a system therefore indicate which sinusoidal frequency ranges are preferentially transmitted or rejected. With a little practice it becomes quite easy to interpret a pole-zero plot in this way. Of course, if the poles and zeros refer to a signal, they indicate which frequencies, or frequency ranges, are most strongly represented. A good example of this is a sine or cosine signal, which has a pair of poles actually on the imaginary axis (see table 6B at the end of the chapter).

The effect of a pole close to the imaginary axis in the s-plane is well illustrated by the tuned circuit considered in worked example E6.2. This has a complex conjugate pole-pair, and its transfer function may be written in the form

$$H(s) = \frac{1}{LC}\frac{1}{s^2 + (s/CR) + (1/LC)} = \frac{1}{LC}\frac{1}{(s + \alpha + j\beta)(s + \alpha - j\beta)} \tag{6.28}$$

As we have shown, $\alpha = 5000$ and $\beta = 25\,000$ radians per second for the particular circuit values chosen. Part (b) of figure 6.3 shows the pole configuration and the two pole vectors P_1 and P_2, for the frequency $\omega = \omega_1$. As ω approaches the value β, it is clear that the length of P_1 must become a minimum. Furthermore, the phase of P_1 changes rapidly as the pole is passed. We therefore expect a resonant peak close to $\omega = \beta$ accompanied by a rapid change of phase. In other words, this is a bandpass system with a well-defined centre frequency. We shall examine the relationships between the Q-factor, damping factor, and s-plane pole locations of second-order systems rather more fully in the next section.

We end this section with a few general remarks about the permissible locations of s-plane poles and zeros. As already mentioned, poles and zeros are always real, or occur in complex conjugate pairs, when the corresponding time function (signal or impulse response) is real. Zeros may in principle be placed anywhere in the s-plane. However, the poles of any stable LTI system, or of any finite signal (that is, one which does not grow without limit), are always confined to the *left-half* of the plane. In other words, they must have negative real parts. This is easily explained by recalling that a pole at $s = \alpha + j\beta$ denotes a complex exponential of the form

$$\exp(st) = \exp(\{\alpha + j\beta\}t) = \exp(\alpha t) \exp(j\beta t) \tag{6.29}$$

Since practical signals, and the impulse responses of stable systems, cannot grow without limit as time progresses, the real part α must be negative. As far as electronic circuits are concerned, it may be shown that the poles of passive RC or RL networks always lie on the negative real axis in the s-plane. The poles of RLC circuits and active filters are often complex, and move closer to the imaginary axis as the damping factor decreases. We shall meet further examples of this effect shortly.

6.3.3 *Continuous LTI systems*

Many aspects of the analysis and design of continuous electronic systems are equally well handled by either the Laplace Transform or the Fourier Transform. There are perhaps two areas where the Laplace Transform is particularly valuable. Firstly, the notion of s-plane poles and zeros is very useful for visualising a system's performance, including its frequency response and stability. In addition, the Laplace Transform offers powerful methods for dealing with systems having initial stored energy. We shall concentrate on these topics in the following pages. Before beginning, however, let us summarise a few key ideas about continuous LTI systems in Laplace notation.

As we have seen, the transfer function $H(s)$ of a system is the Laplace equivalent of the frequency response $H(\omega)$ used in Fourier analysis. Just as $H(\omega)$ and the system's impulse response $h(t)$ form a Fourier Transform pair, so $H(s)$ and $h(t)$ are a Laplace Transform pair. This is easily demonstrated. Equation (6.10) gives

$$Y(s) = X(s)H(s)$$

If the input signal $x(t)$ is a unit impulse $\delta(t)$, table 6B shows that

$$X(s) = 1, \quad \text{and therefore } Y(s) = H(s) \tag{6.30}$$

Since the output signal $y(t)$ is by definition equal to $h(t)$ in this case, its transform $Y(s)$ must equal $H(s)$. In other words, we may write

$$H(s) = \int_0^\infty h(t) \exp(-st)\, dt \tag{6.31}$$

It is interesting to recall that we defined a similar integral for $H(s)$ in equation (6.5), during our discussion of complex exponentials and LTI systems—although we did not at that stage refer to $H(s)$ as a transfer function. In that earlier equation the lower integration limit was taken as $-\infty$. But it makes no difference when we are dealing with causal systems for which $h(t) = 0$ when $t < 0$.

Another important matter is the relationship between the transfer function and differential equation of a continuous LTI system. In general, the differential equation takes the form given by equation (3.43), and quoted again in equation (6.2)

$$\sum_{k=0}^{N} a_k \frac{d^k y(t)}{dt^k} = \sum_{k=0}^{M} b_k \frac{d^k x(t)}{dt^k} \tag{6.32}$$

In section 4.3.1 we saw how to derive the frequency response of a system by taking the Fourier Transform of both sides of such an equation. By taking the Laplace Transform instead, we may obtain the transfer function. This operation requires the time-differentiation property of the Laplace Transform, discussed in section 6.3.1. Differentiation of a signal is equivalent to multiplying its transform by s; forming the second derivative is equivalent to multiplying by s^2, and so on. (There are additional constants involved, which depend on the value of the signal and its derivatives at $t = 0$. However, in forming the transfer function $H(s)$ from equation (6.32) we do not need to include these constants. $H(s)$ is solely a *characteristic of the system*, not of the signals it handles.) Therefore we may write

$$\sum_{k=0}^{N} a_k s^k Y(s) = \sum_{k=0}^{M} b_k s^k X(s) \tag{6.33}$$

or

$$H(s) = \frac{Y(s)}{X(s)} = \frac{\displaystyle\sum_{k=0}^{M} b_k s^k}{\displaystyle\sum_{k=0}^{N} a_k s^k} \tag{6.34}$$

This result, which may be compared with equations (6.21) and (6.22), shows once again that $H(s)$ is a rational function of s. It represents the fundamental method of finding the transfer function of a system. Of course, when possible we prefer to analyse electronic circuits and systems by writing inductive and capacitive impedances as sL and $1/sC$ respectively, and using the normal rules of circuit theory. This convenient shorthand method was employed in worked example E6.2.

We now turn out attention to specific examples of first and second-order systems. The aim is to complement, rather than to repeat, the treatment of such systems in section 4.3.1. We shall see that the Laplace Transform offers some valuable additional insights into their performance.

Little needs to be said on the subject of first-order systems. In worked example E6.2 we saw that a first-order high-pass filter has a zero at the origin of the s-plane, and a pole on the negative real axis at a point determined by the filter's time constant. A first-order low-pass filter has a similar pole, but no zero (see equation (6.13)). It is interesting to relate these locations to the performance of such filters as simple differentiators and integrators. As we saw in section 4.3.1, the high-pass filter acts as an *approximate* differentiator at low frequencies ($\omega \ll 1/CR$). The low-pass version is an *approximate* integrator at high frequencies ($\omega \gg 1/CR$). In terms of Laplace Transforms, a perfect differentiator would have the transfer function $H(s) = s$, and therefore a zero at the origin of the s-plane. A perfect integrator would have the transfer function $H(s) = 1/s$, giving a single pole at the origin. So in this context the high-pass filter has an unwanted pole on the negative real axis. The low-pass filter has its pole placed at $s = -1/CR$ rather than $s = 0$. It is left to the reader to show that these discrepancies have little effect, provided that the input signal frequencies are restricted appropriately.

It is very instructive to consider the s-plane poles of second-order systems. Figure 4.19 showed typical passive and active second-order circuits, and we spent some time analysing their frequency-domain properties. In particular, equation (4.91) expressed the frequency response of a typical system in terms of the undamped natural frequency ω_n and the damping factor ζ

$$H(\omega) = \frac{1}{\left(j\dfrac{\omega}{\omega_n}\right)^2 + 2\zeta\left(j\dfrac{\omega}{\omega_n}\right) + 1} \tag{6.35}$$

Replacing $j\omega$ by s we obtain the corresponding second-order transfer function

$$H(s) = \frac{1}{\dfrac{s^2}{\omega_n^2} + \dfrac{2\zeta}{\omega_n}s + 1} = \frac{\omega_n^2}{s^2 + 2\zeta\omega_n s + \omega_n^2} \tag{6.36}$$

The function has two s-plane poles, but no zeros. The poles are given by the roots of the denominator

$$s = -2\zeta\omega_n \pm \{(2\zeta\omega_n)^2 - 4\omega_n^2\}^{1/2} = \omega_n\{-\zeta \pm (\zeta^2 - 1)^{1/2}\} \tag{6.37}$$

If $\zeta > 1$ we know that the system is overdamped, and equation (6.37) shows that there are two real, distinct poles. When $\zeta = 1$ the system is critically damped, and there are two real, equal poles. If $\zeta < 1$ the system is underdamped, and the poles become a complex conjugate pair. As the damping factor decreases towards zero, the pole locations tend to

$$s = \omega_n\{0 \pm \sqrt{(-1)}\} = \pm j\omega_n \tag{6.38}$$

Therefore a completely undamped system has its pole-pair on the imaginary axis.

These important relationships between the damping factors and s-plane pole locations of second-order continuous systems are illustrated by figure 6.4. Four representative values of ζ have been chosen ($\zeta = 2.0, 1.0, 0.5,$ and 0.25). These values were also used for the frequency response plots of figure 4.19. Note how the poles, which are well separated on the negative real axis when $\zeta = 2.0$, move together and coincide when $\zeta = 1.0$ (critical damping). As the damping factor reduces further, they become a complex conjugate pair and move around a semicircular locus towards the imaginary axis.

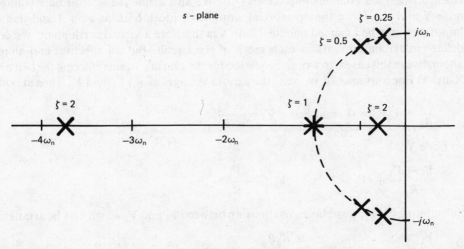

Figure 6.4 s-plane poles of continuous second-order systems as a function of the damping factor ζ.

It is quite straightforward to explain the frequency response characteristics of figure 4.19 in terms of these pole locations and trajectories. We need to consider the variations in length and phase of the two pole vectors with frequency, as described in the previous section. If the system is overdamped or critically damped, the product of the pole vector magnitudes is clearly a minimum when $\omega = 0$. Therefore the system must display its maximum response at DC. However, an underdamped system with poles close to the imaginary axis will show a resonant peak at a frequency which tends to ω_n as ζ tends to zero. Furthermore, there will be a rapid phase change of nearly π radians as the frequency passes through ω_n. These insights into the behaviour of second-order sytsems are very valuable, and time taken to consider them is almost certainly time well spent!

Example E6.3

One type of active filter circuit, based upon a voltage follower, has already been given in section 4.3.1 (see figure 4.19(b)). Another useful circuit is shown in figure E6.3. Find a general expression for its voltage transfer function $H(s)$, assuming the operational amplifier is ideal. In a particular case $R_1 = 10\,\text{k}\Omega$, $R_2 = 1\,\text{k}\Omega$, $R_3 = 100\,\text{k}\Omega$, and $C = 1\,\mu\text{F}$. Find the s-plane poles and zeros of the filter and hence comment on its expected frequency response performance.

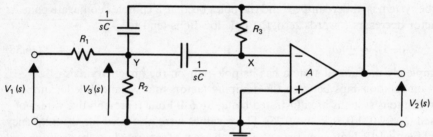

Figure E6.3

Solution

The input and output voltages are considered to be functions of s, and the capacitors are labelled with their complex impedance $1/sC$. We also define the intermediate voltage at node Y as $V_3(s)$. Since the operational amplifier is ideal, both its gain A and its input impedance may be assumed infinite. Node X is therefore a virtual earth point. We could define circulating currents in each mesh of the circuit. But an effective, and simpler, alternative in this case is to write an equation for the sum of currents entering the two nodes X and Y. For convenience, we write the various voltages as V_1, V_2, and V_3. Thus at node X

$$\frac{V_2}{R_3} + V_3 sC = 0 \quad \text{and hence} \quad V_3 = \frac{-V_2}{sCR_3}$$

At node Y

$$\frac{V_1 - V_3}{R_1} + (V_2 - V_3)sC - V_3 sC - \frac{V_3}{R_2} = 0$$

Substituting for V_3, we obtain a relationship between V_1 and V_2 which may be arranged as

$$\frac{V_2}{V_1} = \frac{-sCR_2R_3}{s^2(R_1R_2R_3C^2) + s(2R_1R_2C) + (R_1 + R_2)}$$

Dividing all terms by $(R_1 R_2 R_3 C^2)$ we obtain

$$H(s) = \frac{V_2(s)}{V_1(s)} = \left(\frac{-1}{R_1 C}\right) \frac{s}{s^2 + s\left(\dfrac{2}{R_3 C}\right) + \left(\dfrac{R_1 + R_2}{R_1 R_2 R_3 C^2}\right)}$$

Therefore the filter has two s-plane poles, and a zero at the origin. Comparing the denominator polynomial with equations (6.36) and (6.37) in the main text, we see that

$$\omega_n^2 = \frac{R_1 + R_2}{R_1 R_2 R_3 C^2} \quad \text{and} \quad 2\zeta\omega_n = \frac{2}{R_3 C}$$

For the circuit values given, we obtain

$$\omega_n = 104.9 \text{ radians per second and } \zeta = 0.0953$$

The poles are therefore a complex conjugate pair, located at

$$s = \omega_n\{-\zeta \pm (\zeta^2 - 1)^{1/2}\} = -9.997 \pm j101.4 \text{ radians/s}$$

This represents a bandpass filter, with a Q-factor of

$$Q = \frac{1}{2\zeta} = 5.25$$

and a centre-frequency of about 105 radians per second (about 17 Hz). Its s-plane zero at $s = 0$ gives a true response null at DC.

Although this circuit has one more passive component than the filter shown in figure 4.19(b), it has a s-plane zero at the origin. The resulting rejection of DC signal components may be useful in some applications. It also has the advantage (not explored here) that its peak gain and Q-factor are independently adjustable.

An important feature of the Laplace Transform is its ability to deal with initial stored energy in a system. From a mathematical point of view, the differential equation of such a system has nonzero initial conditions. Physically, this implies that it is still affected by, or responding to, an input signal or excitation applied prior to $t = 0$. Also, in the case of a continuous lumped circuit, it means that there is initial energy stored in capacitors or inductors.

This theme may be developed quite easily by reconsidering the first-order low-pass filter of figure 6.2. We previously derived its transfer function by writing the capacitor's impedance as $1/sC$—see equation (6.13). Let us now return to the differential equation describing the circuit

$$v_2(t) + CR \frac{\mathrm{d}v_2(t)}{\mathrm{d}t} = v_1(t) \tag{6.39}$$

Its solution by Laplace transformation depends upon the form of input signal $v_1(t)$ between $t = 0$ and ∞, and on the initial conditions. For simplicity, let us again take $v_1(t)$ as a unit step. We start by assuming the capacitor to be initially discharged, so that $v_2(t) = 0$ when $t = 0$. Using the differentiation property of the Laplace Transform, equation (6.39) may be transformed to

$$V_2(s) + CR\{sV_2(s) - v_2(0_+)\} = V_1(s) \tag{6.40}$$

giving

$$V_2(s)\{1 + sCR\} = \frac{1}{s} \quad \text{or} \quad V_2(s) = \frac{1/CR}{s\{s + (1/CR)\}} \tag{6.41}$$

The equivalent output signal is

$$v_2(t) = 1 - \exp(-t/CR), \qquad t > 0 \tag{6.42}$$

We may check that $v_2(t)$ satisfies the differential equation by substitution into the left-hand side of expression (6.39)

$$\{1 - \exp(-t/CR)\} + CR \frac{d}{dt}\{1 - \exp(-t/CR)\}$$

$$= 1 - \exp(-t/CR) + \exp(-t/CR) = 1 \tag{6.43}$$

which is indeed the value of $v_1(t)$ for $t > 0$. It also satisfies the initial condition that $v_2(t) = 0$ when $t = 0$.

Let us next assume *nonzero* initial conditions, such as $v_2(0_+) = 3$. In other words, the capacitor is still charged to 3 volts at $t = 0$ because of some previous input signal or excitation. Equation (6.40) becomes

$$V_2(s) + CR\{sV_2(s) - 3\} = V_1(s) = \frac{1}{s} \tag{6.44}$$

Hence

$$V_2(s)\{1 + sCR\} = \frac{1}{s} + 3CR$$

$$\therefore V_2(s) = \frac{(1/s) + 3CR}{1 + sCR} = \frac{1/CR}{s\{s + (1/CR)\}} + \frac{3}{s + (1/CR)} \tag{6.45}$$

The first term on the right-hand side is the same as in equation (6.41). Consulting the table of Laplace Transform pairs (table 6B) at the end of the chapter, we see that

$$v_2(t) = \{1 - \exp(-t/CR)\}u(t) + 3\{\exp(-t/CR)\}u(t) \tag{6.46}$$

or

$$v_2(t) = 1 + 2\exp(-t/CR), \qquad t > 0 \tag{6.47}$$

Once again, it is straightforward to show that the solution satisfies both the differential equation and the stated initial conditions.

Although this is an elementary example, it illustrates several important ideas. Equations (6.42) and (6.47) represent *complete* solutions of the circuit problem for the stated input signal and initial conditions. Therefore the Laplace Transform approach includes the transient and steady-state components of the response, *plus* the effects of any initial energy storage. It does this 'all in one go'. Indeed, it may be hard to disentangle the various components. This calls to mind the discussion of continuous-time convolution and its graphical interpretation in section 3.5. When we convolved a system's impulse response with a 'switched' input signal, we also obtained a complete solution as the impulse response 'moved into' the input signal. This contrasted with our derivation of the homogeneous and particular parts of a solution in section 3.6, where we deliberately split the response of a system into its transient and steady-state components. This gave insight into the character of 'forced' and 'natural' responses.

Actually, in the present example it is also quite easy to separate the various parts of the response—mainly because the circuit and input signal are very simple. Equation (6.42) shows that, with zero initial conditions, $v_2(t) \to 1$ as $t \to \infty$. This is clearly the steady-state response.

The exponential term therefore represents a start-up transient due to the input step at $t = 0$. When the initial condition $v_2(0_+) = 3$ is imposed, equation (6.46) shows that we get an *additional* exponential contribution to the output. This represents a decay towards zero of the initial conditions. Both transient and initial-condition components of the total response are essentially 'natural' rather than 'forced'. They therefore have the same form as the circuit's impulse response—in this case, a decaying real exponential.

We next look rather more carefully at the problem of inverse transformation. We have previously noted that the mathematical integral for the inverse Laplace Transform, equation (6.11), may be difficult to solve *explicitly*. So the common approach is to look up the required time function in a table of transforms. This is called the *implicit* method. If we fail to find the transform pair we need, it is sometimes possible to express the function of s as the sum of two or more simpler functions which *do* appear in the table. (This method was used in equations (6.45) and (6.46).) However, if this ruse fails we must look for another technique. One of the most useful is the algebraic method of partial fractions. This was first introduced in worked example E4.7 in our discussion of a continuous bandpass filter. We now reexamine it from a more general point of view.

Suppose we have a function of s with one s-plane zero and two poles, which does not appear in our table of transforms—for example, the function

$$\frac{K(s + z_1)}{(s + p_1)(s + p_2)} = \frac{Ks + Kz_1}{(s + p_1)(s + p_2)} \tag{6.48}$$

We therefore wish to write the function as the sum of simpler terms which *do* appear. Thus

$$\frac{Ks + Kz_1}{(s + p_1)(s + p_2)} \equiv \frac{A}{(s + p_1)} + \frac{B}{(s + p_2)} \tag{6.49}$$

where A and B are to be determined. The method of partial fractions as described in any fairly advanced textbook of algebra assures us that this can be done, provided the function of s we start with is a *proper rational function* in which the numerator polynomial is of *lesser degree* than the denominator. (This means that the method may be applied to more complicated functions of s than the one we are discussing.) We first multiply both sides of equations (6.49) by the left-hand denominator, giving

$$Ks + Kz_1 \equiv A(s + p_2) + B(s + p_1) \tag{6.50}$$

This is an *identity*, which must hold for all values of s. We may therefore equate equal powers of s. This yields

$$A + B = K \quad \text{and} \quad Ap_2 + Bp_1 = Kz_1 \tag{6.51}$$

from which A and B may be found.

The foregoing discussion outlines the essentials of the method of partial fractions. Various developments are given in more comprehensive texts, but their details are not necessary for our purposes. There is just one special situation deserving mentioned here—that is, when there are two or more *identical* poles. As we have seen, this occurs in a critically damped second-order system. To obtain the correct result in this case, the partial fractions should be specified in the following form

$$\frac{K(s + z_1)}{(s + p_1)^2} = \frac{A}{(s + p_1)} + \frac{B}{(s + p_1)^2} \tag{6.52}$$

We may usefully complete our work on the Laplace Transform by applying such a partial fraction expansion to an example with a practical flavour.

Example E6.4

During our discussion of continuous-time convolution in section 3.5, we tackled a problem on the measurement and recording of oven temperature using a thermocouple (see worked example E3.2). After switching on, the oven's temperature increased at a constant rate of 1°C per second. This produced a ramp output signal from the thermocouple, with a slope of 10 mV per second. A first-order low-pass filter with time constant $CR = 5$ seconds was used to reduce high-frequency noise in the thermocouple signal, and the problem was to find the measurement error introduced by the filter. The solution was found in two ways— by convolution, and by assessing the filter's time-domain response to a ramp input signal. We now wish to solve the same problem in the frequency-domain using the Laplace Transform. (The reader may first find it helpful to refer back to the earlier worked example, to clarify its details.)

Solution

The transfer function of a first-order low-pass filter has already been found (see equation (6.13)) and is given by

$$H(s) = \frac{1/CR}{s + (1/CR)}$$

The thermocouple signal is a voltage ramp of the form $Ar(t)$. Since the Laplace Transform of a unit ramp is $1/s^2$ (see part (a) of worked example E6.1, or table 6B at the end of the chapter), the input signal to the filter has the transform

$$V_1(s) = \frac{A}{s^2}$$

The output signal is therefore given by

$$V_2(s) = V_1(s)H(s) = \frac{A/CR}{s^2\{s + (1/CR)\}}$$

This transform does not appear in table 6B, so we use the method of partial fractions. Note that there are two identical poles at $s = 0$, produced in this case by the input signal rather than the system. Replacing $1/CR$ by K for convenience, we write the identity:

$$\frac{AK}{s^2(s + K)} \equiv \frac{D}{s} + \frac{E}{s^2} + \frac{F}{(s + K)}$$

(We have previously denoted the slope of the ramp by A, so choose symbols D, E, and F for the partial fractions.) Thus

$$AK \equiv Ds(s + K) + E(s + K) + Fs^2$$

for all values of s. Equating coefficients of the different powers of s, we obtain

$$AK = EK \quad \therefore E = A$$

$$DK + E = 0 \therefore D = -E/K = -A/K$$

and

$$D + F = 0 \quad \therefore F = -D = A/K$$

Therefore we may write the output voltage transform as

$$V_2(s) = -\frac{A/K}{s} + \frac{A}{s^2} + \frac{A/K}{(s + K)}$$

$$= -\frac{ARC}{s} + \frac{A}{s^2} + \frac{ARC}{s + (1/RC)}$$

Each of these terms is represented in table 6B (apart from a scaling factor). Hence the output signal from the filter may be written directly as

$$v_2(t) = -ARCu(t) + Ar(t) + ARC \exp(-t/RC)u(t)$$

or

$$v_2(t) = At + ARC \exp(-t/RC) - ARC, \quad \text{for } t > 0$$

This is the result previously obtained in worked example E3.2. The Laplace Transform provides a very compact solution, in spite of the need in this case for a partial fraction expansion. The reader is referred back to the earlier worked example for a discussion of the significance of the various components in $v_2(t)$.

6.4 The z-transform

As we have seen, the Laplace Transform may be thought of as a generalisation of the continuous-time Fourier Transform. In a similar way, the z-transform represents an extension of discrete-time Fourier techniques. Although it is quite possible to use the discrete-time Fourier Series or Transform to describe the frequency-domain properties of discrete signals and systems, the z-transform is tailor-made for the purpose. Its notation is very compact, and proves extremely useful for designing discrete LTI systems such as digital filters and sampled-data control systems. Our development of the z-transform will parallel that of the Laplace Transform in the previous section. In particular, we shall introduce the z-plane pole-zero description of a discrete signal or system, and illustrate its value in analysis and design.

6.4.1 *Definition and properties*

The z-transform of a discrete signal $x[n]$ is defined as

$$X(z) = \sum_{n=0}^{\infty} x[n]z^{-n} \tag{6.53}$$

Since the summation is defined for $0 \leqslant n < \infty$, this is known as the *unilateral* version of the transform. As with the unilateral Laplace Transform, the restriction to positive time is not generally a disadvantage when dealing with practical signals and causal systems. The alternative, *bilateral*, version of the transform is however sometimes required. Bilateral transforms are discussed in section 6.5.

The transform defined by equation (6.53) is rather simple to visualise. $X(z)$ is essentially a *power series* in z^{-1}, with coefficients equal to successive values of the signal $x[n]$. Therefore if we are given a spectral function $X(z)$, we may regenerate the corresponding signal $x[n]$ by expanding $X(z)$ as a power series in z^{-1}. This may not be a very economical way of finding the inverse transform, but it is always possible in principle.

Example E6.5

Find the z-transform of the discrete exponential signal shown in figure E6.5(a), expressing it as compactly as possible. Also, find, and sketch, the signal corresponding to the z-transform

$$X(z) = \frac{0.5}{(z + 1.2)}$$

Solution

For the signal shown in part (a) of the figure, we have

$$X(z) = \sum_{n=0}^{\infty} x[n]z^{-n} = 1 + 0.5z^{-1} + 0.25z^{-2} + 0.125z^{-3} + \ldots$$

$$= 1 + (0.5z^{-1}) + (0.5z^{-1})^2 + (0.5z^{-1})^3 + \ldots$$

$$\therefore X(z) = \frac{1}{(1 - 0.5z^{-1})} = \frac{z}{(z - 0.5)}$$

To find the signal corresponding to the transform

$$X(z) = \frac{0.5}{(z + 1.2)}$$

we may recast $X(z)$ as a power series in z^{-1}. Thus

$$X(z) = \frac{0.5z^{-1}}{(1 + 1.2z^{-1})} = 0.5z^{-1}(1 + 1.2z^{-1})^{-1}$$

$$= 0.5z^{-1}\{1 + (-1.2z^{-1}) + (-1.2z^{-1})^2 + (-1.2z^{-1})^3 + \ldots\}$$

$$= 0.5z^{-1} - 0.6z^{-2} + 0.72z^{-3} - 0.864z^{-4} + \ldots$$

Successive values of $x[n]$, starting at $n = 0$, are therefore

$$0, 0.5, -0.6, 0.72, -0.864, \ldots$$

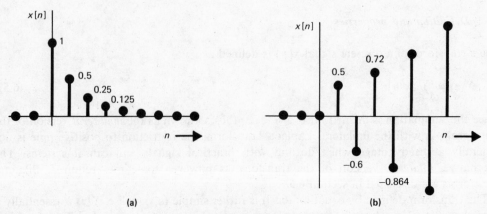

(a)   (b)

Figure E6.5

The signal is sketched in part (b) of the figure. Since it grows without limit as n increases, this particular function could not be observed in practice, nor could it represent the impulse response of a stable system. Note that both signals shown in the figure have exponential envelopes and possess, in theory, an infinite number of terms. Yet their z-transforms are extremely compact.

We saw earlier that the Laplace Transform is very similar to the continuous-time Fourier Transform if the complex frequency variable s is substituted for $j\omega$. Similarly, if we substitute $\exp(j\Omega)$ for z in equation (6.53), we obtain

$$X(j\Omega) = \sum_{n=0}^{\infty} x[n] \exp(-j\Omega n) \tag{6.54}$$

Apart from a change in the lower limit of summation, this is identical to the discrete-time Fourier Transform defined by equation (5.20). Therefore z may also be considered as a complex frequency variable.

An alternative, and probably easier, way of thinking of z is as a *time-shift operator*. Multiplication by z is equivalent to shifting a signal forward in time by one sampling interval. Multiplication by z^{-1} (or division by z) is equivalent to delaying it by the same amount. For example, a discrete unit impulse $\delta[n]$ has a z-transform equal to unity. The same signal delayed by n_0 sampling intervals, $\delta[n - n_0]$, has the transform z^{-n_0}. Notice how the transform converts a shift in the time-domain into a simple *algebraic manipulation* in the frequency-domain.

It is also helpful for our discussion of z-plane poles and zeros in the next section to note that delay by one sampling interval (T) is equivalent, in Laplace notation, to multiplying by $\exp(-sT)$—see table 6A. For this reason we may also consider that

$$z^{-1} \equiv \exp(-sT), \quad \text{or } z \equiv \exp(sT) \tag{6.55}$$

The reader may be surprised that the representation of time-shift by a simple algebraic manipulation should give rise to all the features of a frequency-domain transform. In fact, many properties of such transforms may be simply and elegantly illustrated using the z-transform. Consider for example the *convolution* property, which is common to the continuous and discrete Fourier Transforms, the Laplace Transform, and the z-transform. This states that time-domain convolution is equivalent to frequency-domain multiplication. Let us take two arbitrary, finite-length, discrete signals $x_1[n]$ and $x_2[n]$ with the following sample values

$n = 0$	1	2	3	4	5	6	7	8 ...	
$x_1[n] = 1$	3	1	2	-1	0	0	0	0 ...	(6.56)
$x_2[n] = 1$	-1	2	0	0	0	0	0	0 ...	

We may convolve them by shifting a reversed version of one signal beneath the other, and summing all finite products. This process was explained in section 3.4. The resulting sequence $y[n]$ is easily shown to be

$$y[n] = 1 \quad 2 \quad 0 \quad 7 \quad -1 \quad 5 \quad -2 \quad 0 \quad 0 \quad \ldots \tag{6.57}$$

The z-transforms of $x_1[n]$ and $x_2[n]$ may be written by inspection as

$$X_1(z) = 1 + 3z^{-1} + z^{-2} + 2z^{-3} - z^{-4}$$

and

$$X_2(z) = 1 - z^{-1} + 2z^{-2} \tag{6.58}$$

Their product $Y(z)$ is readily shown to be the power series

$$Y(z) = X_1(z)X_2(z) = 1 + 2z^{-1} + 7z^{-3} - z^{-4} + 5z^{-5} - 2z^{-6} \tag{6.59}$$

The coefficients of this series are indeed the values of $y[n]$ found by time-domain convolution.

In our discussion of the convergence of the unilateral Laplace Transform in section 6.3.1, we mentioned the idea of a *region of convergence*. This also applies in the case of the unilateral z-transform. In general, the z-transform of a signal as defined by equation (6.53) exists only for a suitable range of values of the complex variable z. This range may be indicated by an area of the complex plane, now referred to as the *z-plane*. Fortunately the convergence criteria for the unilateral z-transform do not generally give difficulties when dealing with practical signals and stable systems. This matter is discussed fully in most advanced texts on transform theory.

So far we have considered the z-transforms of signals. However, they apply equally to systems. If the input and output signals of a discrete LTI system have the transforms $X(z)$ and $Y(z)$ respectively, then

$$Y(z) = X(z)H(z) \quad \text{or} \quad H(z) = \frac{Y(z)}{X(z)} \tag{6.60}$$

where $H(z)$ is the transfer function of the system, and equals the z-transform of its impulse response $h[n]$. Thus

$$H(z) = \sum_{n=0}^{\infty} h[n]z^{-n} \tag{6.61}$$

We shall meet examples of these important basic relationships in the following pages.

The question of inverse transformation should now be considered more fully. Formally, the inverse z-transform of a function $X(z)$ is given by

$$x[n] = \frac{1}{2\pi j} \oint X(z)z^{n-1} \, dz \tag{6.62}$$

where the circular symbol on the integral sign denotes a closed circular contour in the complex z-plane. Such *contour integration* is a difficult process, and is outside the scope of this book. In any event, several practical alternative methods are available. Firstly, we may be able to find the function we need in a table of z-transform pairs—such as table 6C at the end of this chapter. If unsuccessful, it may well be possible to decompose the z-transform into the sum of two or more simpler functions which *do* appear in the table. The method of partial fractions is often useful here. A third approach, which we have already met in this section, is to express the z-transform as a power series in z^{-1}. The coefficients of the series are then equal to successive values of $x[n]$.

Example E6.6

Use the method of partial fractions, and the table of z-transforms at the end of this chapter (table 6C) to find the signal corresponding to the z-transform

$$X(z) = \frac{z+1}{z(z-1)^2}$$

Solution

We first note that the denominator of $X(z)$ contains a squared factor. As we shall see in the next section, this means that there are two identical z-plane poles. In line with the procedure for dealing with identical s-plane poles outlined in section 6.3.3, we write the partial fractions as

$$\frac{z + 1}{z(z - 1)^2} \equiv \frac{A}{z} + \frac{B}{(z - 1)} + \frac{C}{(z - 1)^2}$$

$$= \frac{A(z - 1)^2 + Bz(z - 1) + Cz}{z(z - 1)^2}$$

$$= \frac{z^2(A + B) + z(-2A - B + C) + A}{z(z - 1)^2}$$

Equating numerator coefficients of the various powers of z, we obtain

$$A + B = 0; \qquad -2A - B + C = 1; \qquad A = 1$$

Hence

$$A = 1; \qquad B = -1; \qquad C = 1 + B + 2A = 2$$

So that

$$X(z) = \frac{1}{z} - \frac{1}{(z - 1)} + \frac{2}{(z - 1)^2}$$

Referring to table 6C, we see that these partial fractions are not listed as they stand. However the following functions do appear

$$\frac{z}{(z - 1)} \quad \text{and} \quad \frac{z}{(z - 1)^2}$$

Recalling that multiplication by z^{-1} is equivalent to a simple time-shift (delay by one sampling interval), we may write

$$X(z) = z^{-1} \left\{ 1 - \frac{z}{(z - 1)} + \frac{2z}{(z - 1)^2} \right\}$$

The three terms in brackets produce the inverse transform

$$\delta[n] - u[n] + 2r[n]$$

so the required function $x[n]$ is given by

$$x[n] = \delta[n - 1] - u[n - 1] + 2r[n - 1]$$

By superposing these three components, we find that successive values of $x[n]$ (starting at $n = 0$) are

$$0, 0, 1, 3, 5, 7, 9, 11, 13 \ldots$$

The reader may wish to check this result by expressing $X(z)$ as a power series. This may readily be done by a standard long-division of the numerator by the denominator.

The z-transform, like the Fourier and Laplace Transforms, has a number of useful properties. Some of the important ones are given in table 6A. A comparison with the properties of the Laplace Transform listed in the same table, or with those of the discrete-time Fourier Transform in table 5B, reveals obvious parallels and similarities. In addition, we have already demonstrated the convolution property of the z-transform in this section, and have described the role of z as a time-shift operator. For all these reasons, the properties of *linearity*, *time-shifting*, and *convolution* should appear quite straightforward. As far as *time-differentiation* and *time-integration* are concerned, the reader may check the equivalence of these properties with those of the discrete-time Fourier Transform, if z is substituted for $\exp(j\Omega)$. The only noteworthy difference is that time-integration in the case of the Fourier Transform produces additional frequency-domain terms related to the mean value of the signal. This is a rather detailed and complicated point, which need not concern us here.

Now that we have obtained some familiarity with z-transform notation and properties, it is time to introduce the idea of z-plane poles and zeros, and to illustrate the application of z-transform techniques to some practical problems.

6.4.2 *z-plane poles and zeros*

The z-transform of a real discrete signal or an LTI system is always a rational function of z and may be expressed in the form

$$X(z) = \frac{N(z)}{D(z)} = \frac{K(z - z_1)(z - z_2)(z - z_3)\ldots}{(z - p_1)(z - p_2)(z - p_3)\ldots} \tag{6.63}$$

where the constant K is a gain factor. As with the Laplace Transform (see equation (6.22)) the numerator polynomial $N(z)$ has been factorised to indicate the zeros of the function $(z_1, z_2, z_3 \ldots)$, and the denominator polynomial $D(z)$ has been factorised to indicate the poles $(p_1, p_2, p_3 \ldots)$. $N(z)$ and $D(z)$, expressed as power series, always have real coefficients. This means that the poles and zeros of $X(z)$ must be either real, or occur in complex conjugate pairs. They may be plotted on a complex-plane diagram, referred to as the z-*plane*. Such a plot gives a useful visual representation of a z-transform, from which we may infer the corresponding spectrum or frequency response.

To understand the relationships between s-plane and z-plane poles and zeros, it is helpful to consider equivalent locations in the two planes. This may be done by *mapping* the s-plane into the z-plane. In the previous section we outlined the role of z as a time-shift operator, and showed in equation (6.55) that it is equivalent in Laplace terms to $\exp(sT)$, where T is the sampling interval of the signal or system. Given this equivalence, we may select various typical points in the complex s-plane, and map them into corresponding points in the z-plane. For example, suppose that s is purely imaginary, represented by a point on the imaginary axis in the s-plane. Then

$$s = j\omega \quad \text{and} \quad z = \exp(j\omega T) = \cos \omega T + j \sin \omega T \tag{6.64}$$

Therefore as ω varies, the locus of z traces out a circle of unit radius in the z-plane, starting on the real axis when $\omega = 0$ and repeating its trajectory at intervals of $\omega = 2\pi/T$. This is known as the *unit circle*. Next, suppose that s is real, giving

$$s = \sigma \quad \text{and} \quad z = \exp(\sigma T) \tag{6.65}$$

If σ is positive, z has a real positive value greater than unity; if σ is negative, z is still real and positive, but with a value less than unity. Finally, allowing s to be complex, we have

$$s = \sigma + j\omega \quad \text{and} \quad z = \exp(\sigma T) \exp(j\omega T) \tag{6.66}$$

This value of z may be represented by a z-plane vector of length σT, making an angle ωT radians

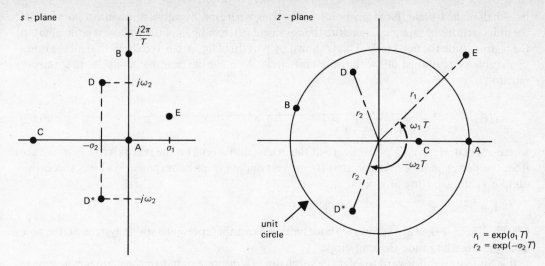

Figure 6.5 Mapping various s-plane points into the z-plane.

with the positive real axis. Note also that a complex conjugate pair of points in the s-plane maps into another complex conjugate pair in the z-plane. Several typical s-plane locations, and their z-plane equivalents, are shown in figure 6.5.

Actually, figure 6.5 does not tell quite the whole story. For whereas any point in the s-plane maps into a *unique* location in the z-plane, the converse is not true. We may show this by considering a set of s-plane points separated by $2\pi/T$ in the direction of the imaginary axis

$$s = \sigma_1 + j(\omega_1 + 2\pi k/T), \qquad k = \ldots -2, -1, 0, 1, 2 \ldots \tag{6.67}$$

These map into the z-plane as follows

$$z = \exp(\{\sigma_1 + j\omega_1 + 2\pi k/T\}T) = \exp(\sigma_1 T)\exp(j\omega_1 T)\exp(j2\pi k) \tag{6.68}$$

However, $\exp(j2\pi k) = 1$ for all integer values of k. So the *complete* set of s-plane points maps into a *single* point in the z-plane. Conversely, a single z-plane point represents an infinitely repeating set of points in the s-plane. This is illustrated by part (a) of figure 6.6.

Another important matter concerns system stability. We have shown in section 6.3.2 that the poles of a stable, continuous LTI system always have negative real parts. They lie in the left-

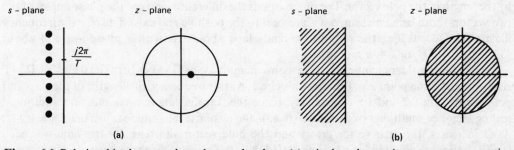

Figure 6.6 Relationships between the s-plane and z-plane: (a) a single z-plane point represents a repeating set of points in the s-plane; (b) the complete left-half s-plane maps into the area inside the unit circle in the z-plane.

hand half of the s-plane. Now any point $s = \sigma + j\omega$, where σ is negative, maps into a point *inside* the unit circle in the z-plane. Therefore the complete left-hand half of the s-plane is equivalent to the region inside the unit circle. This is shown by part (b) of figure 6.6. It follows that all the poles of a stable system must fall within the unit circle. As a simple example, consider the transfer function

$$H(z) = \frac{z}{(z - \alpha)} = \frac{1}{(1 - \alpha z^{-1})} = 1 + \alpha z^{-1} + \alpha^2 z^{-2} + \alpha^3 z^{-3} + \alpha^4 z^{-4} + \ldots \qquad (6.69)$$

where α is real. $H(z)$ has a z-plane zero at the origin, and a pole on the real axis at $z = \alpha$. We see from the power series expansion that the corresponding impulse response $h[n]$ has successive sample values (starting at $n = 0$)

$$1, \alpha, \alpha^2, \alpha^3, \alpha^4, \ldots$$

Clearly, if $|\alpha| > 1$ then $h[n]$ grows without limit and cannot represent a stable system. So the pole at $z = \alpha$ must lie inside the unit circle.

It is quite straightforward to infer the spectrum of a discrete signal, or the frequency response of a system, from a knowledge of its z-plane poles and zeros. The method is to construct *pole vectors* and *zero vectors* in the z-plane, in a way analogous to that described for the s-plane in section 6.3.2. However, the imaginary axis in the s-plane is equivalent to the unit circle in the z-plane. The vectors must therefore be drawn from the various poles and zeros to a point on the unit circle representing the sinusoidal frequency of interest. The technique is sometimes referred to as the geometric evaluation of the discrete-time Fourier Transform in the z-plane.

Suppose, for example, we have a system with the transfer function

$$H(z) = \frac{(z - 0.8)}{(z + 0.8)} = \frac{(z - z_1)}{(z - p_1)} \qquad (6.70)$$

Substituting $\exp(j\Omega)$ for z we obtain a discrete-time Fourier Transform which defines the frequency response of the system

$$H(j\Omega) = \frac{\{\exp(j\Omega) - 0.8\}}{\{\exp(j\Omega) + 0.8\}} \qquad (6.71)$$

At a particular sinusoidal frequency (say $\Omega = \Omega_1$) the numerator of $H(j\Omega)$ is represented by a vector Z_1 drawn from the zero at $z = 0.8$ to the relevant point on the unit circle, and the denominator by a vector P_1 drawn from the pole at $z = -0.8$ to the same point. These are shown in figure 6.7(a). The magnitude of the response equals the length of the zero vector divided by the length of the pole vector. The phase equals the difference between the phase angles of the two vectors (both being measured with respect to the positive real axis). Thus for the frequency illustrated ($\Omega_1 \approx 0.36\pi$), the response magnitude is about 0.6, with a phase angle of about $112° - 35° = 77°$, or 0.43π radians.

Let us now consider changes in the response magnitude as Ω varies between 0 and 2π. $\Omega = 0$ corresponds to the point $z = 1$ on the unit circle. At this frequency, the lengths of the zero and pole vectors are 0.2 and 1.8 respectively. Since the transfer function contains no additional scaling factor or multiplier (see equation (6.63)), the response magnitude is just $0.2/1.8 = 0.111$. As Ω increases, the zero vector grows and the pole vector shortens. By the time we reach $\Omega = \pi/2$, they are equal in length, giving $|H(j\Omega)| = 1$. The peak response must clearly occur at $\Omega = \pi$, where the pole vector has minimum length, and the zero vector maximum length. Here $|H(j\omega)| = 1.8/0.2 = 9.0$. As Ω increases further, we continue to move anticlockwise around the

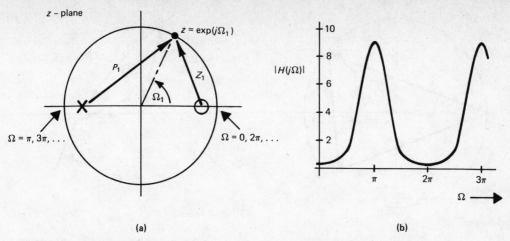

Figure 6.7 The geometric evaluation of a discrete-time Fourier Transform in the z-plane.

unit circle, reaching our starting point when $\Omega = 2\pi$. The whole cycle then repeats. Therefore we generate a *periodic* frequency response which repeats at intervals in Ω of 2π. $|H(j\Omega)|$ is shown plotted to linear scales in part (b) of the figure. Since a system's performance over the range $0 < \Omega < \pi$ defines its effect on any adequately sampled signal (see section 5.4), this is a high-pass system.

The procedure just described underlines once again the economy of the z-transform for describing a discrete signal or system. A single pole (or zero) in the z-plane is equivalent to a whole series of poles (or zeros) in the s-plane. The inherently periodic nature of discrete-time spectra and frequency responses is therefore automatically catered for by the z-plane representation.

Example E6.7

In previous worked example E4.8, we discussed the design of a continuous, second-order, bandpass filter for reducing mains supply interference from an electroencephalogram (EEG) signal. The filter was required to transmit signal components between 10 Hz and 14 Hz, and to provide relative discrimination of about 50:1 (34 dB) between its centre-frequency of 12 Hz and the mains frequency of 50 Hz.

It is now required to transfer such filtering to a microcomputer. The EEG signal will be sampled at 100 Hz. Investigate the possibility of achieving the above performance with a discrete system based upon a complex-conjugate pair of z-plane poles. Compare its performance at the passband edges (10 Hz and 14 Hz) with that of the continuous filter, and, if appropriate, suggest improvements to the design. Specify the time-domain recurrence formula of the filter, and sketch its impulse response.

Solution

There are many techniques for designing digital filters and discrete systems and, as with most design problems, there is no 'correct' solution. Here we aim to produce a filter with approximately the same frequency response performance as the continuous filter described in worked example E4.8. Since the filter is to be based initially on a pair of complex z-plane poles, and the frequency response is not tightly specified, we may develop the design using a geometric evaluation in the z-plane.

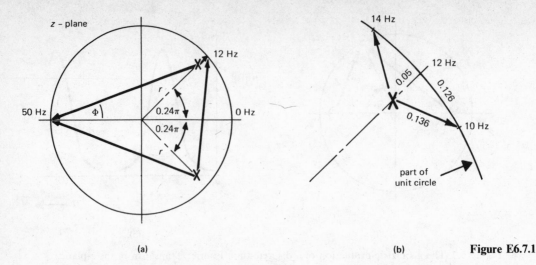

(a)   (b)   **Figure E6.7.1**

With a sampling frequency of 100 Hz, signal components up to 50 Hz will be adequately represented according to the Sampling Theorem. 50 Hz corresponds to $\Omega = \pi$. The required centre-frequency of 12 Hz corresponds to $\Omega = 12\pi/50 = 0.24\pi$. The pair of complex-conjugate poles must therefore be placed close to the unit circle in the z-plane as shown in part (a) of figure E6.7.1. If their radius r is close to unity, a well-defined resonant peak will occur in the region of 12 Hz. Pole vectors are drawn for the two sinusoidal frequencies 12 Hz and 50 Hz.

Given that r is close to unity, and noting that the angle ϕ is close to 0.12π, we may approximate the pole vector lengths as follows

(a) at 12 Hz

Shorter pole-vector length $= (1 - r)$
Longer pole-vector length $\approx 2\sin(0.24\pi)$

(b) at 50 Hz

Length of both pole vectors $\approx d\,\mathrm{cosec}(0.12\pi)$
where d is the perpendicular distance from each pole to the real axis. Hence $d \approx \sin(0.24\pi)$.

The magnitude of the filter's response at 12 Hz is therefore approximately $\{2(1 - r)\sin(0.24\pi)\}^{-1}$, and at 50 Hz it is approximately $\{\sin(0.24\pi)\,\mathrm{cosec}(0.12\pi)\}^{-2}$. The *relative* discrimination against the 50 Hz interference is

$$\frac{\{\sin(0.24\pi)\,\mathrm{cosec}(0.12\pi)\}^2}{2(1 - r)\sin(0.24\pi)} = \frac{2.53}{(1 - r)}$$

This is required to equal about 50, so that

$$(1 - r) = 0.0506, \quad \text{or } r = 0.9494 \approx 0.95$$

Let us now consider the filter's gain at the passband edges of 10 Hz and 14 Hz. The shorter pole vector is drawn for these two frequencies in part (b) of the figure, to an expanded scale. A complete trajectory around the unit circle, equal to an arc length of 2π, corresponds to a frequency interval of 100 Hz. Hence the arc length equivalent to an interval of 2 Hz is $4\pi/100 = 0.126$. Over this short arc the unit circle is approximately a straight-line, so the pole vector length for frequencies of 10 Hz and 14 Hz is about $(0.05^2 + 0.126^2)^{1/2} = 0.136$. This is marked on the figure. As we go from the centre-frequency of 12 Hz to the passband edges, this pole vector increases in length from 0.05 to 0.136, giving a reduction in response magnitude to $0.05/0.136 = 37$ per cent of its peak value at 12 Hz. (This assumes that variations in length of the other, longer, pole vector over this frequency range are negligible.) This is unlikely to be an acceptable performance, and compares unfavourably with the 62 per cent figure for the continuous filter described in the earlier worked example.

The difficulty is, of course, that we have initially chosen the pole radius r to meet the criterion for rejection of the 50 Hz interference. Also, we now find that the passband performance is poor (note that we cannot improve matters by changing the value of r: an *increased* passband width implies a *smaller* value of r, giving *worse* discrimination at 50 Hz). However, an attractive solution is available. We may place a z-plane zero at $z = -1$, corresponding to the frequency 50 Hz. This will give complete steady-state rejection of the 50 Hz interference. The pole radius may now be altered to give a satisfactory passband performance. For example, let us specify a 3 dB reduction in the response magnitude at the passband edges of 10 Hz and 14 Hz. This is a commonly used criterion. At 12 Hz, the length of the smaller pole vector must be 0.126, rather than 0.05 as shown in the figure. This will make its length greater by a factor of $\sqrt{2}$ (3 dB) at 10 Hz and 14 Hz. Hence $r = (1 - 0.126) = 0.874$. (We are once again ignoring changes in the length of the second pole vector, and of the new zero vector, over this comparatively small frequency range.)

When specifying complex-conjugate z-plane poles (or zeros) it is very convenient to use polar coordinates. The required filter's transfer function may be written as

$$H(z) = \frac{(z + 1)}{\{z - r \exp(j\theta)\}\{z - r \exp(-j\theta)\}}$$

$$= \frac{(z + 1)}{(z^2 - 2rz \cos\theta + r^2)} = \frac{Y(z)}{X(z)}$$

where, as already discussed, $\theta = 0.24\pi$ and $r = 0.874$.

$$\therefore \frac{Y(z)}{X(z)} = \frac{(z + 1)}{(z^2 - 1.274z + 0.764)}$$

or

$$Y(z)(z^2 - 1.274z + 0.764) = X(z)(z + 1)$$

This is a frequency-domain description of the filter. To recast it into a time-domain *recurrence formula*, we recall that multiplication by z is equivalent to a time-advance by one sampling period. Multiplication by z^2 is equivalent to time-advance by two sampling intervals. Hence we may write the following relation between input and output signals by inspection

$$y[n + 2] - 1.274y[n + 1] + 0.764y[n] = x[n + 1] + x[n]$$

Since this is a recurrence formula which applies for all values of n, we may subtract 2 from all the terms within square brackets. This gives the required relationship between the present and *previous* values of input and output

$$y[n] - 1.274y[n-1] + 0.764y[n-2] = x[n-1] + x[n-2]$$

or

$$y[n] = 1.274y[n-1] - 0.764y[n-2] + x[n-1] + x[n-2]$$

Note that the present output value $y[n]$ depends on previous inputs $x[n-1]$ and $x[n-2]$. This implies an unnecessary delay of one sampling interval in the output sequence, and may be corrected by writing

$$y[n] = 1.274y[n-1] - 0.764y[n-2] + x[n] + x[n-1]$$

In terms of the filter's transfer function, we have added a z-plane zero at the origin. This does not affect the filter's characteristics, other than eliminating the unnecessary delay in the output. We have now specified the required recurrence formula.

The above design procedure involves a number of approximations and simplifications— particularly concerning the geometric evaluation of the filter's frequency response in the z-plane. In deriving the recurrence formula from the transfer function $H(z)$, we have also introduced some new ideas and techniques which the reader may find a little hard to follow. These will be discussed more carefully in the next section. The main purpose of this example has been to show the possibilities—and limitations—for the design of simple discrete-time filters using pole vectors and zero vectors in the z-plane. It must be emphasised that the rather 'hit-and-miss' approach adopted here would hardly be adequate for most filter design problems!

Finally, we may use the filter's recurrence formula to find its impulse response. If the input signal is a unit impulse $\delta[n]$, the output must be the impulse response $h[n]$. Therefore

$$h[n] = 1.274h[n-1] - 0.764h[n-2] + \delta[n] + \delta[n-1]$$

This formula may be used to evaluate the $h[n]$ term-by-term, using a calculator or simple computer program. It is shown in part (a) of figure E6.7.2. For the sake of completeness, and to check that our design assumptions and calculations are reasonably accurate, this impulse response has been accurately transformed back into the frequency-domain using a 128-point FFT (as described in sections 5.3.3 and 5.4). The magnitudes of the first 64 spectral coefficients are shown in part (b) of the figure. These are samples of the underlying

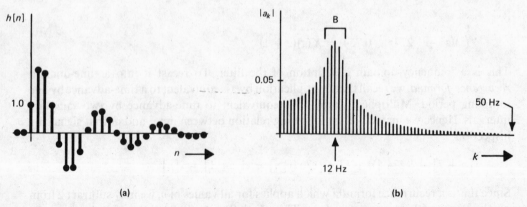

(a)   (b)

Figure E6.7.2

function $|H(j\Omega)|$. To aid interpretation, the 12 Hz and 50 Hz points are indicated, and also the passband (B) between 10 and 14 Hz.

6.4.3 *Discrete LTI systems*

The z-transform offers a compact and convenient notation for the analysis and design of discrete LTI systems in the frequency-domain. Most of the necessary groundwork has already been laid in earlier chapters and sections of this book. For example, we have already noted that the transfer function $H(z)$ and impulse response $h[n]$ of a discrete LTI system are a z-transform pair (equation (6.61)). We have seen that the poles of $H(z)$ must lie within the unit circle in the z-plane, if the system is to be stable. Furthermore, in our discussion of the geometrical evaluation of the discrete-time Fourier Transform in the previous section, we have visualised the frequency responses of two discrete systems from a knowledge of their z-plane poles and zeros. Going back a little further in our story, the work on difference equations in section 3.6, and on the description of systems by the discrete-time Fourier Transform in section 5.4, is directly relevant to the present discussion. So we begin this section with a brief review of some of this earlier material, consolidating and developing it in relation to the z-transform.

In section 3.6 we showed that a discrete LTI system obeys a difference equation of the general form

$$\sum_{k=0}^{N} a_k y[n-k] = \sum_{k=0}^{M} b_k x[n-k] \tag{6.72}$$

This is the fundamental relationship describing the operation of the system in the time-domain. By transforming both sides of the equation, we may derive an equivalent frequency-domain description. For example, in section 5.4 we used the discrete-time Fourier Transform to define the frequency response $H(\Omega)$—see equation (5.39). Substituting z for $\exp(j\Omega)$, or using the time-shifting property of the z-transform, we may readily find the system's transfer function $H(z)$.

The opposite process, of deriving the difference equation from the transfer function, is also quite straightforward. Let us illustrate this with a second-order transfer function which will be useful to us later in this section

$$H(z) = \frac{Y(z)}{X(z)} = \frac{z^2}{\{z - r\exp(j\theta)\}\{z - r\exp(-j\theta)\}} = \frac{z^2}{z^2 - 2rz\cos\theta + r^2} \tag{6.73}$$

The function has two identical zeros (generally referred to as a *second-order* zero) at the origin of the z-plane, and a complex-conjugate pole pair. As in worked example E6.7, the poles are specified by their radius r in the z-plane, and by their angle with respect to the positive real axis. We may write

$$(z^2 - 2rz\cos\theta + r^2)Y(z) = z^2 X(z)$$

or

$$z^2 Y(z) - 2r\cos\theta\, zY(z) + r^2 Y(z) = z^2 X(z) \tag{6.74}$$

To derive the difference equation we must effectively carry out an inverse z-transformation. This is quite easy if we recall that z may be thought of as a time-shift operator. Thus if the inverse transform of $Y(z)$ is written as $y[n]$, $zY(z)$ becomes $y[n+1]$, $z^2 Y(z)$ becomes $y[n+2]$, and so on. In this case we obtain the difference equation

$$y[n+2] - 2r\cos\theta\, y[n+1] + r^2 y[n] = x[n+2]$$

or

$$y[n + 2] = 2r \cos \theta \, y[n + 1] - r^2 y[n] + x[n + 2] \qquad (6.75)$$

Since we normally prefer to work in terms of present and *previous* values of input and output signals, it is helpful to subtract 2 from each term in square brackets, giving

$$y[n] = 2r \cos \theta \, y[n - 1] - r^2 y[n - 2] + x[n] \qquad (6.76)$$

(This is permissible because the equation is a *recurrence formula* which applies to *all* values of *n*.)

During the discussion of difference equations in section 3.6, it was mentioned that an equation is known as *recursive* if the present output signal value $y[n]$ depends on one or more previous outputs. This implies feedback, and we now see that it is a consequence of using one or more z-plane poles. A *nonrecursive* system, on the other hand, has a transfer function specified entirely in terms of z-plane zeros. When we use a time-domain recurrence formula to find the output signal from a system, we are effectively convolving the input signal with the system's impulse response. This is fairly obvious with a nonrecursive system, since the multiplier coefficients equal the various terms of the impulse response. The convolution is then *explicit*. But when—as in the present example—the system is recursive, the convolution is *implicit* and not nearly so apparent.

If the input signal to a system is the unit impulse $\delta[n]$, then the output is by definition the impulse response $h[n]$. This gives us a useful way of evaluating $h[n]$ term-by-term from the difference equation (a technique we have already used several times in this book). In the present case, equation (6.76) becomes

$$h[n] = 2r \cos \theta \, h[n - 1] - r^2 h[n - 2] + \delta[n] \qquad (6.77)$$

Since $\delta[n]$ is nonzero only when $n = 0$, it only contributes directly to h[0]. Thereafter the system is 'on its own' and the impulse response is self-generating. By using the system's difference equation in this way, we are effectively completing the inverse z-transformation from $H(z)$ to $h[n]$. The technique may therefore be viewed as an additional way of obtaining an inverse transform. One other point deserves mention here. In most cases, $h[n]$ is found to continue for many sampling intervals (see, for example, figure E6.7.2). This means that a nonrecursive version of the same system, although theoretically feasible, would require many multiplications on input signal values only. This would generally make it much less economic than the recursive version.

When the numerator and denominator polynomials of a transfer function are of equal order, the function has an equal number of poles and zeros. Its impulse response $h[n]$ begins at $n = 0$. If there are more poles than zeros, $h[n]$ begins after $n = 0$. This implies an unnecessary delay in the output from the system. On the other hand, if there are more zeros than poles, $h[n]$ begins before $n = 0$ and the system is noncausal. It is therefore usual to specify an equal number of poles and zeros. This may always be achieved by placing an appropriate number of poles, or zeros, at the origin of the z-plane. Since these introduce a pure time-shift in the output signal, they affect only the phase response of the system—not its magnitude response. We have already met this technique in worked example 6.7, where a single zero was placed at the origin. The present transfer function (equation (6.73)) includes two zeros at the origin, which 'balance' the two poles. And equation (6.77) confirms that $h[n]$ begins at $n = 0$.

It is now time to consider some particular first and second-order systems. Probably the most helpful approach is to look back at various examples already used in this book, and comment on them in relation to the z-transform. This will allow us to see them from a rather different viewpoint.

First-order systems have a single z-plane pole on the real axis, and offer simple low-pass or high-pass properties. Their impulse responses follow real exponential envelopes. We have already met a number of such systems in this book. Worked example E3.1 considered the time-domain performance of a low-pass system with its pole at $z = 0.8$. Another system, with a pole at $z = 0.5$, was used as a digital filter for smoothing an oven temperature signal in worked example E3.3. However, at this state we were not in a position to discuss frequency-domain properties in any detail. In section 5.4 we looked at the frequency responses of first-order discrete systems with some care, illustrating typical examples in figure 5.12. These systems had their z-plane pole at $z = 0.9$ and 0.6 (low-pass), and at $z = -0.9$ and -0.6 (high-pass). The closer the pole to the unit circle, the more prolonged is the impulse response, and the more selective the frequency response. The action of a high-pass filter of this type was illustrated by figure 5.13. Finally, we examined two first-order z-transforms in worked example E6.5 in this chapter; a low-pass function with its pole at $z = 0.5$, and a high-pass one with its pole at $z = -1.2$. Although we considered the corresponding time functions to be *signals*, they could just as well represent the impulse responses of *systems*. The second of these systems would of course be unstable, with its pole lying outside the unit circle.

We have previously noted that first-order RC circuits are commonly used as approximate differentiators and integrators. And in section 6.3.3 we compared their s-plane poles and zeros with those of ideal differentiators and integrators. Corresponding ideas apply to discrete systems and the z-plane. Differentiation of a signal $x[n]$ is normally taken to mean forming its *first-order difference* $x[n] - x[n - 1]$. A system to achieve this has the transfer function

$$H(z) = 1 - z^{-1} = \frac{(z - 1)}{z} \tag{6.78}$$

It therefore has a zero at $z = 1$ and a pole at the origin. Conversely, discrete-time integration involves forming the *running sum* of an input signal. This is achieved in the time-domain with the recurrence formula

$$y[n] = y[n - 1] + x[n] \tag{6.79}$$

In other words, each new output value equals the previous value, updated by the new input value $x[n]$. The required transfer function is

$$H(z) = \frac{1}{(1 - z^{-1})} = \frac{z}{(z - 1)} \tag{6.80}$$

This has a pole at $z = 1$ and a zero at the origin. Such a system is widely referred to as an *accumulator*. (Note that since its pole is actually *on* the unit circle, it is not strictly stable. Its response to a unit impulse is a unit step, which continues forever. However, since the impulse response does not *grow* we normally regard an integrator as *marginally stable*.) The discrete-time integrator, as defined by equation (6.80), is clearly the inverse of the differentiator defined by equation (6.78).

The earliest example of a second-order discrete system met in this book occurred in section 3.6. The following recurrence formula was used to investigate the particular and homogeneous components of an output signal

$$y[n] = y[n - 1] - 0.5y[n - 2] + x[n] \tag{6.81}$$

Comparing with equation (6.76), we see that $2r \cos \theta = 1$ and $r^2 = 0.5$, giving $r = 0.7071$ and $\theta = 45°$. The transfer function of this system may therefore be written in the same form as equation (6.73)

$$H(z) = \frac{z^2}{\{z - 0.7071 \exp(j\pi/4)\}\{z - 0.7071 \exp(-j\pi/4)\}} \qquad (6.82)$$

A complex-conjugate pole pair with these values of r and θ gives an impulse response of damped oscillatory form at a frequency close to $\Omega = \pi/4$. This corresponds to 8 samples per cycle. It is interesting to note that the homogeneous component of the solution shown in figure 3.15(d) is of this type.

The frequency response characteristics of typical second-order discrete LTI systems were investigated in section 5.4 (see equations (5.47) to (5.51)). We concentrated there on the difference equation

$$y[n] + a_1 y[n-1] + a_2 y[n-2] = x[n] \qquad (6.83)$$

Making the substitutions $a_1 = -2r \cos \theta$ and $a_2 = r^2$, the corresponding frequency response was found to be

$$H(\Omega) = \frac{1}{1 - 2r \cos \theta \exp(-j\Omega) + r^2 \exp(-j2\Omega)} \qquad (6.84)$$

This was illustrated in figure 5.14 for various values of r and θ, and we noted that these two parameters primarily affect the peak gain and centre-frequency of the system respectively. Recalling that $z = \exp(j\Omega)$, we now see that the above frequency response is equivalent to the transfer function

$$H(z) = \frac{1}{1 - 2r \cos \theta\, z^{-1} + r^2 z^{-2}} = \frac{z^2}{z^2 - 2rz \cos \theta + r^2} \qquad (6.85)$$

which is the same as equation (6.73). Therefore the frequency responses already shown in figure 5.14 refer to typical second-order systems having a pole pair with polar coordinates r and θ. The reader is encouraged to review this earlier figure, relating it to our new knowledge about z-plane poles and zeros.

Towards the end of section 6.3.3, we saw how the unilateral Laplace Transform may be used to deal with initial stored energy in a continuous system. In a similar way, the unilateral z-transform can deal with nonzero initial conditions in a discrete system. In this situation it, too, evaluates the output signal 'all in one go'—the steady-state and transient components, *plus* the modifications to the response caused by the initial conditions. To illustrate this aspect of the z-transform, we need to modify the time-shifting property listed in table 6A. This is quoted as

$$x[n - n_0]u[n - n_0] \leftrightarrow X(z)z^{-n_0} \qquad (6.86)$$

Thus a signal shifted forward by n_0 sampling intervals has its z-transform multiplied by z^{-n_0}. Note, however, that the shifted signal is multiplied by the shifted step function $u[n - n_0]$, to ensure that it is zero prior to $n = n_0$. If we are to use the shifting property of the z-transform to solve difference equations with nonzero initial conditions, we need to remove this restriction. Let us therefore consider a signal $y_1[n]$ equal to a shifted version of a general signal $x[n]$, which may not be zero prior to $n = 0$

$$y_1[n] = x[n - 1]$$

Therefore

$$Y_1(z) = \sum_{n=0}^{\infty} x[n-1]z^{-n} = x[-1] + \sum_{n=1}^{\infty} x[n-1]z^{-n}$$

$$\therefore\ Y_1(z) = x[-1] + z^{-1}\left\{\sum_{n=0}^{\infty} x[n]z^{-n}\right\} = x[-1] + z^{-1}X(z) \tag{6.87}$$

By similar arguments it may be shown that if

$$y_2[n] = x[n-2]$$

then

$$Y_2(z) = x[-2] + x[-1]z^{-1} + z^{-2}X(z) \tag{6.88}$$

The use of equations (6.87) and (6.88) may conveniently be illustrated by a worked example.

Example E6.8

A second-order discrete system is shown in part (a) of figure E6.8. Use the z-transform to find its response to the input signal $x[n] = \delta[n]$ where (a) the initial conditions are zero, and (b) the initial conditions are $y[-1] = -1.25$ and $y[-2] = -0.52083$.

Solution

The difference equation of the system is, by inspection

$$y[n] = -0.2y[n-1] + 0.48y[n-2] + x[n]$$

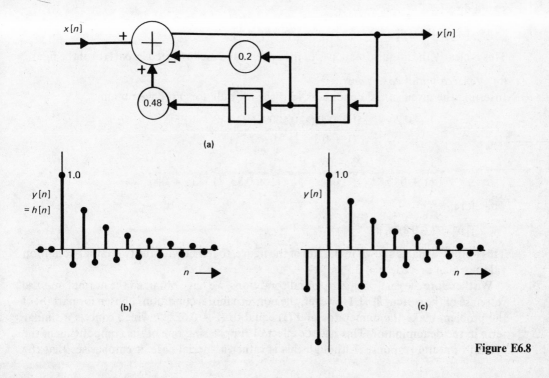

(a)

(b)

(c)

Figure E6.8

hence

$$y[n] + 0.2y[n - 1] - 0.48y[n - 2] = x[n]$$

Using equations (6.87) and (6.88) we take the z-transform of both sides of the equation, allowing for nonzero initial conditions

$$Y(z) + 0.2\{y[-1] + z^{-1}Y(z)\} - 0.48\{y[-2] + y[-1]z^{-1} + z^{-2}Y(z)\} = X(z)$$

This gives

$$Y(z) = \frac{X(z) - 0.2y[-1] + 0.48y[-2] + 0.48y[-1]z^{-1}}{(1 + 0.2z^{-1} - 0.48z^{-2})}$$

(a) *Zero initial conditions*
Since $x[n] = \delta[n]$, $X(z) = 1$. All other numerator terms are zero, so that

$$Y(z) = \frac{1}{(1 + 0.2z^{-1} - 0.48z^{-2})} = \frac{z^2}{(z^2 + 0.2z - 0.48)}$$

The denominator may be factorised to give

$$Y(z) = \frac{z^2}{(z + 0.8)(z - 0.6)}$$

This z-transform does not appear in table 6A, so we use the partial fraction expansion

$$\frac{z^2}{(z + 0.8)(z - 0.6)} = \frac{Az}{(z + 0.8)} + \frac{Bz}{(z - 0.6)}$$

which yields $A = 0.5714$ and $B = 0.4286$. Using the table, we may now write the output signal directly

$$y[n] = 0.5714(-0.8)^n u[n] + 0.4286(0.6)^n u[n]$$

This is clearly the impulse response of the system, and is illustrated in part (b) of the figure.

(b) *Nonzero initial conditions*
Inserting the given initial conditions into the formula for $Y(z)$, we obtain

$$Y(z) = \frac{1 - 0.2(-1.25) + 0.48(-0.52083) + 0.48(-1.25)z^{-1}}{(1 + 0.2z^{-1} - 0.48z^{-2})}$$

$$= \frac{1 + 0.25 - 0.25 - 0.6z^{-1}}{(1 + 0.8z^{-1})(1 - 0.6z^{-1})} = \frac{1}{(1 + 0.8z^{-1})} = \frac{z}{(z + 0.8)}$$

Therefore

$$y[n] = (-0.8)^n u[n]$$

This output signal is shown in part (c) of the figure, together with the two initial-condition values which precede $n = 0$.

We therefore see that, with zero initial conditions, we have obtained the normal impulse response of the system $h[n]$. However, the nonzero initial conditions chosen for part (b) of the problem make the numerator of $Y(z)$ equal to $(1 - 0.6z^{-1})$, which cancels a similar term in the denominator. This has the effect of suppressing one of the components in the system's natural response. Although this is rather a special case, it emphasises that the response of an LTI system to a unit impulse is only a complete and valid description of the system when the initial conditions are zero. Otherwise, the response may be quite different in form. Finally, we should note that the z-transform has produced the complete solution to the problem, 'all in one go'. Transient and steady-state components, plus the 'after-effects' of nonzero initial conditions, are all superimposed—and may be hard to disentangle. In this respect, the unilateral Laplace Transform and the z-transform are very similar.

6.5 **Bilateral transforms**

Bilateral versions of the Laplace Transform and the z-transform are defined as follows

$$X(s) = \int_{-\infty}^{\infty} x(t) \exp(-st) \, dt \quad \text{and} \quad X(z) = \sum_{n=-\infty}^{\infty} x[n]z^{-n} \tag{6.89}$$

Comparison with equations (6.7) and (6.53) respectively shows that the only difference between these bilateral transforms and their unilateral counterparts is the lower limit of integration, or summation. Bilateral transforms take account of a signal over all time, whereas unilateral transforms take account only of positive time. Of course, if a signal is zero before $t = 0$ (or $n = 0$), then there is no difference between the two versions of its transform. Conversely, two signals which are identical over positive time, but different over negative time, will have the same unilateral transform—but different bilateral transforms.

Generally speaking, analysis and design problems in electronic and electrical engineering may be handled by the unilateral transforms already described in this chapter. A signal may usually be considered zero before some reference time, or switching instant, which may be taken as the origin. As far as LTI systems are concerned, the great majority are *causal*, with impulse responses which begin at or after $t = 0$ (or $n = 0$). Clearly, in these cases a unilateral transform is quite adequate for deriving the corresponding frequency responses or transfer functions. Also, as we have seen, if a causal system is still responding to some *previous* input signal or excitation when we apply a new signal, we may take account of this by incorporating suitable initial conditions.

However, we must be careful not to dismiss bilateral transforms entirely! The Fourier Transform, in both its continuous-time and discrete-time versions, *is* bilateral. It deals with signals which in principle may exist over all time, analysing them into imaginary exponentials which are also 'eternal'. Clearly, if we have to find a frequency-domain representation of a signal which is finite within the range $-\infty < t < 0$ (or $-\infty < n < 0$), a bilateral transform is necessary. Such signals sometimes arise—for example, in antenna theory and sonar systems as well as in standard electronic engineering. Bilateral transforms do therefore find practical application. Even in our own discussions, we have met one example of a noncausal LTI system—the digital filter used to smooth pre-recorded temperature data in section 3.4—for which the unilateral z-transform would be inappropriate.

The main disadvantage of bilateral transforms lies in their convergence criteria. These are more stringent than the criteria of unilateral transforms. For example, we have seen in chapter 4 that the continuous-time Fourier Transform fails to converge for certain quite common signals—such as DC levels or step functions—which continue forever. The unilateral Laplace Transform overcomes such difficulties by multiplying the signal by $\exp(-st) = \exp(-\sigma t) \exp(-j\omega t)$, before integration. The term $\exp(-\sigma t)$ may be thought of as a *convergence factor*, with a rate of decay in positive time which is sufficient to counteract any tendency of the signal to continue, or grow without limit. However, it is clear that values of σ which ensure convergence in positive time may well produce divergence in negative time. This is the basic reason why convergence is a more troublesome question with bilateral transforms than with unilateral ones. A proper understanding of the bilateral Laplace Transform and z-transform would therefore require a fuller discussion of regions of convergence in the s-plane and z-plane—a topic which we have mentioned very briefly in sections 6.3.1 and 6.4.1.

Problems to chapter 6

Section 6.3

Q6.1.   Find the Laplace Transforms of the following signals

  (a) $x(t) = \exp(-t)u(t)$
  (b) $x(t) = u(t) + u(t - t_0)$
  (c) $x(t) = \delta(t - t_0) - 2\delta(t - 2t_0)$
  (d) $x(t) = t \exp(-\alpha t)u(t).$

Q6.2.   Using only the answer to part (a) of Q6.1, and the properties of the Laplace Transform, find the transforms of the signals shown in figure Q6.2 (the exponentials have a time constant of 1 second).

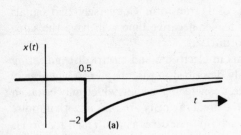
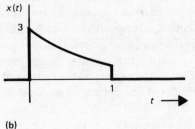

Figure Q6.2

Q6.3.   Use table 6B at the end of the chapter, and the method of partial fractions (if necessary), to find the signals corresponding to the following Laplace Transforms

  (a) $X(s) = \dfrac{1}{s(s + 2)}$

  (b) $X(s) = \dfrac{(s + 1)}{(s^2 + 1)}$

  (c) $X(s) = \dfrac{s + 3}{s(s + 1)(s + 2)}.$

Q6.4.   Find the voltage step responses of the first-order high-pass filter, and the RC bandpass filter, shown in figure Q6.4.

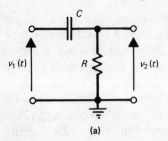
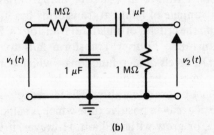

Figure Q6.4

Q6.5.   In section 3.5 (see also figure 3.14) we considered the start-up transient caused by applying a sinewave of voltage at $t = 0$ to a first-order low-pass filter. The signal frequency was 1 kHz and the filter's time constant 0.4 ms. Use table 6B to solve this problem by the Laplace Transform, obtaining an expression for the filter's output voltage $v_2(t)$. (Ignore any subsequent transient caused by switching off the input signal.) Infer from your result: (a) the steady-state voltage gain of the circuit, (b) the steady-state phase shift, and (c) the initial value of the transient component in the output.

Q6.6.   Use the Laplace Transform to find the current that flows in the circuit shown in figure Q6.6, if the switch is closed at $t = 0$. What is the Q-factor of the circuit?

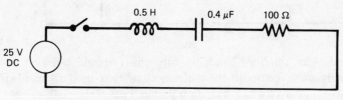

Figure Q6.6

Q6.7.   Find the s-plane poles and zeros of the voltage transfer functions which describe the circuits shown in figure Q6.4.

Q6.8.   An active, second-order, low-pass filter is shown in figure Q6.8. Assuming the operational amplifier is ideal, find a general expression for its voltage transfer function $V_2(s)/V_1(s)$. In a particular case, circuit values are as follows

$$R_1 = 1125 \,\Omega \qquad R_2 = 1010 \,\Omega \qquad R_3 = 11.25 \text{ k}\Omega$$

$$C_1 = 2.2 \,\mu\text{F} \qquad C_2 = 0.1 \,\mu\text{F}$$

Find the locations of the filter's s-plane poles, and hence sketch the magnitude of its frequency response. Also estimate: (a) the gain of the filter at very low frequencies, and (b) its cut-off slope (in dB per decade) at very high frequencies.

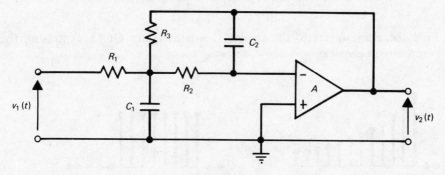

Figure Q6.8

Q6.9. Two first-order low-pass filters are cascaded and buffered with an ideal voltage follower, as shown in figure Q6.9. What is the transfer function of the overall system, and where are its *s*-plane poles located? Find the impulse response $h(t)$ by convolving the impulse responses of the two individual circuits, and check that its Laplace Transform is equal to the transfer function already determined.

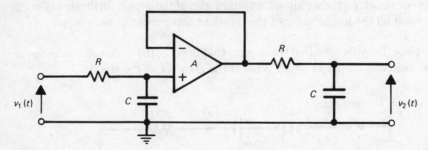

Figure Q6.9

Q6.10. A second-order, high-Q, bandpass filter has *s*-plane poles at $s = -\alpha \pm j\omega_0$. By considering pole vectors in the *s*-plane, show that its 3 dB bandwidth (that is, the frequency range over which its gain is within 3 dB of the peak value) is approximately equal to 2α.

Q6.11. A continuous LTI system is described by the following differential equation relating input and output signals

$$\frac{d^3 y(t)}{dt^3} + 3\frac{d^2 y(t)}{dt^2} + 103\frac{dy(t)}{dt} + 101 y(t) = \frac{d^2 x(t)}{dt^2} + 9x(t)$$

Find its transfer function $H(s)$, and the locations of its *s*-plane poles and zeros. Hence sketch the magnitude of its frequency–response characteristic.

Q6.12. A system is described by the following linear differential equation with constant coefficients

$$\frac{d^2 y(t)}{dt^2} + 3\frac{dy(t)}{dt} + 2y(t) = x(t)$$

Use the Laplace Transform to find its response to a unit impulse, given the following initial conditions

(a) $y(0_+) = 0$, $y'(0_+) = 0$
(b) $y(0_+) = 0$, $y'(0_+) = 1$
(c) $y(0_+) = 2$, $y'(0_+) = -3$

Which of these is the true 'impulse response' of the system?

Section 6.4

Q6.13. Find the *z*-transforms of the signals shown in figure Q6.13, expressing them as compactly as possible.

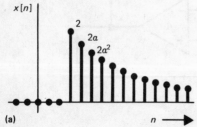

(a)

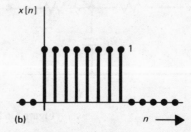

(b)

Figure Q6.13

Q6.14. Using only the properties of the z-transform, and the answers to problem Q6.13, find the z-transform of the signal shown in figure Q6.14.

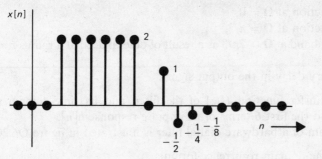

Figure Q6.14

Q6.15. Two discrete-time signals are as follows

$$x_1[n] = \delta[n] + \delta[n-1] - \delta[n-3]$$
$$x_2[n] = 2\delta[n-1] + 2\delta[n-2] + \delta[n-3]$$

Write down their respective z-transforms $X_1(z)$ and $X_2(z)$. Convolve the two signals to form a third signal $x_3[n]$, and show that its z-transform equals $X_1(z)X_2(z)$.

Q6.16. Refer to the table of z-transforms at the end of the chapter (table 6C), and use partial fraction expansions if necessary, to find the signals corresponding to the z-transforms

(a) $X(z) = \dfrac{z/2}{z^2 - z + \frac{1}{2}}$

(b) $X(z) = \dfrac{(z - 0.5)}{z(z - 0.8)(z - 1)}$

Q6.17. Find the z-plane poles and zeros of the following transfer functions. Which, if any, represent unstable or noncausal systems?

(a) $H(z) = \dfrac{z^2 - z - 2}{z^2 - 1.3z + 0.4}$

(b) $H(z) = \dfrac{z^2 - z + 1}{z^2 + 1}$

(c) $H(z) = \dfrac{z^3 - z^2 + z - 1}{z^2 - 0.25}$.

Q6.18. Find and sketch the poles and zeros of the transfer function

$$H(z) = \dfrac{(z^3 - z^2 + 0.8z - 0.8)}{z^3 + 0.8z^2}$$

Using the geometrical evaluation of the discrete-time Fourier Transform in the z-plane, visualise and sketch the magnitude of the system's frequency response in the range $0 \leqslant \Omega \leqslant 2\pi$.

Q6.19. Using the smallest possible number of z-plane poles and zeros, design a discrete-time filter with the following performance

(a) complete rejection at $\Omega = 0$,
(b) complete rejection at $\Omega = \pi/3$,
(c) a narrow passband at $\Omega = 2\pi/3$ as a result of poles placed at a radius $r = 0.9$ in the z-plane, and
(d) no unnecessary delay in the output signal.

Specify the transfer function $H(z)$ of the filter, and its time-domain recurrence formula. Also find the first 6 terms of its impulse response $h[n]$.

Q6.20. The block diagram of a hardware digital filter is illustrated in figure Q6.20.

(a) Specify its time-domain recurrence formula.
(b) Find its transfer function $H(z)$.
(c) Find its z-plane poles and zeros, and sketch their locations in the z-plane.
(d) Sketch its frequency–response magnitude characteristic in the range $0 \leqslant \Omega \leqslant \pi$.

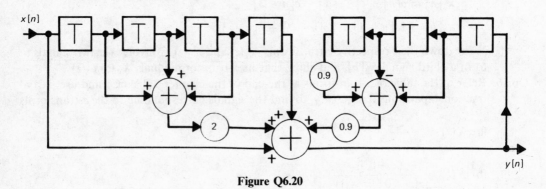

Figure Q6.20

Q6.21. A recursive LTI system has the following difference equation

$$y[n] - y[n-1] = \tfrac{1}{8}\{x[n] - x[n-8]\}$$

Find its impulse response $h[n]$, and satisfy yourself that the system acts as a moving-average low-pass filter. Specify the difference equation of a nonrecursive filter with the same performance.

Q6.22. By entering the impulse response $h[n]$ found in Q6.21 as data in the FFT program listed in section 5.3.3 (program no. 5), confirm that the filter's frequency–response is of the low-pass type. (It is suggested that you use a 64-point zero-padded FFT.) How many 'sidelobes' are there in the range $0 \leqslant \Omega \leqslant \pi$? Also, how do these relate to the poles and zeros of the z-transform found in part (b) of problem Q6.13?

Q6.23. A discrete LTI system is shown in figure Q6.23. Find the z-transform of its output signal, if a unit impulse $\delta[n]$ is delivered to its input side, given the following initial conditions

(a) $y[-1] = 0,$ $y[-2] = 0$
(b) $y[-1] = -2,$ $y[-2] = 2$

Which of these results represents the true transfer function of the system?

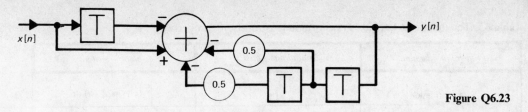

Figure Q6.23

What initial values of $y[-1]$ and $y[-2]$ would result in the output signal being zero for $0 \leqslant n \leqslant \infty$, if a unit impulse is delivered to the input at $n = 0$? Can you account for this apparently surprising result?

Table 6A The unilateral Laplace Transform and z-transform: properties

Property or operation	Continuous signal	Laplace Transform
transformation	$x(t)$	$\int_0^\infty x(t) \exp(-st)\,dt$
inverse transformation	$\dfrac{1}{2\pi j} \int_{\sigma-j\infty}^{\sigma+j\infty} X(s) \exp(st)\,ds$	$X(s)$
linearity	$a_1 x_1(t) + a_2 x_2(t)$	$a_1 X_1(s) + a_2 X_2(s)$
time-shifting	$x(t - t_0)\, u(t - t_0)$	$X(s) \exp(-st_0)$
time-scaling	$x(at)$	$\dfrac{1}{|a|} X\!\left(\dfrac{s}{a}\right)$
time-differentiation	$\dfrac{d}{dt} x(t)$	$sX(s) - x(0_+)$
time-integration	$\int_0^t x(t)\,dt$	$\dfrac{X(s)}{s}$
convolution	$x_1(t) * x_2(t)$	$X_1(s)\, X_2(s)$

Property or operation	Discrete signal	z-transform
transformation	$x[n]$	$\displaystyle\sum_{n=0}^{\infty} x[n]\, z^{-n}$
inverse transformation	$\dfrac{1}{2\pi j} \oint X(z)\, z^{n-1} dz$	$X(z)$
linearity	$a_1 x_1[n] + a_2 x_2[n]$	$a_1 X_1(z) + a_2 X_2(z)$
time-shifting	$x[n - n_0]\, u[n - n_0]$	$X(z)\, z^{-n_0}$
time-differentiation	$x[n] - x[n-1]$	$X(z)\, (1 - z^{-1})$
time-integration	$\displaystyle\sum_{k=0}^{n} x[k]$	$X(z) \left(\dfrac{z}{z-1}\right)$
convolution	$x_1[n] * x_2[n]$	$X_1(z)\, X_2(z)$

Table 6B The unilateral Laplace Transform: pairs

Waveform	Signal $x(t)$	Spectrum $X(s)$	s-plane poles and zeros
unit step	$u(t)$	$\dfrac{1}{s}$	
unit impulse	$\delta(t)$	1	
unit ramp	$r(t)$	$\dfrac{1}{s^2}$	
exponential	$\exp(-\alpha t)\, u(t)$	$\dfrac{1}{(s + \alpha)}$	
	$\{1 - \exp(-\alpha t)\}\, u(t)$	$\dfrac{\alpha}{s(s + \alpha)}$	
	$\dfrac{1}{\beta - \alpha}\{\exp(-\alpha t) - \exp(-\beta t)\}\, u(t)$	$\dfrac{1}{(s + \alpha)\,(s + \beta)}$	
cosine	$\cos \omega_0 t\, u(t)$	$\dfrac{s}{(s^2 + \omega_0^2)}$	
sine	$\sin \omega_0 t\, u(t)$	$\dfrac{\omega_0}{(s^2 + \omega_0^2)}$	
damped sine	$\exp(-\alpha t) \sin \omega_0 t\, u(t)$	$\dfrac{\omega_0}{(s + \alpha + j\omega_0)\,(s + \alpha - j\omega_0)}$	
	$\dfrac{\sin(\omega_0 t - \theta) + \exp(-\alpha t) \sin \theta}{(\alpha^2 + \omega_0^2)^{\frac{1}{2}}}$ where $\theta = \tan^{-1}\dfrac{\omega_0}{\alpha}$	$\dfrac{\omega_0}{(s + \alpha)\,(s^2 + \omega_0^2)}$	

Table 6C The unilateral z-transform: pairs

Waveform	Signal $x[n]$	Spectrum $X(z)$	z-plane poles and zeros
unit step	$u[n]$	$\dfrac{z}{(z-1)}$	
unit impulse	$\delta[n]$	1	
unit ramp	$r[n]$	$\dfrac{z}{(z-1)^2}$	
exponential	$a^n\,u[n]$	$\dfrac{z}{(z-a)}$	
	$(1-a^n)\,u[n]$	$\dfrac{z(1-a)}{(z-a)(z-1)}$	
cosine	$\cos n\Omega_0\,u[n]$	$\dfrac{z(z-\cos\Omega_0)}{(z^2-2z\cos\Omega_0+1)}$	
sine	$\sin n\Omega_0\,u[n]$	$\dfrac{z\sin\Omega_0}{(z^2-2z\cos\Omega_0+1)}$	
damped sine	$a^n\sin n\Omega_0\,u[n]$	$\dfrac{az\sin\Omega_0}{(z^2-2az\cos\Omega_0+a^2)}$	

7 Feedback

"The report of my death was an exaggeration."
Mark Twain (1835–1910), in a cable from
Europe to the Associated Press

"Well, if I called the wrong number, why did you answer the phone?"
James Thurber (1894–1962)

7.1 Introduction

The principles and applications of feedback are of the greatest importance in electronic engineering. Most electronic systems of any complexity employ feedback in one way or another. Sometimes the feedback is an obvious and deliberate part of the design; in other cases it is more subtle. Occasionally it is unintentional.

Feedback often falls into one of two major categories, negative or positive. *Negative* feedback tends to stabilise a system, making it less subject to outside disturbances. As a general rule it also reduces the gain of the system and increases its bandwidth. This kind of feedback is widely used in such diverse systems as electronic amplifiers and automatic control systems. *Positive* feedback, on the other hand, tends to reduce stability and may lead to inherent oscillations in a system. Although it is put to good use in electronic oscillators and signal generators, its effects are sometimes very undesirable. For example, if the microphone and loudspeaker of a public-address system are placed close together, positive feedback may produce a high-pitched whine. Clearly, the ability to analyse feedback systems, and to exploit their many advantages in engineering design, is of great importance to the electronic engineer.

The principles of feedback are also important in other fields. These include other branches of engineering, biology, psychology, and economics. At its most general, the word 'feedback' simply implies a transfer of information between the output and input of a system. A great many situations—technical, biological, and organisational—may usefully be viewed in this way. Let us very briefly mention two examples. The human eye automatically compensates for overall changes in light intensity by adjusting the size of the pupil. In this system, negative feedback is used to achieve a roughly constant illumination of the retina. A second example may be taken

273

from economics. If a government tries to raise its revenue by taxing a product, there is a natural tendency for consumers to buy less of it. Such 'consumer resistance' may be thought of as a type of feedback (again negative) which reduces the effect desired by the government. We therefore see that the general ideas of feedback may be very widely applied. However, a word of warning is necessary. While technological feedback systems are often linear and time-invariant, the same is rarely true of biological or economic ones.

The term feedback has already been used frequently in this book, and we have met a number of examples of practical feedback systems. As early as section 1.4.3 we noted that several standard operational amplifier circuits use negative feedback to stabilise gain and increase overall bandwidth. In section 2.3.2 it was mentioned that instability in a system is intimately associated with the ideas of feedback. It was also pointed out that when a nominally linear system becomes unstable, some *nonlinear* mechanism must sooner or later come into play to limit the growth of its output signal. Section 2.3.3 demonstrated the use of feedback connections for building up the block diagram of a system from its differential or difference equation. In subsequent chapters we have met various first and second-order systems involving feedback. For example, several continuous active filters with feedback connections around an operational amplifier have been analysed (figure 4.19, and worked examples E4.8 and E6.3). In the case of discrete systems, we have examined the performance of simple recursive systems in some detail in section 5.4, and in section 6.4.3 we have seen how z-plane poles are directly related to the feedback terms in a difference equation. Chapter 6 has also introduced the idea that the poles of a transfer function must be confined to certain regions of the s-plane or z-plane if they are to represent a stable system.

We have therefore already met a number of ideas concerning feedback and stability. However, their introduction has been rather piecemeal. The aim of this chapter is to develop and consolidate these ideas by taking a broader view of the topic of feedback, showing how it is applied in a variety of electronic systems.

7.2 General aspects of feedback

The simple control system shown in figure 7.1 demonstrates some important general aspects of feedback. The antenna of a tracking radar is driven by a motor-gearbox, labelled M. The input to the system is a signal representing the *desired* position of the antenna. This is compared with a

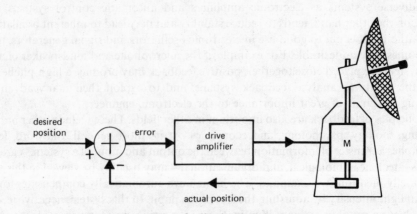

Figure 7.1 A feedback control system.

feedback signal giving the *actual* position, derived from a transducer attached to the antenna shaft. Any difference between the desired and actual positions constitutes an *error* signal which activates the drive amplifier. This turns the motor and reduces the error. This classic type of *servomechanism* is in true equilibrium only when the error signal is zero. For obvious reasons, the type of arrangement shown in the figure is often referred to as *closed-loop* control.

It is important to realise that such a system is only self-aligning and stable if the feedback is negative. In other words, the output from the drive amplifier must turn the motor in such a direction as to *reduce the error*. If the polarity of one of the signals in the control loop were reversed, the feedback would become positive. Any error would then be *increased* by the feedback signal, causing a 'runaway' situation with potentially disastrous consequences. Such polarity reversal might be due to a faulty connection. But it might also be caused by time-delays or phase-shifts in the control loop, which sometimes turn a nominally stable system into an unstable one. It is a major challenge of feedback system design to ensure that this does not happen.

Since the use of feedback generally involves some risk of instability, we might consider the alternative option of *open-loop* control. This would involve estimating the precise input signal needed to move the antenna to its desired position, and delivering this signal directly to the drive amplifier. To do this, we would need very exact knowledge of the electrical and mechanical properties of the system, and any discrepancy in the control would go uncorrected. Furthermore, disturbances of the antenna position—caused, for example, by wind forces— would not produce any automatic correcting action. For all these reasons, open-loop control is rarely adequate in practice.

Our prime interest in this book is, of course, electronic circuits and systems—many of which do not involve 'control' in any obvious sense. In addition, feedback in such systems may not always be classed as simply 'negative' or 'positive'. So while the control system shown in figure 7.1 offers some valuable general insights, we must now quantify the discussion and look more carefully at electronic systems.

We start by considering the two LTI feedback systems in figure 7.2. One of these is continuous, the other discrete. Both have a *forward-path* subsystem and a *feedback* subsystem, characterised by their respective transfer functions G and H. The input and feedback signals are combined by an adder unit to produce the net input signal (E) to the forward-path subsystem. Since we have given frequency-domain descriptions for the subsystems, the various signals are represented by their Laplace Transform or z-transform.

Several additional points are worth noting. Firstly, many practical feedback systems do not have this particular structure; however, their block diagrams may quite often be arranged to appear like those in the figure. Secondly, although the signal E is sometimes an 'error' (as in figure 7.1), in many applications this term is inappropriate. Finally, we must not assume that addition of the feedback signal to the input signal necessarily implies positive feedback, or that

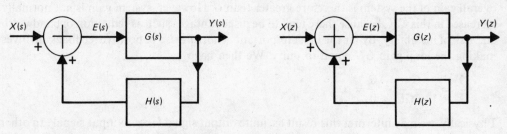

Figure 7.2 Basic LTI feedback systems.

subtraction implies negative feedback. The type of feedback depends on whether the feedback signal, having passed *right around the closed loop*, reinforces or detracts from input signal X. This in turn depends on the *total number* of polarity changes (also called inversions, or phase reversals) around the loop.

The overall transfer functions of these systems may readily be derived. Omitting the variables s or z for convenience, we may write

$$Y = EG \quad \text{or} \quad E = \frac{Y}{G}, \quad \text{and} \quad E = X + HY \tag{7.1}$$

Elimination of the signal E yields

$$\frac{Y}{X} = \frac{G}{1 - GH} \tag{7.2}$$

Examination of this apparently simple result gives important clues about the properties of feedback systems. These may be summarised as follows.

Negative feedback. The product GH is negative. Hence the denominator in expression (7.2) is greater than unity, giving an overall system gain which is less than G. In many practical applications, the so-called *loop gain* is much greater than unity; that is, $|GH| \gg 1$. This gives

$$\frac{Y}{X} = \frac{G}{1 - GH} \approx \frac{G}{-GH} = \frac{-1}{H} \tag{7.3}$$

Thus the overall transfer function becomes largely independent of the precise gain, or properties, of the subsystem G, and depends only on H. This important effect is widely exploited in negative feedback amplifiers, where G is typically an amplifier of high but ill-defined gain, and H is a passive feedback network with very stable component values and large bandwidth.

If there is *direct* feedback from output to input, then $H = 1$. If, furthermore, the feedback signal is *subtracted* from the input signal, then the expression for the overall transfer function changes to

$$\frac{Y}{X} = \frac{G}{1 + GH} = \frac{G}{1 + G} \approx 1 \tag{7.4}$$

In other words the output equals, or 'follows', the input. This is the basis of the type of automatic control system shown in figure 7.1. As we shall see in the next section, it also applies to *follower circuits* based upon operational amplifiers or other active electronic devices.

Positive feedback. In the systems illustrated in figure 7.2, the product GH is positive. If the loop gain is less than unity, the denominator of expression (7.2) is between 1 and zero. The overall gain of the system is therefore greater than G. However, system gain is not normally increased in this way, because there tend to be disadvantages such as reduction of bandwidth and risk of instability. By far the most important *deliberate* use of positive feedback involves making the loop gain GH equal to unity. We then have

$$\frac{Y}{X} = \frac{G}{1 - GH} = \frac{G}{0} = \infty \tag{7.5}$$

Physically, we may interpret this result as 'finite output signal for zero input signal'. In other words the system is unstable, generating its own output signal with no input signal applied,

This forms the basis of a wide range of practical oscillators and signal generators. The condition for instability in a positive feedback system is *unity loop gain*. This is sometimes called the *Barkhausen criterion*. If the system is designed to meet it at only one frequency, then we may expect to see a 'single-frequency' oscillation at the output—in other words, a sinusoidal waveform.

As we have already noted, it is not always possible to describe feedback as clearly positive or negative. The subsystems *G* and *H* in figure 7.2 are generally frequency-dependent, and phase-shifts around the closed loop must be expected to change with frequency. Even when electronic systems are designed for a particular type of feedback, the required conditions will generally only be met at certain frequencies, or over limited frequency ranges. This makes it difficult to categorise many feedback systems—such as the active filters met in section 4.3.1 and worked example E6.3—as simply 'negative' or 'positive'. In spite of these qualifications, equation (7.2) offers some valuable insights into the expected behaviour of feedback systems. The reader may find it helpful to refer back to this section after we have considered some more specific circuit applications.

7.3 Feedback in continuous systems

The topic of feedback in continuous systems is a very large one, and we restrict ourselves here to a few key applications in electronic engineering. Fortunately, many of the principles involved may be illustrated using operational amplifier circuits. As we pointed out in section 1.4.3, the performance of operational amplifiers may be represented quite accurately by a few simple equations. This removes the need to consider electronic feedback circuits in great detail. However the reader is asked to bear in mind that operational amplifiers are by no means suitable for all practical applications, because of their inadequate high-frequency performance, power output, or other factors. The circuits explored in the following pages are generally best suited to low-frequency low-power applications.

7.3.1 *Negative feedback amplifiers*

The use of negative feedback in high-gain electronic amplifiers was pioneered by H.S. Black in the mid-1920s. His discovery was described by one employee at the Bell Laboratories as having "all the initial impact of a blow with a wet noodle." However, its virtues are now very widely accepted. They include improvements in stability and bandwidth, together with a reduction of distortion and noise. Performance becomes relatively insensitive to the precise characteristics of active components, or to the effects of ageing. About the only disadvantages are increased circuit complexity—normally quite modest—and a reduction in overall gain. However the gain may usually be made up by cascading an additional amplifier stage, or stages.

The present section focuses on three aspects of this important subject. Firstly, we will look rather more carefully at the standard operational amplifier circuits introduced in section 1.4.3, discussing their action as negative feedback systems. This will be followed by brief discussions of the role of negative feedback for enhancing stability, and for improving the impedance characteristics of amplifiers.

Section 1.4.3 and figure 1.14 gave a simplified account of three standard feedback amplifier configurations based on operational amplifiers. These are the inverting amplifier, the noninverting amplifier, and the voltage follower. The approach was to assume an *ideal* operational amplifier, with infinite voltage gain and input impedance. We then used the *virtual-earth* concept to estimate the voltage gain of the overall systems. However, although the term 'feedback' was introduced, it was not fully explained. It is therefore interesting and instructive to draw block diagrams for the three configurations, comparing them with the continuous feedback system shown in figure 7.2. To do this, we now assume that the integrated circuit operational amplifier at the heart of each configuration has a *finite* voltage gain A. (We could also include the effects of finite input and output impedances. However, this would complicate the analysis, without offering particular advantages in the present context.)

We start with the inverting amplifier configuration. For convenience this is drawn again at the top of figure 7.3(a). Since the operational amplifier is now assumed to have a finite voltage gain, the voltage at its inverting input point may not be taken as zero (virtual earth). Instead, let us denote it by V_3. Since no current flows into the operational amplifier, we may write

$$\frac{V_1 - V_3}{R_1} = \frac{V_3 - V_2}{R_2} \tag{7.6}$$

and furthermore

$$-AV_3 = V_2 \tag{7.7}$$

It is simple to eliminate V_3, giving the following relationship between V_2 and V_1

$$\frac{V_2}{V_1} = \frac{-AR_2}{R_2 + R_1(1 + A)} = \frac{-A}{1 + \dfrac{R_1}{R_2}(1 + A)} \tag{7.8}$$

Now for practical purposes $A \gg 1$, so that

$$\frac{V_2}{V_1} = \frac{-A}{1 + \dfrac{AR_1}{R_2}} \tag{7.9}$$

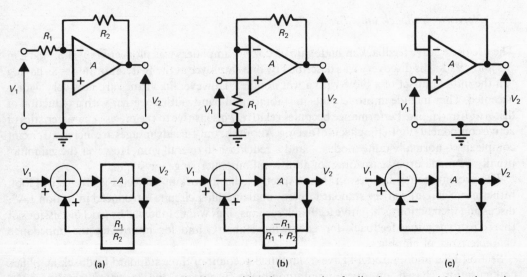

(a)   **(b)**   **(c)**

Figure 7.3 Operational amplifier circuits considered as negative feedback systems: (a) the inverting amplifier, (b) the noninverting amplifier, and (c) the voltage follower.

This result is identical to equation (7.2) if

$$G = -A, \quad \text{and} \quad H = \frac{R_1}{R_2} \tag{7.10}$$

The corresponding system block diagram is shown in the lower part of figure 7.3(a). We see that the inverting amplifier configuration may be recast as a forward-path subsystem with gain $-A$, together with a feedback subsystem of gain R_1/R_2. If the loop gain is much greater than unity, then

$$|GH| = \frac{AR_1}{R_2} \gg 1, \quad \text{and} \quad \frac{V_2}{V_1} \approx \frac{-A}{\dfrac{AR_1}{R_2}} = \frac{-R_2}{R_1} \tag{7.11}$$

Thus the gain of the overall amplifier approximates $-1/H$ (see equation (7.3)), and is determined by the values of R_1 and R_2. These may be accurately selected, and very stable. This is a major advantage of using negative feedback.

We must be careful to distinguish between the two representations of this system given in the figure. The *circuit diagram* indicates the basic electrical connections and components required to build an inverting amplifier (even though, as explained in section 1.4.3, the DC power supply and certain other subsidiary connections to the operational amplifier are often omitted). The *block diagram*, on the other hand, indicates information flow and system function. It views the system as a signal processor, which in this case happens to be processing voltages.

The standard noninverting amplifier configuration at the top of figure 7.3(b) may be analysed in a very similar way. Since the input impedance of the operational amplifier is assumed infinite, resistors R_1 and R_2 act as a potential divider which feeds back a fraction of the output signal to the inverting input. Again denoting the voltage at this input point by V_3, we have

$$V_3 = \frac{R_1}{(R_1 + R_2)} V_2 \tag{7.12}$$

and also

$$A(V_1 - V_3) = V_2 \tag{7.13}$$

Eliminating V_3, we readily obtain

$$\frac{V_2}{V_1} = \frac{A(R_1 + R_2)}{R_2 + R_1(1 + A)} = \frac{A}{1 + \dfrac{AR_1}{(R_1 + R_2)}} \tag{7.14}$$

Comparing this result with equation (7.2), we see that

$$G = A, \quad \text{and} \quad H = \frac{-R_1}{(R_1 + R_2)} \tag{7.15}$$

The corresponding block diagram is shown in the figure. The forward-path subsystem now has positive gain, but the feedback factor H is negative. Since there is one inversion as we travel right around the closed loop, the feedback is also negative. Assuming the loop gain is much greater than unity, we have

$$|GH| = \frac{AR_1}{(R_1 + R_2)} \gg 1, \quad \text{and} \quad \frac{V_2}{V_1} \approx \frac{A}{\dfrac{AR_1}{(R_1 + R_2)}} = \frac{(R_1 + R_2)}{R_1} \tag{7.16}$$

The overall gain of the system is once more determined by the values of two passive, external components.

The voltage follower circuit shown at the top of part (c) of the figure may be considered as a particular case of the noninverting amplifier, with $R_1 = \infty$ and $R_2 = 0$. Hence

$$G = A, \quad \text{and} \quad H = \frac{-R_1}{(R_1 + R_2)} = -1 \tag{7.17}$$

The feedback factor of -1 may be conveniently incorporated in the block diagram by *subtracting* the output signal from the input signal. This amounts to *comparing* the output voltage V_2 with the input voltage V_1. Any difference between them produces an 'error' signal which drives the forward-path amplifier and tends to reduce the error. This explains why the output signal tries to 'follow' the input. The circuit displays a number of close and interesting parallels with the servomechanism illustrated in figure 7.1.

We have so far assumed that the voltage gain of the integrated-circuit operational amplifier is a constant, A. In fact this *open loop gain*, which at DC and very low frequencies may be as high as 10^5 (100 dB) or more, reduces with frequency. In a cheap device the fall-off may begin as low as a few hertz. This means, of course, that the impressive gain figure quoted in the manufacturer's data sheet is only available over a very limited frequency range. A major advantage of negative feedback is that it extends the bandwidth of the amplifier. Let us consider, for example, the standard noninverting amplifier with a performance specified by equation (7.14)

$$\frac{V_2}{V_1} = \frac{A}{1 + \dfrac{AR_1}{(R_1 + R_2)}} \tag{7.18}$$

Equation (7.16) shows that if the loop gain is much greater than unity, the overall gain of the system is close to $(R_1 + R_2)/R_1$. Let us denote this closed-loop gain by K. Furthermore, let us assume that the frequency response of the integrated circuit itself may be represented by

$$A(\omega) = \frac{A_0}{(1 + j\omega\tau)} \tag{7.19}$$

This is a first-order characteristic with a DC gain equal to A_0, a 3 dB cut-off frequency given by $\omega = 1/\tau$, and a high-frequency cut-off rate of 20 dB/decade (as discussed in section 4.3.1). In fact many operational amplifiers are designed to have this form of response. Substituting in equation (7.18), we obtain the frequency response of the overall noninverting amplifier

$$\frac{V_2}{V_1}(\omega) = \frac{\dfrac{A_0}{(1 + j\omega\tau)}}{1 + \dfrac{A_0}{(1 + j\omega\tau)}\dfrac{1}{K}}$$

$$\therefore \frac{V_2}{V_1}(\omega) = \frac{A_0}{1 + j\omega\tau + A_0/K} = \frac{K}{1 + K/A_0 + j\omega\tau K/A_0}$$

Providing $K \ll A_0$ we may write

$$\frac{V_2}{V_1}(\omega) \approx \frac{K}{1 + j\omega\tau K/A_0} \tag{7.20}$$

Therefore the closed-loop system is also of first order, with a DC gain equal to K and a 3 dB cut-off frequency given by $\omega = A_0/K\tau$.

We may readily use these results to show that as the degree of negative feedback is varied, *the product of gain times bandwidth remains fixed*. With no feedback applied (equation (7.19)) we have a nominal gain A_0 and a 3 dB bandwidth equal to $1/\tau$. The gain–bandwidth product is A_0/τ radians per second or $A_0/2\pi\tau$ Hz. The gain is reduced to K when feedback is applied, but the bandwidth increases to $A_0/K\tau$ (equation (7.20)). Their product is unchanged. We therefore see that gain may be traded for bandwidth. This is an important principle of negative feedback amplifier design, and gives rise to the notion of the *gain–bandwidth product* of an amplifier.

These ideas are illustrated by the Bode plots in figure 7.4. The dotted line, labelled (a), represents the open-loop voltage gain of a typical, inexpensive, operational amplifier. Its nominal gain of 100 dB ($A_0 = 10^5$) is only available up to about 10 Hz. Thereafter the gain falls off at 20 dB/decade, reaching 0 dB at a frequency of 1 MHz. The thick lines, labelled (b) to (e), represent the effects of various amounts of negative feedback. For example, feedback sufficient to reduce the nominal gain to 60 dB ($K = 10^3$) causes the bandwidth to increase to 1 kHz. A voltage follower with a nominal gain of 0 dB ($K = 1$) has a much higher bandwidth. The gain–bandwidth product remains constant at a value of 1 MHz in this illustration.

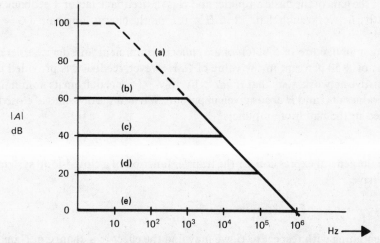

Figure 7.4 The effects of negative feedback on an amplifier's gain–frequency characteristic.

We next consider the beneficial effects of negative feedback on the stability of an amplifier. 'Stability' may imply several different things. Firstly, there is the meaning already used many times in this book. A stable system has an impulse response which decays with time; the faster the rate of decay, the more stable the system. In terms of transfer function poles and zeros, a very stable continuous LTI system has poles lying well to the left of the imaginary axis in the s-plane. As a general rule, the application of negative feedback does indeed tend to move s-plane poles further away from the imaginary axis, and increase system damping.

A rather different aspect of amplifier stability concerns device and component tolerances. Active devices, and to a lesser extent passive components, often have quite wide manufacturing tolerances. For example, the gain parameter of individual transistors may vary over a 2:1 or 3:1 range, even for devices of the same nominal type. If a large batch of amplifiers is manufactured, their characteristics therefore tend to vary quite widely. This problem may be largely offset by incorporating negative feedback in the design.

Apart from manufacturing tolerances, electronic components are often affected to a marked extent by temperature change. Once again, this is particularly true of active devices. However, when negative feedback is used the overall characteristics of an amplifier become largely dependent on a passive feedback network. This can be made relatively stable with temperature. Finally, by 'stability' we may mean unchanging performance over the lifetime of a system— perhaps 15 years or more. Clearly, if 'ageing' of devices and components causes their values to drift significantly over the years, overall performance is likely to suffer. Such effects may be greatly reduced by incorporating a highly stable negative feedback network.

Example E7.1

(a) Show that any changes in the gain of an amplifier are reduced by a factor equal to the loop gain when negative feedback is employed. Assume the loop gain is much greater than unity.

(b) The overall voltage gain of a negative feedback amplifier is given by

$$\frac{V_2}{V_1} = \frac{G}{1 - GH}$$

where G is the gain of the basic amplifier and H is the feedback factor. Feedback is provided by a resistive network, such that $-1 < H < 0$. Find the closed-loop gain if $G = 10\,000$ and $H = -0.1$.

(c) During manufacture of a batch of amplifiers, component and device tolerances cause variations of ± 50 per cent in the value of G. However, feedback is provided by a highly stable resistive network, such that H varies by only ± 1 per cent from its nominal value. The nominal values of G and H are as given in part (b). What range of values of closed-loop gain is expected in the batch of amplifiers?

Solution

(a) Using the general expression for the transfer function of a closed-loop system (equation (7.2)) we have

$$\frac{Y}{X} = \frac{G}{1 - GH} = F$$

By differentiating with respect to G, we may find the effect of a change in G on the overall system gain, F. Thus

$$\frac{dF}{dG} = \frac{(1 - GH) - G(-H)}{(1 - GH)^2} = \frac{1}{(1 - GH)^2} = \frac{F}{G(1 - GH)}$$

Therefore

$$\frac{dF}{F} = \frac{1}{(1 - GH)}\frac{dG}{G} \approx \left(\frac{-1}{GH}\right)\frac{dG}{G}, \quad \text{if } |GH| \gg 1$$

This shows that a fractional change in G gives rise to a fractional change in F which is smaller by a factor equal to the loop gain.

(b)

$$\frac{V_2}{V_1} = \frac{10\,000}{1 - 10\,000(-0.1)} = 9.990$$

Hence the closed-loop voltage gain is 9.990 (or 19.99 dB).

(c) The largest closed-loop gain occurs when G is maximum and the amount of feedback is minimum, that is $G = 15\,000$ and $H = -0.099$. Then

$$\frac{V_2}{V_1} = \frac{15\,000}{1 + 15\,000(0.099)} = 10.094$$

The smallest closed-loop gain occurs when G is minimum and the amount of feedback is maximum, that is $G = 5000$ and $H = -0.101$. Then

$$\frac{V_2}{V_1} = \frac{5000}{1 + 5000(0.101)} = 9.881$$

Therefore the gain values are expected to fall in the range 9.881 to 10.094 (a variation of 0.185 dB).

The application of negative feedback to an electronic system generally also affects its input and output impedances. Indeed, feedback is sometimes used for this reason alone. Such effects need not surprise us—after all, a circuit with feedback components added is not the same circuit as it was before! The actual changes to impedance levels depend upon the manner in which negative feedback is applied. Broadly speaking, a signal representing either output voltage or output current can be fed back to the input either in series or in parallel. Of these four possibilities, the *voltage-series* feedback is the most common. This is illustrated in simplified form in the combined system–circuit diagram of figure 7.5(a), which shows an electrical load connected to the output side. The output voltage V_2 is multiplied by a voltage feedback factor H_V to produce the feedback voltage V_F. This is placed in series with the input signal. Clearly, connections around the closed loop must be such that the input and feedback signals are in *series-opposition*; in other words, they must subtract. Another possibility—*current-shunt* feedback—is illustrated in part (b) of the figure. Here a feedback signal proportional to output current is subtracted from the input current. The other two types of negative feedback (voltage-shunt and current-series) may readily be imagined as variations on the schemes shown in the figure.

The impedance changes caused by the four types of negative feedback are summarised in the following table.

	Type of negative feedback			
	voltage-series	*current-shunt*	*voltage-shunt*	*current-series*
Input impedance	increases	decreases	decreases	increases
Output impedance	decreases	increases	decreases	increases

A detailed explanation of these effects will not be attempted here. However, a few general remarks may be helpful. We see that the popular voltage-series connection increases input impedance. This useful effect may be explained as follows. Since the feedback signal detracts from the input signal, the *net* voltage applied to the forward-path subsystem is reduced by such feedback. The subsystem therefore draws less current. The feedback and input voltages are in *series*, so this reduced current equals the current demanded from the input signal source. The input impedance must therefore be greater. The standard noninverting amplifier and voltage follower circuits shown in figure 7.3 use this type of feedback, and both have very high input

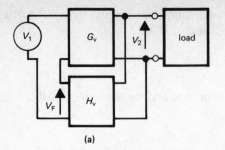
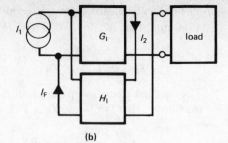

Figure 7.5 Two types of negative feedback connection in continuous electronic systems: (a) voltage-series feedback, and (b) current-shunt feedback.

impedances. The voltage follower is normally used for precisely this reason, acting as a *buffer* between a relatively high-impedance signal source and low-impedance load.

The reader familiar with electrical circuit theory will recognise the *duality* shown in the table. Voltage is the dual of current, and series is the dual of parallel (or shunt). So it need come as no surprise that the impedance changes caused by voltage-series feedback are precisely opposite to those caused by current-shunt feedback. Comparable duality exists between the voltage-shunt and current-series connections.

7.3.2 *Oscillators*

An oscillator generates a periodic output signal without requiring any input. Very often the output is a sinusoidal or square waveform, and sometimes its frequency and amplitude are adjustable. Sinusoidal oscillators are widely used in electronic systems—for example, radio, radar, and television receivers. Square wave oscillators find application as 'clocks' which control the sequence of operations in digital systems, including computers. Oscillators are also at the heart of signal generators. These are among the most widely used laboratory instruments.

Positive feedback is employed in an oscillator to produce a deliberately unstable system. The system needs no input signal—only a power supply. It channels DC energy from this supply into AC signal energy, arranging that the conditions for oscillation are met only at the desired signal frequency. We have already seen what these conditions are in section 7.2. There must be positive feedback, and unity loop gain. In practice, the loop gain of an analog system cannot be made *precisely* unity. Even if it could, small changes in device and component parameters due to ambient temperature fluctuations would very likely cause the loop gain to fall slightly. The output signal would then decay to zero. So the loop gain must be made somewhat greater than unity. This means that when the oscillator's power supply is first switched on, the output signal increases in amplitude. As in any unstable system, its growth must sooner or later be halted by some nonlinear mechanism. This was first discussed in section 2.3.2. It is an important part of oscillator design to ensure that such *limiting* occurs at the desired signal amplitude, without causing unacceptable distortion of the output waveform.

We start by describing the well-known *Wien oscillator*. This is particularly suitable for generating sinusoidal signals up to (say) a few hundred kilohertz. It is based upon a noninverting amplifier, plus an *RC* feedback network which provides zero phase shift at the required oscillation frequency. Rather than introduce its circuit diagram directly, it is helpful to consider the closely related feedback system shown in figure 7.6(a). This will allow us to view the operation of the Wien oscillator as an extension of our previous work on *s*-plane poles and system stability.

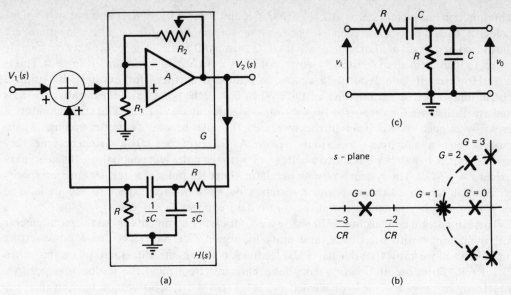

Figure 7.6 Development of a Wien oscillator.

The figure shows a noninverting amplifier whose gain G may be altered by adjusting R_2. We assume that G is independent of frequency. A resistor–capacitor network is used to provide a feedback signal which is added to normal input signal (note that *input* terminals of the network are on the *right-hand* side in this figure, and the *output* terminals are on the *left*). The frequency response of this network was previously found in worked example E4.7

$$H(\omega) = \frac{j\omega CR}{1 + 3j\omega CR - (\omega CR)^2} \tag{7.21}$$

This is a simple bandpass function having a peak gain of $1/3$ at the frequency $\omega_1 = 1/CR$. The phase-shift characteristic starts at $\pi/2$ when $\omega = 0$, passes through zero when $\omega = \omega_1$, and approaches $-\pi/2$ at high frequency—see figure E4.7(b). Substituting s for $j\omega$ we obtain the corresponding transfer function relating input and output voltage signals

$$H(s) = \frac{sCR}{1 + 3sCR + s^2C^2R^2} \tag{7.22}$$

This function has a single zero at $s = 0$, and two s-plane poles. It is straightforward to show that these are real, with values $s = -0.382/CR$ and $s = -2.617/CR$.

Let us now find the transfer function of the overall feedback system. We assume that the input impedance of the adder unit is very high, so that the output of the feedback network is effectively open-circuit. Equation (7.22) then holds. Comparing the present system with the generalised feedback system in figure 7.2, and using equation (7.2), we obtain

$$\frac{V_2(s)}{V_1(s)} = \frac{G}{1 - GH(s)} = \frac{G}{1 - G\left(\dfrac{sCR}{s^2C^2R^2 + 3sCR + 1}\right)}$$

$$\therefore \frac{V_2(s)}{V_1(s)} = \frac{G(s^2C^2R^2 + 3sCR + 1)}{s^2C^2R^2 + sCR(3 - G) + 1} \tag{7.23}$$

This function has s-plane zeros at $s = -0.382/CR$ and $s = -2.617/CR$. It also has two s-plane poles, *at locations which depend on the value of the amplifier gain G*. These locations are illustrated in part (b) of figure 7.6 for values of G between 0 and 3. (The reader may reasonably object that adjustment of resistor R_2 would not allow us to obtain gain values below 1.0. This is true. However, it would be quite simple to reduce G further—for example, by using a potentiometer across the amplifier output.) When $G = 0$, the poles lie on the negative real axis and are distinct. As G increases to 1.0, they come together at $s = -1/CR$. This corresponds to a critically damped system. If G is further increased, the poles become a complex-conjugate pair, moving round a semicircular locus in the s-plane. As G approaches 3.0 the system becomes very underdamped. Instability is reached when $G = 3$, with the poles lying actually *on* the imaginary axis at $s = \pm j/CR$. The system is now an oscillator. Since the poles of a transfer function specify its natural response—the response it exhibits *on its own*—we expect to see undamped oscillations at the system output at the sinusoidal frequency $\omega = 1/CR$.

These important conclusions tie in neatly with our earlier comments about the requirements for oscillation: positive feedback, and unity loop gain. We have specified a noninverting amplifier, and we know that this particular feedback network introduces zero phase shift when $\omega = 1/CR$. Therefore at this frequency (and *only* this frequency) the feedback is positive. Furthermore, the gain of the feedback network is 1/3 at $\omega = 1/CR$. So we must have an amplifier gain of at least 3 to give unity gain right around the loop.

Although these oscillation conditions can be established without considering the s-plane poles of the system, the approach we have adopted illustrates a number of important ideas very graphically. In particular, we see that a stable feedback system can become unstable merely by altering the gain of one of its subsystems.

If the gain of the amplifier in figure 7.6(a) is 3.0 (or, in practice, slightly above 3.0), and the system has become an oscillator, there is no need for an input signal. Therefore the adder unit on the input side is redundant, and the feedback signal may be applied directly to the operational amplifier's noninverting input. Another point to note is that the RC network shown in part (c) of the figure is often used as an alternative feedback network. Perhaps surprisingly, its transfer function is also given by equation (7.22). Taking these two points together, we may redraw the circuit diagram so that the various resistors and capacitors form a bridge network. This produces the oscillator circuit shown in figure 7.7(a). For obvious reasons, it is widely known as the *Wien bridge* oscillator. Since the gain of a standard noninverting amplifier equals

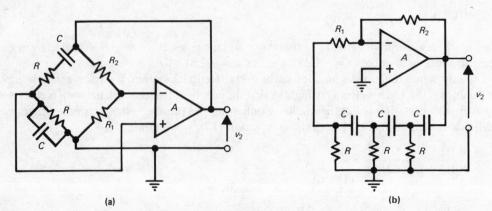

(a)   (b)

Figure 7.7 Two common forms of continuous oscillator: (a) the Wien bridge, and (b) the phase-shift oscillator.

$(1 + R_2/R_1)$, we expect the oscillator to work if R_2 is slightly greater than $2R_1$. Also, by adjusting component values on the other side of the bridge, the oscillation frequency may be controlled.

It may not seem at all obvious why this oscillator—or any other—should 'start up' when its power supply is first switched on. In fact, there is always a certain amount of random noise present in any electronic system, and some of its energy will be at or close to the oscillation frequency. Provided the loop gain is slightly greater than unity, this noise is sufficient to initiate a growing oscillation in the circuit. As already mentioned, some nonlinear mechanism must sooner or later halt the growth of the output signal. We will return to this important matter at the end of the section.

The *phase-shift oscillator* shown in part (b) of figure 7.7 may be considered an alternative to the Wien oscillator. It is based on an inverting amplifier, together with a feedback network which gives 180° phase-shift at the oscillation frequency. It requires two more components in the feedback network compared with the Wien oscillator and, as we shall see, a rather higher value of amplifier gain. However, it is quite widely used as a simple sinusoidal oscillator—particularly at low and medium frequencies. Since we have looked carefully at the workings of the Wien oscillator, we may tackle the phase-shift oscillator in less detail. The basic ideas involved are very similar.

Example E7.2

Establish the oscillation conditions for the phase-shift oscillator shown in figure 7.7(b) of the main text. Choose suitable component values to give an output frequency of 10 kHz.

Solution

The feedback network is redrawn in figure E7.2 (remember that its input terminals are on the right-hand side in figure 7.7(b)). We may find its voltage transfer function $H(s)$ by labelling three circulating currents as shown. Writing the various voltages and currents in

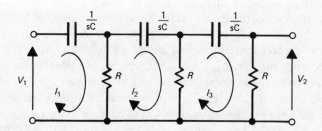

Figure E7.2

terms of their transforms, the mesh equations are

$$V_1 = I_1/sC + (I_1 - I_2)R$$
$$0 = (I_2 - I_1)R + I_2/sC + (I_2 - I_3)R$$
$$0 = (I_3 - I_2)R + I_3/sC + I_3R$$

and

$$V_2 = I_3R$$

It is straightforward, although a little lengthy, to eliminate the three currents and obtain a relationship between V_1 and V_2. This is

$$H(s) = \frac{V_2(s)}{V_1(s)} = \frac{(sCR)^3}{(sCR)^3 + 6(sCR)^2 + 5(sCR) + 1}$$

Substitution of $j\omega$ for s yields the corresponding frequency response

$$H(\omega) = \frac{(j\omega CR)^3}{(j\omega CR)^3 + 6(j\omega CR)^2 + 5(j\omega CR) + 1}$$

Since we are using an inverting amplifier and require positive feedback, the feedback network must also provide an inversion, or 180° phase-shift. $H(\omega)$ must therefore be real and negative. Its numerator is purely imaginary, so its denominator must also be imaginary. This occurs only when

$$-6(\omega CR)^2 + 1 = 0, \quad \text{or} \quad \omega = \frac{1}{CR\sqrt{6}}$$

At this frequency

$$H(\omega) = \frac{(j\omega CR)^3}{(j\omega CR)^3 + 5(j\omega CR)} = \frac{(j\omega CR)^2}{(j\omega CR)^2 + 5} = \frac{-1/6}{(-1/6) + 5} = \frac{-1}{29}$$

For oscillation to commence, the loop gain must be unity. The amplifier must therefore have a gain of -29.

Capacitor values are normally kept below about 1 μF if possible, to save on size and cost. Let us try $C = 0.01$ μF. For an oscillation frequency of 10 kHz, we require that

$$R = \frac{1}{\omega C\sqrt{6}} = \frac{1}{2\pi(10^4)(10^{-8})\sqrt{6}} = 650\,\Omega$$

Our analysis of the feedback network assumes that it is open-circuit. The input impedance 'looking into' the inverting amplifier must therefore be much greater than the output impedance of the network. A value of (say) 33 kΩ for R_1 is therefore sensible. Since we need an amplifier gain of -29, resistor $R_2 = 29 \times 33$ kΩ = 957 kΩ. A value of 1 MΩ should give a loop gain slightly greater than unity, and ensure oscillation.

This discussion of component values is necessarily sketchy, but should give the reader some idea of the choices to be made. In practice, it may be sensible to make R_1 a 50 kΩ variable resistor, and adjust it until oscillation just commences. Note also that the values of C and R must be accurate if the oscillation frequency is to be close to the required 10 kHz. (Standard carbon resistors often have a tolerance of ± 5 per cent or ± 10 per cent on their stated values. Capacitors may typically be ± 20 per cent.)

Our analysis of the phase-shift oscillator has been much less thorough than that of the Wien oscillator. We have not looked with care at the frequency response of the feedback network, nor at the locations of the circuit's s-plane poles as a function of amplifier gain. Two problems based upon these topics are included at the end of the chapter.

The feedback networks of the Wien and phase-shift oscillators contain no inductors. This is an attraction for low-frequency applications, where inductors tend to be bulky, expensive, and non-ideal. However at higher frequencies (say above 1 MHz), an oscillator with an LC feedback network is often chosen. Such a network may generally be designed with a high Q-factor. This means that the phase shift conditions required for positive feedback and oscillation occur at a more sharply defined frequency.

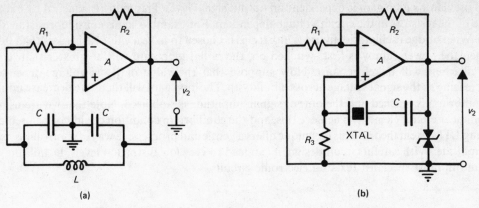

Figure 7.8 (a) Colpitts oscillator, and (b) crystal oscillator.

One of the best-known circuits of this type is the *Colpitts oscillator* illustrated in figure 7.8(a). It should again be stressed that in many high-frequency applications an operational amplifier would not be suitable as the amplifying device. However, our aim here is to show the basic circuit configuration. The loop gain and phase-shift requirements for oscillation are met only at the resonant frequency of the tuned feedback network. In the *Hartley oscillator*, which works in a very similar manner, the inductive and capacitive feedback components are interchanged.

Many practical applications of oscillators require an extremely stable output frequency. For example, the frequency of a broadcast transmitter must be controlled with great accuracy. At a more mundane level, a cheap digital watch with an accuracy of a few minutes per year needs an internal oscillator with a frequency stability of about 1 part in 100 000! Apart from the difficulty and expense of securing feedback network components with the required values, the effects of temperature and component ageing make such performance virtually impossible to achieve using the simple oscillators already described.

Fortunately a cheap and highly effective solution to this difficulty is provided by the *piezoelectric crystal*, normally made of quartz. This has the properties that a voltage applied across two of its faces causes mechanical distortion, and that mechanical strain gives rise to an electrical output signal. Viewed from its electrical terminals, the crystal behaves like a tuned *LC* circuit with an extremely high Q-factor—typically 20 000. Furthermore, its natural frequency is determined by the original cut of the crystal, and is highly stable. In particularly demanding applications, the crystal may be housed in a temperature-controlled oven.

Figure 7.8(b) illustrates—once more in a simplified form, using an operational amplifier—the principle of using a quartz crystal in an electronic oscillator. In this circuit the crystal is connected as a series element in the feedback path. The crystal's impedance is a minimum at its so-called *series-resonant* frequency, giving a maximum amount of feedback. The total phase-shift around the loop is zero at resonance, making the feedback positive. Clearly, the values of the various resistors in the circuit must be chosen to give the required loop gain. In this particular example, we have also shown two *Zener diodes* connected back-to-back across the oscillator output. These are not essential to the operation of the oscillator, but provide one means of limiting the output amplitude. The diodes conduct when the peak-to-peak output voltage exceeds a certain level. This produces a *clipping* of the output, and if the loop gain of the linear part of the circuit is high, an approximately square output waveform is obtained.

Diode clipping is an effective way of limiting signal amplitude, but introduces unacceptable distortion if a pure sinusoidal output is required. In this case a better approach is to arrange that the oscillator's loop gain is dependent on output signal level. This may be achieved by making one of the resistors in the circuit voltage-dependent. For example, let us consider resistor R_1 in the Wien bridge oscillator of figure 7.7(a). If this is chosen to have a value rather less than $0.5R_2$ when the power supply is first switched on, the initial loop gain will be greater than unity. Oscillations will therefore start. Now suppose that the value of R_1 is voltage-dependent, increasing as the signal voltage across it builds up. The loop gain will therefore decrease until an equilibrium is reached and the output signal amplitude is stabilised. Note that we are using a nonlinear circuit element to achieve this, and the equilibrium condition could not be predicted using LTI system theory. This technique offers a gentle and progressive way of controlling signal amplitude. With careful circuit design, it can lead to very low distortion levels. Details may be found in most specialist texts on electronic circuits.

7.4 Feedback in discrete LTI systems

The general attributes of feedback described in section 7.2 also apply to discrete-time systems. Negative feedback tends to reduce gain, increase bandwidth, and enhance stability. Positive feedback increases gain and may lead to instability. The purpose of this section is to demonstrate such features as they apply to discrete systems, and to outline some applications.

We should first note that one of the main roles of feedback in analog electronic systems—its application in negative feedback amplifiers—is hardly relevant to the digital case. Distortionless wideband amplification of a discrete signal is a relatively simple matter—we merely multiply all sample values by a constant! On the other hand, the design of discrete-time oscillators and signal generators using positive feedback is a practical matter of some interest. However, it involves few of the frequency and amplitude stability problems associated with analog oscillators. Moving away from feedback which is clearly either negative or positive, we should remember that *all* recursive discrete systems involve feedback connections. Viewed in this wider context, feedback is very commonly employed.

Apart from ever-increasing application in signal processing and communication, discrete feedback systems are extremely useful in the field of automatic control. The great flexibility and accuracy of discrete-time methods make it very attractive to include a digital computer or microprocessor in the feedback loop of many automatic control systems—industrial plant and processes, machine tools, aircraft autopilots, and so on. Most of these systems are essentially *hybrid*, involving a mix of continuous and discrete subsystems.

Let us first demonstrate the main properties of negative and positive feedback by some simple examples. Inside the large rectangular box in figure 7.9(a) is a first-order low-pass discrete filter (since we are working in terms of z-transforms, its delay unit is labelled z^{-1}). We ignore, for the moment, the feedback within this filter, and focus on the additional feedback path right around the system. This has gain α. Comparing with figure 7.2 we see that

$$G(z) = \frac{1}{(1 - 0.95z^{-1})} = \frac{z}{(z - 0.95)}, \quad \text{and } H(z) = \alpha \tag{7.24}$$

The overall transfer function of the feedback system is given by equation (7.2)

$$\frac{Y(z)}{X(z)} = \frac{G(z)}{1 - G(z)H(z)} = \frac{\dfrac{z}{(z - 0.95)}}{1 - \dfrac{\alpha z}{(z - 0.95)}} = \frac{1}{(1 - \alpha)} \frac{z}{\left\{ z - \dfrac{0.95}{(1 - \alpha)} \right\}} \tag{7.25}$$

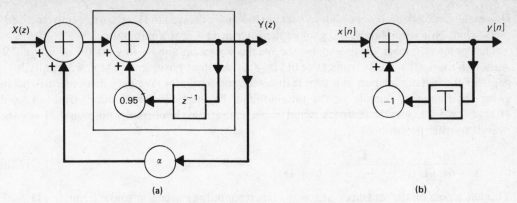

(a) (b)

Figure 7.9 Discrete LTI systems involving feedback.

If there is no feedback ($\alpha = 0$) we obtain

$$\frac{Y(z)}{X(z)} = \frac{z}{(z - 0.95)} \qquad (7.26)$$

This is, of course, the transfer function of the low-pass filter within the rectangular box. Its pole at $z = 0.95$ denotes a system of narrow bandwidth.

Negative feedback may be applied by making α negative, for example $\alpha = -1$. With this value, the overall transfer function becomes

$$\frac{Y(z)}{X(z)} = 0.5 \frac{z}{(z - 0.475)} \qquad (7.27)$$

This has had two effects. First, the overall gain of the system has been reduced; and second, the pole has moved away from the unit circle, giving a more stable system. In terms of its frequency response, the system is still low-pass, but it has a wider bandwidth. These are the expected effects of negative feedback.

If we apply positive feedback by making α positive, the effects are reversed. Overall gain increases, and stability reduces. Equation (7.25) shows that if $\alpha = 0.05$ the pole reaches the unit circle at $z = 1$, and the system becomes unstable. Higher values of α are not allowed, since they imply an impulse response which grows without limit. Thus although negative feedback may be applied with any value of α in the range $-\infty < \alpha < 0$, in this case positive feedback up to the point of system instability is covered by the narrow range $0 < \alpha < 0.05$.

The reader is asked not to assume that feedback would necessarily be incorporated in the way shown in figure 7.9(a). The attraction of this particular connection is that it demonstrates the typical effects of feedback in a simple and graphic manner.

When the feedback path is a direct connection from output to input (perhaps including a scalar multiplier), it is easy to see whether the feedback is positive or negative. But as soon as we include one or more delay elements in the feedback path, the situation becomes more complicated. This is because a pure time-delay gives rise to a phase-shift proportional to frequency. So the feedback may well be positive at some frequencies and negative at others. A good example of this is the low-pass filter subsystem just discussed. It includes a feedback path with a single delay unit, and the loop gain of 0.95 denotes a stable system. At first sight the feedback may appear to be positive. This is indeed the case at zero frequency, $\Omega = 0$ (and at other frequencies separated from this by 2π). It gives the filter its low-pass properties. But at

$\Omega = \pi$, the feedback becomes negative, because the single delay in the loop corresponds to a 180° phase-shift. Not surprisingly, the gain of the filter at $\Omega = \pi$ is a minimum.

This point is further illustrated by the feedback system shown in part (b) of figure 7.9. Although the feedback is here negative at $\Omega = 0$, it becomes positive at $\Omega = \pi$, with unity loop gain. So the system behaves as a simple discrete-time oscillator. We may demonstrate this in either the frequency-domain or the time-domain. In the frequency-domain, $G(z) = 1$; and $H(z) = -z^{-1}$, because the feedback signal is *subtracted* from the normal input signal. Hence the overall transfer function is

$$\frac{G(z)}{1 - G(z)H(z)} = \frac{1}{(1 + z^{-1})} = \frac{z}{(z + 1)} \tag{7.28}$$

This has a pole on the unit circle at $z = -1$ (corresponding to the sinusoidal frequency $\Omega = \pi$), so we expect an unstable system with a natural response which neither grows nor decays with time. The time-domain recurrence formula of the system is

$$y[n] = -y[n-1] + x[n] \tag{7.29}$$

and its impulse response is given by

$$h[n] = -h[n-1] + \delta[n] \tag{7.30}$$

$h[n]$ has successive sample values, starting at $n = 0$

$$1, -1, 1, -1, 1, -1, \ldots$$

This represents a continuing oscillation at the discrete frequency $\Omega = \pi$. Clearly, by placing poles at other points on the unit circle, we can design a whole series of digital oscillators with different output frequencies.

Example E7.3

Specify the recurrence formula of a discrete-time oscillator to produce a sinusoidal signal at the frequency $\Omega = \pi/20$. Adjust the design to give an output of unit amplitude when the initial excitation is a unit impulse. Check the operation of the oscillator using a digital computer.

Solution

We require a complex conjugate pole pair on the unit circle at angles $\pm\pi/20$ to the real positive axis. These give the transfer function

$$H(z) = \frac{Y(z)}{X(z)} = \frac{1}{\{z - \exp(j\pi/20)\}\{z - \exp(-j\pi/20)\}}$$

$$\therefore H(z) = \frac{1}{z^2 - 2z\cos(\pi/20) + 1}$$

The corresponding time-domain recurrence formula is

$$y[n+2] - 2\cos(\pi/20)y[n+1] + y[n] = x[n]$$

or

$$y[n] = 1.97537668y[n-1] - y[n-2] + x[n]$$

Since this is an unstable system it does not need an ongoing input signal to drive it.

However, some initial excitation is required 'to get the system going', and the question specifies a unit impulse. If this is applied at $n = 0$, then $x[0] = 1$ and the recurrence formula shows that $y[0] = 1$.

Given the initial conditions $y[-1] = 0$ and $y[0] = 1$, and no further input excitation, the recurrence formula produces oscillations of peak amplitude about ± 6.4. Therefore its gain must be reduced. The exact reduction required may be found by consulting the table of z-transforms at the end of chapter 6 (table 6C). This includes the z-transform pair

$$\sin(n\Omega_0)u[n] \leftrightarrow \frac{z \sin \Omega_0}{z^2 - 2z \cos \Omega_0 + 1}$$

A system with a sinusoidal impulse response of *unit* amplitude needs this form of transfer function. With $\Omega_0 = \pi/20$ we obtain the recurrence formula

$$y[n] = 1.975\,376\,68y[n-1] - y[n-2] + 0.156\,434\,465x[n-1]$$

Note that $x[n-1]$ is now specified in place of $x[n]$. This gives the correct phase for a sine output signal. Again applying a unit impulse function at $n = 0$, we obtain $y[1] = 0.156\,434\,465$. The required oscillator may therefore be specified as follows

$$y[n] = 1.975\,376\,68y[n-1] - y[n-2], \qquad n \geqslant 2$$

given that

$$y[0] = 0 \quad \text{and} \quad y[1] = 0.156\,434\,465$$

The multiplier coefficients of recurrence formulae have always previously been quoted to about 4-figure accuracy. Here, however, we have given 9 decimal figures. The reason is that the oscillator's z-plane poles should lie *exactly* on the unit circle. Otherwise the oscillation amplitude will grow or decay with time. Even with 9-figure accuracy, the pole locations will not be perfect. (A sensible way round this problem would be initially to *store* one complete period of the output signal, subsequently reading it out from memory over and over again. However, this is possible only when the required output frequency implies a strictly periodic output signal—as discussed in section 2.2.3.)

The following BASIC program (program no. 6) implements the oscillator. Rather than dimension an array to hold the output signal, we have merely specified three storage locations Y0, Y1, and Y2. These are updated on each recursion, the old values being lost. A plot or print option is available for the output (if *only* the print option is required, then lines 120, and 150 to 180 inclusive, may be omitted). In a test on a microcomputer, 25 000 complete periods of the oscillation were completed (1 million sample values). The final oscillation amplitude departed from the desired value of 1.0 by less than 0.01 per cent. So the poles must have been extremely close to the unit circle!

```
100 REM ******  PROGRAM NO.6        DISCRETE-TIME OSCILLATOR  *****
110 X=0
120 PRINT "SELECT PLOT OPTION (+1) ,OR PRINT OPTION (-1)":INPUT K
130 Y0=0:Y1=0.156434465
140 Y2=1.97537668*Y1-Y0
150 IF K=-1 THEN GOTO 190
160 IF X=0 THEN CLS
170 X=X+2:IF X>600 THEN X=0
180 PLOT X,200:DRAW X,200+Y0*150:GOTO 200
190 PRINT Y0;
200 Y0=Y1:Y1=Y2:GOTO 140
210 REM ************************************************************
```

Problems to chapter 7

Section 7.2

Q7.1. A generalised feedback system is shown in figure Q7.1. Determine whether the feedback is negative or positive under the following conditions

(a) $G = 10$; $H = 0.5$

(b) $G = -5$; $H = 0.1$

(c) G introduces a phase shift of $3\pi/2$; H introduces a phase shift of $\pi/2$.

(d) $G = G(\omega) = \dfrac{100}{1 + j\omega\tau}$; $H = H(\omega) = \dfrac{j\omega\tau}{1 + j\omega\tau}$; $\omega = \dfrac{1}{\tau}$

(e) $G = G(z) = \dfrac{1 - 2z}{5z}$; $H = H(z) = \dfrac{1}{z^2}$; input signal frequency is zero.

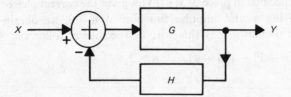

Figure Q7.1

Section 7.3

Q7.2. The open-loop voltage gain of an integrated-circuit operational amplifier is 10^5. Its input and output impedances may be assumed infinite and zero respectively.

(a) It is used in the standard inverting amplifier configuration with $R_1 = 10\,\text{k}\Omega$ and $R_2 = 1\,\text{M}\Omega$. Viewed as a negative feedback amplifier, what is the effective feedback factor and loop gain?

(b) It is used in the standard noninverting amplifier configuration with $R_1 = 1\,\text{k}\Omega$ and $R_2 = 10\,\text{k}\Omega$. What is the effective voltage feedback factor and loop gain? If the integrated circuit is replaced by another having an open-loop voltage gain of 5×10^4, what is the percentage change in closed-loop gain?

(c) The integrated circuit has a frequency response characteristic which falls off at $20\,\text{dB/decade}$ at high frequencies. Its gain–bandwidth product is $5\,\text{MHz}$ and its gain at very low frequencies is 10^5. What bandwidth (to the $-3\,\text{dB}$ frequency) is expected in parts (a) and (b) of this problem, and also if the operational amplifier is connected as a voltage follower?

Q7.3. During manufacture of a large batch of amplifiers, device and component tolerances result in voltage gain values between $60\,\text{dB}$ and $70\,\text{dB}$. Negative feedback is then incorporated to reduce and stabilise the gain. Resistor tolerances in the feedback network give feedback factors in the range 0.1 ± 2 per cent. What total spread of gain values is expected in the feedback amplifiers? Express your answer in decibels.

Q7.4. The voltage transfer function of a continuous amplifer may be represented by

$$G(s) = \frac{10^8}{s + 10^6}$$

What is its DC gain, and 3 dB bandwidth in hertz? Negative feedback is incorporated around the amplifier with a feedback factor α. What value of α will cause the bandwidth to be increased by a factor of 5?

Q7.5. A Wien bridge oscillator is shown in figure 7.7(a) in the main text. Select suitable component values to give an oscillation frequency of (a) 25 Hz and (b) 100 kHz, using a cheap, standard, operational amplifier.

Q7.6. A system and circuit diagram having many similarities with the phase-shift oscillator described in the main text is shown in figure Q7.6. Find an expression for its overall transfer function $V_2(s)/V_1(s)$. Satisfy yourself that when $G = -29$ the system has an imaginary pair of s-plane poles at $s = \pm j/CR\sqrt{6}$, as implied by worked example E7.2. What is the location of the third s-plane pole at this value of G? Also, at what frequency will the system oscillate if $C = 1\ \mu F$ and $R = 100\ k\Omega$?

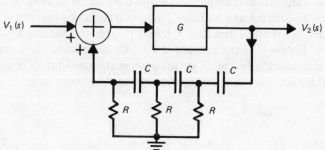

Figure Q7.6

Q7.7. An expression for the frequency response of the feedback network used in a phase-shift oscillator is given in worked example E7.2. Sketch the magnitude and phase of this function over the range $0 < \omega < 2/CR$. What information do your sketches give about the requirements for the amplifier in the phase-shift oscillator? Why is a feedback network with at least three RC sections needed in this type of oscillator?

Q7.8. A continuous linear feedback system is shown in figure Q7.8. Find the locations of its s-plane poles and zeros when the amplifier gain A is (a) 1.0, and (b) 100. Do your findings confirm the general effect that increasing the gain decreases the system stability? Is there any positive value of A above which this system would become unstable?

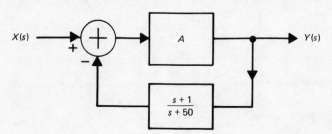

Figure Q7.8

Section 7.4

Q7.9. Figure Q7.9 shows a discrete LTI filter. At what signal frequency (or frequencies) in the range $0 < \Omega < \pi$ does the feedback become negative, or positive? What type of filtering

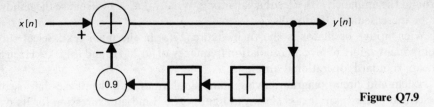

Figure Q7.9

action do you expect this system to produce? Check your conclusion by finding the locations of its z-plane poles and zeros.

Q7.10. Specify the recurrence formula of a discrete-time oscillator to produce a cosinusoidal output signal with 64 samples per cycle. What initial conditions will ensure that the output starts at $n = 0$ and has unit amplitude? If you have access to a digital computer, check your formula by writing and running a simple computer program.

Q7.11. Find a second-order recurrence formula which may be used to generate a table of the function $\sin \theta$, at $1°$ intervals in the range $0 < \theta < 90°$. Implement the formula on a digital computer, and check a few of its results against standard tables or a scientific calculator. Does their accuracy worsen significantly as θ becomes larger?

8　Signal Processing

> "I have a right to be blind sometimes ... I really do not see the signal."
> Horatio, Viscount Nelson (1758–1805),
> putting a telescope to his blind eye
> during the Battle of Copenhagen

8.1 Introduction

The practical applications of electronic signal processing range from aircraft autopilots to medical diagnosis, from satellite communications to the automatic reading of fingerprints. It has been said that, of all the branches and topics into which electronic engineering is now divided, signal processing is the most pervasive. It is not hard to see why. If we take the word *processing* to mean the modification of a signal as it passes through a circuit or system, it is clear that almost every electronic application involves some type of signal processing. In this chapter we develop a few important topics in this field. Most of them have already been mentioned in this book, and are strongly related to the analytical methods of earlier chapters.

8.2 Signal sampling and reconstitution

When a continuous signal is represented by a set of sample values, it may be transmitted or processed digitally, and finally converted back into analog form using a reconstituting filter. The availability of cheap and highly reliable digital circuits and computers gives these processes ever-increasing practical importance. (The reader may find it helpful to refer back to the description of analog-to-digital and digital-to-analog conversion in section 1.3.) At first it may seem surprising that any continuous signal can be completely represented by a set of samples. But the Sampling Theorem quoted in chapter 1 assures us that it may, provided the signal is bandlimited, and provided we sample it often enough. Our purpose here is to explain the reasoning behind this important result, and to outline its practical consequences.

The three diagrams on the left-hand side of figure 8.1 illustrate sampling in the time-domain. At the top is shown a portion of a typical continuous signal $x_1(t)$. Beneath it is a signal $x_2(t)$

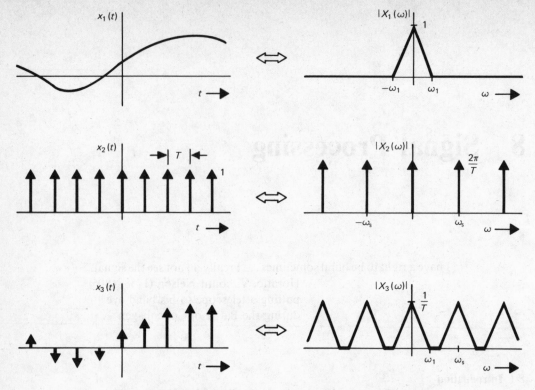

Figure 8.1 Signal sampling in the time and frequency domains.

consisting of a train of continuous unit impulses spaced T apart. Multiplying $x_1(t)$ by $x_2(t)$, we obtain the sampled signal $x_3(t)$. In this version of the signal, each impulse in $x_2(t)$ is *weighted* by the value of $x_1(t)$ at the appropriate instant. It is clear that sampling, which is a form of modulation process, involves *time-domain multiplication*.

It is more difficult to describe this process in the frequency-domain; but the effort is well worthwhile, because it provides the key to understanding the Sampling Theorem. The relevant spectral functions (for convenience we show only their magnitudes) are illustrated on the right of the figure. Although the detailed *shape* of $|X_1(\omega)|$ does not affect the following derivation, it *is* important that this spectrum is bandlimited, with no energy above some frequency ω_1. To explain the spectrum $X_2(\omega)$ of the unit impulse train, we first note that $x_2(t)$ is a strictly periodic signal. It must therefore have a Fourier Series and a line spectrum. We may use equation (4.31) to find its exponential Fourier Series coefficients (noting that in this case the period of the signal is T)

$$a_k = \frac{1}{T} \int_{-T/2}^{T/2} x(t) \exp(-2\pi jkt/T)\, dt \tag{8.1}$$

Now $x_2(t)$ is zero between $-T/2$ and $T/2$, apart from a unit impulse at $t = 0$. Hence

$$a_k = \frac{1}{T} \exp(-2\pi jkt/T)|_{t=0} = \frac{1}{T} \tag{8.2}$$

Therefore the signal has a cosine series in which all harmonics are equally represented.

For the present discussion we wish to work in terms of the Fourier Transform, rather than the Series. We may change from one to the other using a result derived in section 4.2.3.1 (see also table 4B)

$$\cos \omega_0 t = \tfrac{1}{2} \exp(j\omega_0 t) + \tfrac{1}{2} \exp(-j\omega_0 t) \leftrightarrow \pi\delta(\omega + \omega_0) + \pi\delta(\omega - \omega_0) \tag{8.3}$$

Thus an eternal cosine may be represented *either* by a pair of Fourier Series coefficients of value 1/2, *or* by a pair of Fourier Transform 'impulses' of value π. Returning to the unit impulse train in figure 8.1, we have just found that all its Fourier Series coefficients are equal to $1/T$. By analogy, we infer that its Fourier Transform must consist of a train of frequency-domain impulses of magnitude $2\pi/T$.

The next step is to consider the spectrum of the sampled signal $x_3(t)$. Since time-domain multiplication is equivalent to frequency-domain convolution, $X_3(\omega)$ may be found by convolving $X_1(\omega)$ and $X_2(\omega)$. Fortunately, the convolution of two functions is quite straightforward to visualise when one of them consists of an impulse train. The effect is to *repeat the other function at each point where an impulse occurs*. In other words the spectrum of $x_3(t)$ must be a repetitive version of the spectrum of $x_1(t)$. This is also illustrated in figure 8.1.

The above argument will now be summarised mathematically. The impulse train $x_2(t)$ is given by

$$x_2(t) = \sum_{n=-\infty}^{\infty} \delta(t - nT) \tag{8.4}$$

Therefore the sampled version of the signal is

$$x_3(t) = x_1(t)x_2(t) = \sum_{n=-\infty}^{\infty} x_1(t)\delta(t - nT) = \sum_{n=-\infty}^{\infty} x_1(nT)\delta(t - nT) \tag{8.5}$$

Using the modulation property of the continuous-time Fourier Transform (see table 4A), we have

$$X_3(\omega) = \frac{1}{2\pi} \{X_1(\omega) * X_2(\omega)\} \tag{8.6}$$

As argued a little earlier, the transform of a train of unit impulses consists of a repetitive train of frequency-domain impulses of magnitude $2\pi/T$. These are separated by ω_s. Hence

$$X_2(\omega) = \frac{2\pi}{T} \sum_{k=-\infty}^{\infty} \delta(\omega - k\omega_s) \tag{8.7}$$

Finally we obtain

$$X_3(\omega) = \frac{1}{2\pi} \{X_1(\omega) * X_2(\omega)\} = \frac{1}{T} \sum_{k=-\infty}^{\infty} X_1(\omega - k\omega_s) \tag{8.8}$$

This shows, once again, that the spectrum of the sampled signal is the sum of a repeating set of replicas of the original spectrum. They are separated by ω_s along the frequency axis, and scaled in magnitude by $1/T$.

We now have all the information we need to infer the Sampling Theorem. Provided the various replicas of $X_1(\omega)$ contained in $X_3(\omega)$ *do not overlap*, we may reconstitute the original signal from its sampled version using a low-pass filter. This must select out the replica of $X_1(\omega)$ centred at $\omega = 0$, but eliminate all the others. The lower right-hand diagram in figure 8.1 shows that spectral overlap is only avoided if $\omega_s \geqslant 2\omega_1$, giving

$$f_s = \frac{\omega_s}{2\pi} \geqslant \frac{\omega_1}{\pi} = 2f_1, \quad \text{or} \quad T = \frac{1}{f_s} \leqslant \frac{1}{2f_1} \tag{8.9}$$

The Sampling Theorem may therefore be stated as follows

"A continuous signal containing frequency components up to some maximum frequency f_1 Hz may be completely represented by regularly spaced samples taken at a rate of at least $2f_1$ samples per second."

Too low a sampling rate would lead to spectral overlap, or *aliasing*. The original signal could not then be recovered with a linear filter.

In practice, the maximum frequency f_1 may not be accurately known. So it is quite common to filter the original signal before sampling, to ensure it is bandlimited. A filter used for this purpose is known as an *anti-aliasing filter*.

The reconstitution of a continuous signal from its sample values is summarised by figure 8.2. The upper diagram shows the situation in the frequency-domain. In this case we have assumed that $\omega_s = 2\omega_1$, so that aliasing is just avoided. The reconstituting filter needs an ideal low-pass characteristic—constant transmission in the range $-\omega_1 < \omega < \omega_1$, zero transmission elsewhere. This is shown dotted on the diagram.

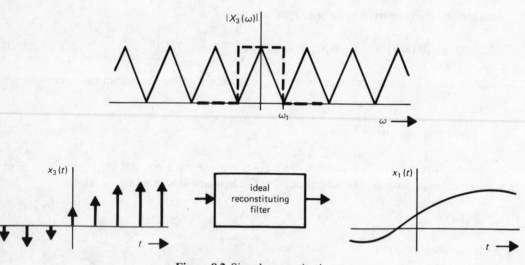

Figure 8.2 Signal reconstitution.

The lower part of the figure illustrates signal reconstitution in the time-domain. It is interesting to consider the action of the ideal filter rather more carefully. Assuming it has unity transmission in the passband $(-\omega_1 < \omega < \omega_1)$, its impulse response is found by inverse Fourier transformation

$$h(t) = \frac{1}{2\pi} \int_{-\infty}^{\infty} H(\omega) \exp(j\omega t)\, d\omega = \frac{1}{2\pi} \int_{-\omega_1}^{\omega_1} \exp(j\omega t)\, d\omega \tag{8.10}$$

The integral is readily evaluated, giving

$$h(t) = \frac{\omega_1}{\pi} \left(\frac{\sin \omega_1 t}{\omega_1 t} \right) = \frac{\omega_1}{\pi} \text{ sinc } \omega_1 t$$

$$= \frac{1}{T} \text{ sinc } \omega_1 t \tag{8.11}$$

Each impulse in $x_3(t)$ therefore produces a weighted sinc function at the filter output. The total output may be found by superposition, as shown in figure 8.3. Note how each sinc function, arranged around the input impulse which causes it, passes through zero at all *other* sampling instants. The reconstituted waveform, shown dotted, must therefore pass through all the sample values. (The figure ignores the $1/T$ multiplier in equation (8.11). However, this only affects the overall scale of the output signal, not its shape.) In effect, an ideal reconstituting filter *interpolates* between the various sample values, producing a continuous signal from an impulse sequence. Its action is sometimes referred to as *ideal bandlimited interpolation*, and may be

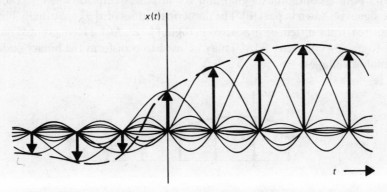

Figure 8.3 The action of an ideal reconstituting filter in the time-domain.

summarised by the following equation

$$x(t) = \sum_{n=-\infty}^{\infty} x_1(nT) \text{ sinc } \omega_1(t - nT) \tag{8.12}$$

Unfortunately, the ideal reconstituting filter cannot be realised in practice. We have assumed an infinitely sharp cut-off at $\omega = \pm\omega_1$, and zero phase-shift. Such a filter is noncausal. The best we can actually hope to achieve is a rapid cut-off beginning at $\pm\omega_1$, and a phase-shift roughly proportional to frequency. The reconstituted signal will then be a reasonably faithful, but delayed, version of the original signal prior to sampling. Its quality may be improved by using a sampling rate rather higher than that specified by the Sampling Theorem. This introduces a *guardband* (B) in the spectrum of the sampled signal, and the reconstituting filter is designed so that its response falls to a very low value as the guardband is crossed. These points are illustrated by figure 8.4. Although the practical sampling and reconstitution of signals falls somewhat short of the idealised situation shown in figures 8.1 to 8.3, the foregoing analysis gives valuable insight into the sampling process and its theoretical basis.

We have so far assumed that a sampled signal is a continuous-time function, consisting of a sequence of weighted impulses. The reader may feel this is rather artificial, because we cannot generate and transmit infinitely narrow electrical impulses in a practical system. In fact the

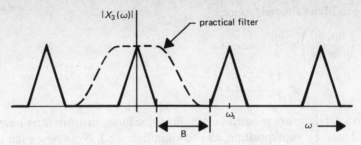

Figure 8.4 Signal reconstitution using a practical filter characteristic.

sample values of a continuous signal are almost always coded into binary form using an analog-to-digital converter (ADC). So rather than work with continuous-time impulse trains (as shown in figures 8.1 to 8.3), we normally convert them into equivalent discrete-time signals. In effect, a sampled signal than becomes just a sequence of numerical values. This is illustrated in figure 8.5. Part (a) shows both a continuous signal and its 'impulse-sampled' version. The equivalent discrete-time signal is shown in part (b). The numerical values of $x[n]$ are usually binary-coded, and may be stored, transmitted, or processed in digital form. As we have pointed out in section 1.3, a digital-to-analog converter (DAC) may be used to transform the binary code back into equivalent analog voltages.

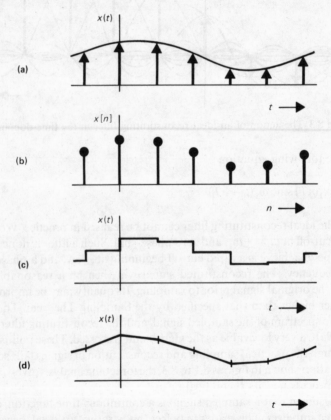

Figure 8.5 Various types of sampled signal: (a) impulse-sampled continuous signal, (b) discrete-time signal, (c) zero-order hold signal, and (d) first-order hold signal.

A DAC normally produces a *zero-order hold* output, in which each analog voltage level is 'held' until the next binary-coded sample value is delivered on the input side. This type of output is shown in figure 8.5(c). Clearly, it represents a simple form of signal reconstitution. Although rather crude compared with the idealised reconstitution of figure 8.3, it is often quite adequate in practice. For example, if one draws a graph or picture on the display of a digital computer, individual lines are generally seen to be made up of a series of discrete steps. In effect these are zero-order hold versions of the 'underlying' continuous lines.

An alternative reconstitution technique is *first-order hold*, also known as *linear interpolation*. Adjacent sample points are joined by a straight line, as illustrated in part (d) of the figure. This gives a considerably better approximation to the underlying analog signal, but is more difficult and expensive to achieve than first-order hold. Needless to say, both zero-order and first-order hold techniques represent well-defined filtering effects in the frequency-domain. These are discussed in more advanced texts on signal sampling and reconstitution.

Parts (a) and (b) of figure 8.5 emphasise the similarity between impulse-sampled continuous signals and discrete signals. Not surprisingly, there are also close relationships between them in the frequency-domain. A continuous signal such as $x_3(t)$ in figure 8.1 has a repetitive spectrum. Similarly, the spectra of all discrete-time signals repeat indefinitely along the frequency axis. We have discussed this aspect of discrete-time functions at various places in this book (and especially in sections 5.2 and 5.3.1). In all cases the spectral repetitions are an inevitable consequence of working with sampled data, and of representing signals by impulse trains.

We next consider the topic of *sampling in the frequency domain*. This has also been touched on previously. For example, in section 4.2.3.1 we described a BASIC computer program for synthesising an isolated rectangular pulse from its spectral components. The program used frequency-domain samples of the underlying continuous spectrum. Also, in section 5.3.1 we saw that the spectral coefficients a_k of a discrete periodic signal may be regarded as samples of an underlying spectrum $X(\Omega)$ representing an aperiodic version of the same signal. This was illustrated by figure 5.4.

The duality between time and frequency domains, and the essential symmetry of Fourier transformation, should surely lead us to expect a frequency-domain version of the Sampling Theorem. We have already seen how a *bandlimited* signal may be completely defined by a set of *time-domain* samples. So we should expect that a *time-limited* signal may be defined by a set of *frequency-domain* samples. This is indeed the case.

Figure 8.6 shows a continuous spectrum $X_1(\omega)$, a unit impulse train $X_2(\omega)$, and a sampled spectrum $X_3(\omega)$. For convenience, all three spectra are assumed real. This figure is the frequency-domain counterpart of the time-domain sampling shown on the left-hand side of figure 8.1. Since $X_3(\omega)$ is the product of $X_1(\omega)$ and $X_2(\omega)$, the corresponding time functions must be related by

$$x_3(t) = x_1(t) * x_2(t) \tag{8.13}$$

Using analogous arguments to those summarised by equations (8.4) to (8.8) for time-domain sampling, it may be shown that

$$x_3(t) = \frac{1}{\omega_0} \sum_{k=-\infty}^{\infty} x_1(t - kT_0), \quad \text{where } T_0 = \frac{2\pi}{\omega_0} \tag{8.14}$$

In other words $x_3(t)$ consists of a repeating set of replicas of $x_1(t)$, separated along the time axis by T_0. Provided the duration of $x_1(t)$ is less than T_0, these replicas will not overlap, and there will be no 'time-domain aliasing'. Clearly, any one of these replicas defines the signal $x_1(t)$. The

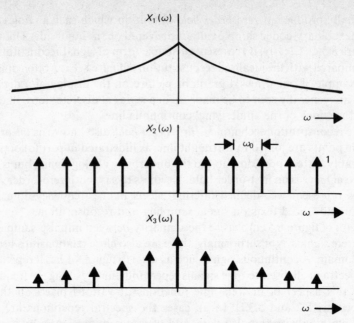

Figure 8.6 Sampling in the frequency-domain.

Sampling Theorem in the frequency domain may therefore be stated as follows

"A continuous signal of total duration T_0 seconds may be recovered from a sampled version of its spectrum, provided the frequency-domain samples are spaced not more than $2\pi/T_0$ radians per second apart."

Although we have discussed this important idea in relation to continuous signals, an equivalent result holds in discrete time. A time-limited discrete signal $x[n]$ may be completely represented by, or recovered from, a limited set of spectral coefficients. These are samples of its underlying continuous spectrum $X(\Omega)$. This matter has been discussed in some detail in sections 5.2 and 5.3, and forms the basis of the discrete and fast Fourier Transforms.

Example E8.1

We sometimes need to display extremely high-frequency signals on an oscilloscope screen (for example, well above 1000 MHz). The restricted bandwidth of normal oscilloscopes prevents us from doing this directly. However, if a signal is periodic, a special (and expensive!) instrument known as a *sampling oscilloscope* may be used.

The operating principle of a sampling oscilloscope is illustrated by figure E8.1.1. For simplicity, the high-frequency signal $x_1(t)$ is assumed to be cosinusoidal. It is multiplied by the unit sample train $x_2(t)$ to produce the sampled signal $x_3(t)$. Sampling occurs once per period, at a slightly later point in each period. $x_3(t)$ is then passed through a suitable reconstituting filter, giving an output (shown dotted) which is a slowed-down, or 'stretched', version of $x_1(t)$. This output may be displayed on a conventional oscilloscope screen.

Interpret the sampling oscilloscope's operation in the light of the Sampling Theorem, and draw an equivalent set of frequency-domain diagrams. For the particular set of waveforms shown, what 'guardband' is available to the reconstituting filter?

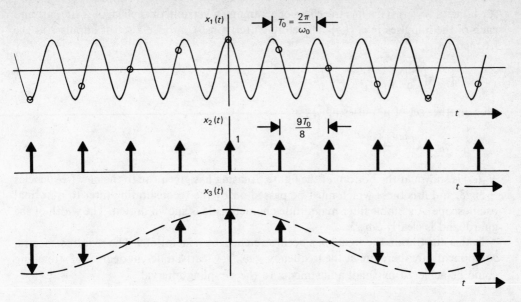

Figure E8.1.1 The principle of a sampling oscilloscope. Sampling points on the signal $x_1(t)$ are indicated by small circular symbols.

Solution

The Sampling Theorem tells us that a signal with components up to f_1 Hz must be sampled at least $2f_1$ times per second to avoid aliasing. This implies at least *two* samples per cycle of the highest frequency present. In this example $x_1(t)$ is being sampled slightly less than *once* per cycle. Therefore the sampling oscilloscope clearly does not avoid aliasing. Rather, it *uses* aliasing to achieve 'stretching' of the signal.

The spectrum of $x_1(t)$ is shown at the top of figure E8.1.2. In the middle is the spectrum of the unit sample train. Since the sample spacing is $9T_0/8$, the impulses in $X_2(\omega)$ are separated by $8\omega_0/9$. To aid interpretation, the positive frequency axes are marked off in steps of $\omega_0/9$. The spectrum $X_3(\omega)$ of the sampled signal $x_3(t)$ may be found by convolving

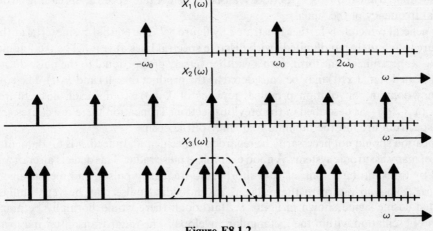

Figure E8.1.2

$X_1(\omega)$ with $X_2(\omega)$. This has the effect of arranging a version, or replica, of $X_2(\omega)$ around each of the impulses in $X_1(\omega)$. Therefore $X_3(\omega)$ must comprise a set of impulses at the frequencies

$$\omega_0 \pm k\left(\frac{8\omega_0}{9}\right), \qquad -\infty < k < \infty$$

plus another set of impulses at

$$-\omega_0 \pm k\left(\frac{8\omega_0}{9}\right), \qquad -\infty < k < \infty$$

$X_3(\omega)$ is shown at the bottom of the figure. Aliasing has given rise to the new frequencies $\pm\omega_0/8$, and it is these which must be passed on by the reconstituting filter to a normal oscilloscope. A suitable filter magnitude characteristic is shown dotted. The width of the guardband is clearly $2\omega_0/3$.

In this illustration the signal has been 'stretched' by a factor of 9. The required spectral components are therefore at the frequency $\pm\omega_0/9$. Clearly, different degrees of stretching could be achieved by small adjustments to the sampling interval.

8.3 Signal truncation and windowing

In practical situations we are forced to deal with truncated signals—that is, signals which are zero outside certain time-limits. Truncation occurs whenever a signal is switched on or off, or is observed or recorded over a finite time-interval. It tends to produce sudden discontinuities which lead to a spreading of spectral energy. In this section we investigate truncation in both time and frequency domains, and introduce an important signal processing technique for reducing its effects.

We have already met some aspects of truncation in sections 4.2.3.1 and 5.3.1. Figure 4.11 showed how the bandwidth of a rectangular pulse increases as the pulse shortens. If we think of such a pulse as a DC level which is switched on and off, it is clear that such truncation leads to a broadening of the spectrum. Figure 5.6 illustrated the spectral effects of truncating a discrete sinusoidal signal. When the waveform contained two complete periods, its spectrum was 'well behaved'. But truncation to $1\frac{1}{2}$ periods caused considerable spectral spreading around the nominal frequency of the signal.

This general principle is further illustrated by figure 8.7. The eternal cosine $x_1(t)$ at the top of the figure is 'infinitely bandlimited', with discrete spectral lines at $\pm\omega_1$. The rectangular pulse $x_2(t)$ has a spectrum of sinc form, with a width inversely proportional to the pulse duration T_0. The truncated signal $x_3(t)$ may be considered as the product of $x_1(t)$ and $x_2(t)$. The equivalent frequency-domain convolution produces replicas of $X_2(\omega)$ around each discrete frequency present in $X_1(\omega)$—as described in the previous section. Truncation therefore causes spreading of the spectrum around the nominal frequency of the cosine.

Truncation should not necessarily be regarded as accidental. Indeed, it is fundamental to the design of many electronic systems. A good example is pulse radar. This detects aircraft and other targets by transmitting a train of very short radio-frequency pulses, and measuring the time taken for echoes to return to the receiver. An individual pulse may be very similar to the truncated cosine signal shown in figure 8.7 (although there would normally be many more periods of oscillation within the rectangular envelope). The radar transmitter may work at a

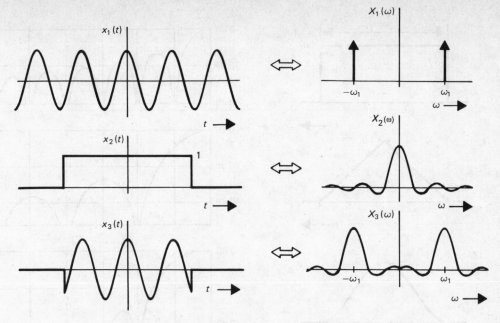

Figure 8.7 Truncation of an eternal cosine signal.

frequency of (say) 1000 MHz, but the spectrum of each pulse spreads considerably around the nominal frequency. The design of the receiver must take this into account.

In other situations, however, truncation is more incidental. We quite often record a signal over a restricted time-interval, assuming it to be zero elsewhere. In effect, we are multiplying it by a rectangular pulse, or *observation window*, of the type shown in figure 8.7. This causes spectral spreading, in which the 'true' signal spectrum is convolved with a sinc function. Although it may not be practicable to reduce spreading by increasing the observation time, we are free to multiply the signal by some *other* form of window if it suits us better. Various alternative functions have been devised for this purpose. Their use in signal processing is referred to as *windowing*.

Figure 8.8 illustrates three common types of window. Part (a) shows a rectangular window of duration T_0, of the type already discussed. It is, so to speak, the 'do-nothing' window, which makes no attempt to reduce the effects of truncation. Its spectrum is of sinc form, and is drawn on the right-hand side (we have used a logarithmic (dB) amplitude scale and a linear frequency scale, to clarify the relative magnitudes and spacing of the various sidelobes).

Part (b) of the figure shows a triangular, or *Bartlett*, window. If we multiply an observed signal by this function, we clearly avoid the major 'on' and 'off' discontinuities at the start and end of the waveform. In the frequency-domain, we now convolve the signal spectrum with a function whose main lobe is twice the width of that of the rectangular window, but with considerably smaller sidelobes. Taken overall, the spectral spreading effects of the Bartlett window are generally less severe.

Even more useful in many applications is the *Hanning* window shown in figure 8.8(c). This takes the form of one complete period of a 'raised cosine'—that is, a cosine plus a DC level. Its smooth transitions further reduce spectral spreading, with much smaller sidelobes. Other types of window—for example, the Hamming and Kaiser windows—are sometimes used. They offer

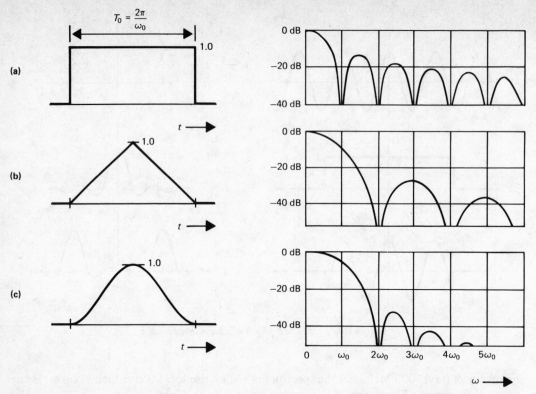

Figure 8.8 Observation windows and their spectra: (a) rectangular, (b) triangular, or Bartlett, and (c) Hanning.

different compromises between main lobe width and sidelobe level. A problem on the Hamming window is included at the end of the chapter.

We have introduced these windows as continuous-time functions, but the practical windowing of signals and data is generally achieved with a digital computer. Given a discrete signal $x[n]$ and a finite duration window $w[n]$, the windowed signal is

$$y[n] = x[n]w[n] \tag{8.15}$$

A discrete rectangular window with $(2N_1 + 1)$ unit sample values is defined as

$$
\begin{aligned}
w_1[n] &= 1, \qquad -N_1 \leqslant n \leqslant N_1 \\
&= 0, \qquad \text{elsewhere}
\end{aligned}
\tag{8.16}
$$

A Bartlett window of the same duration is given by

$$
\begin{aligned}
w_2[n] &= 1 - \frac{|n|}{(N_1 + 1)}, \qquad -N_1 \leqslant n \leqslant N_1 \\
&= 0, \quad \text{elsewhere}
\end{aligned}
\tag{8.17}
$$

Whereas the Hanning window is

$$
\begin{aligned}
w_3[n] &= \tfrac{1}{2}\{1 + \cos(\pi n/N_1)\}, \qquad -N_1 \leqslant n \leqslant N_1 \\
&= 0, \quad \text{elsewhere}
\end{aligned}
\tag{8.18}
$$

Since these are sampled functions, their spectra are repetitive versions of those shown in figure 8.8. But provided N_1 is large, their performance is very similar to their continuous-time counterparts.

Practical signals are generally considered to begin at or after $n = 0$, whereas window functions are invariably shown as symmetrical about $n = 0$. This need cause no difficulty. We may either shift the window forward in time, or the signal backwards in time, for the purposes of windowing. In either case the only effect is to introduce a phase term proportional to frequency. Spectral magnitudes are unaffected.

Example E8.2

Write a BASIC program to estimate the values of a 21-point Hanning window, and apply the window to a signal $x[n]$ with 21 finite values defined by a DATA statement. Load the windowed signal into an array Y.

Solution

Program no. 7 satisfies the above requirements. The signal values specified in line 150 are arbitrary.

```
100 REM ********  PROGRAM NO.7        HANNING DATA-WINDOW  *******
110 REM
120 DIM X(21),W(21),Y(21)
130 FOR J=1 TO 21:N=J-11:W(J)=0.5*(1+COS(PI*N/10)):NEXT J
140 FOR K=1 TO 21:READ X(K):Y(K)=X(K)*W(K):NEXT K
150 DATA -2,-1,-1,0,-1,-6,5,3,0,-4,-5,-1,1,2,-3,-2,-1,-1,2,1,1
160 REM
170 REM ******************** PLOT OPTION ********************
180 REM *** (WINDOW ABOVE,DATA IN MIDDLE,WINDOWED DATA BELOW) **
190 REM **********  PLOTS SCALED TO SAME PEAK VALUE  *********
200 XMAX=0:FOR J=1 TO 21:X1=ABS(X(J)):IF X1>XMAX THEN XMAX=X1
210 NEXT J:CLS:FOR K=1 TO 21:L=100+16*K
220 PLOT L,300:DRAW L,300+W(K)*50:PLOT L,200
230 DRAW L,200+X(K)*50/XMAX:PLOT L,100:DRAW L,100+Y(K)*50/XMAX
240 NEXT K
250 REM
260 REM ***  PRINT OPTION   (PAIRS OF WINDOW AND OUTPUT VALUES)**
270 FOR J=1 TO 21:PRINT W(J),Y(J):NEXT J
280 REM ***************************************************
```

There is sometimes confusion over the width of such an observation window. Of the 21 values loaded into array W, the first and last are zero because of the shape of the Hanning function. If we wish to avoid eliminating the first and last signal values when we multiply by the window, a 23-point window should be used instead.

Such windowing is often used as a prelude to Fourier transformation. Program statements similar to those in lines 120 to 150 could readily be included at the start of the FFT program given in section 5.3.3 (program no. 5).

We now give a practical illustration of windowing. Part (a) of figure 5.5 showed a signal representing traffic flow along a busy highway. A fortnight's data were included, consisting of 56 sample values taken at a rate of 4 samples per day. The lower part of the figure showed the magnitude of the signal's spectral coefficients, estimated using a discrete Fourier Transform program. Since we used exactly a fortnight's data, the natural periodicity of the signal was not significantly disturbed by truncation, and the resulting spectrum was 'well behaved'. In other words, the spectral coefficients accurately reflected frequencies present in the underlying signal.

    Let us now imagine that the person responsible for recording traffic flow left his (her?) post late on the second Saturday afternoon (better things to do!). As a result, the last 5 sample values are missing. Such truncation produces an unnatural discontinuity in the signal. We further assume that its spectrum is to be found using the FFT program listed in section 5.3.3 (program no. 5). This requires a number of samples equal to an integer power of 2. Since there are only 51 sample values in our data, we must use a 64-point transform with zero-padding. This introduces further discontinuities. All in all, we may expect the computed spectrum to be a rather distorted and spread version of the 'true' one.

    The top left-hand diagram in figure 8.9 shows the traffic signal once again, drawn to smaller scales. The last 5 values are now missing, and 13 zero-values have been included to make the signal up to the required length. The magnitudes of the first 32 coefficients of its 64-point FFT are shown on the right-hand side (the next 32 coefficients are simply a mirror-image set, since the signal is a real time function). Comparing with figure 5.5(b), and bearing in mind that the different length of transform has altered the frequency scale slightly, we see quite a lot of

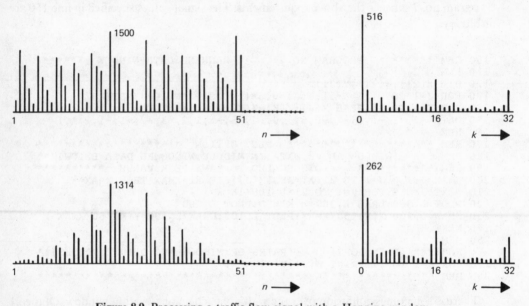

Figure 8.9 Processing a traffic-flow signal with a Hanning window.

evidence of spectral spreading. The new transform is not so clear or 'well behaved'. Many of its coefficients are larger, and appear somewhat random in size. It is hard to know which spectral features are genuine, and which are caused by signal discontinuities.

    The lower part of the figure shows the same signal after multiplication by a 53-point Hanning window. The modified spectrum is shown on the right-hand side. Although the results of such windowing are complicated, it is clear that the gross effects of truncation and zero-padding have been removed. Note that the window has caused considerable spreading immediately to either side of the largest spectral coefficients, but reduced it elsewhere. The spectrum is now much better-behaved and, to an expert eye, probably easier to interpret.

    Before ending this brief account of windowing techniques, we should note that windows are quite often used in the design of discrete systems, as well as for the processing of signals. We shall meet an example of this later, during our discussion of digital filters.

8.4 Filtering

Filtering is of central importance in electronic engineering. Practical filters range from the humble first-order *RC* circuit, to complicated high-order designs with elaborate specifications. Filter design is a huge topic, represented by many large volumes on library bookshelves! We must limit ourselves here to a brief account of some widely used filter families and design approaches.

First-order filters were introduced early in this book, and used to illustrate some important ideas in signal and system theory. Subsequently, we looked rather carefully at the filtering properties of first and second-order LTI systems. Continuous systems were explored in section 4.3.1, and illustrated in figures 4.18 and 4.19; discrete systems in section 5.4, and figures 5.12 and 5.14. We also considered the frequency responses and pole-zero configurations of such systems in chapter 6.

8.4.1 *Analog filters*

The historical development of electric and electronic filters was closely associated with the needs of radio broadcasting. However, the applications of analog filters have expanded enormously over the past 30 years, and a wide range of design techniques is available. Active filters are now commonly used in low and medium frequency applications, and we shall concentrate on these in this section.

Any frequency-dependent system may be thought of as a filter. But common usage of the term is reserved for systems which transmit certain frequencies or frequency ranges, and reject others. Most filters may therefore be classed as low-pass, high-pass, bandpass, or bandstop. In many applications we start with an ideal frequency response characteristic, and then try to approximate it with a circuit of given order. This explains why filter design is often referred to as an *approximation problem*. For example, figure 8.10(a) shows an ideal magnitude characteristic for an analog low-pass filter. Also shown, dotted, are typical approximations obtained with a first-order circuit, and a slightly underdamped second-order circuit. Part (b) of the figure represents an ideal bandpass characteristic, and an approximation based on a high-*Q* second-order system.

The approximations shown in the figure are not very impressive, and would be inadequate in many practical applications. A common way of improving them is to specify either a

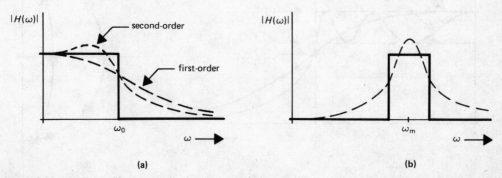

Figure 8.10 Idealised filter magnitude characteristics, and approximations: (a) low-pass, and (b) bandpass.

Butterworth, or *Chebyshev*, characteristic. Although we introduce these by reference to low-pass filters, it is quite possible to derive equivalent high-pass, bandpass, and bandstop designs. A low-pass Butterworth filter of nth order and nominal cut-off frequency ω_0 is defined by the magnitude response

$$|H(\omega)| = \frac{1}{\left\{1 + \left(\dfrac{\omega}{\omega_0}\right)^{2n}\right\}^{1/2}} \tag{8.19}$$

Regardless of the value of n, this function has the value 1.0 at $\omega = 0$, and passes through 0.7071 (-3 dB) at $\omega = \omega_0$. But as n increases, so does the cut-off rate in the region of ω_0. At high frequency the cut-off rate tends to $-20n$ dB/decade. The passband performance, which also improves with increasing n, is referred to as *maximally flat*. A Butterworth characteristic of 5th order is illustrated in figure 8.11(a).

The Chebyshev approximation achieves a sharper initial cut-off, at the expense of some passband *ripple*. The amount of ripple is specified by the designer. The magnitude function is given by

$$|H(\omega)| = \frac{1}{\left\{1 + \varepsilon^2 C_n^2\left(\dfrac{\omega}{\omega_0}\right)\right\}^{1/2}} \tag{8.20}$$

where the parameter ε controls the ripple, and C_n denotes the so-called *Chebyshev polynomial* of nth order. Over the range $0 < \omega < \omega_0$, $|H(\omega)|$ oscillates between 1.0 and $(1 + \varepsilon^2)^{-1/2}$, displaying an *equiripple characteristic*. The larger n, the greater the number of oscillations. A 5th-order Chebyshev characteristic is also shown in figure 8.11(a). Note how the oscillations become more compressed as the cut-off frequency is approached.

A Butterworth or Chebyshev low-pass filter of nth order has n poles located in the left-half s-plane. By substituting s/j for ω in equation (8.19), it is straightforward to prove that the Butterworth poles lie on a semicircle of radius ω_0. The poles of a Chebyshev filter are arranged on a semi-ellipse, with its major axis along the imaginary axis in the s-plane. The greater the

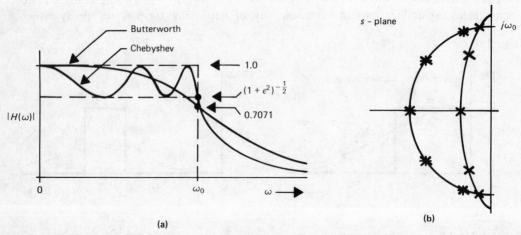

(a)   (b)

Figure 8.11 The magnitude functions and s-plane poles of typical Butterworth and Chebyshev analog low-pass filters.

passband ripple, the more elongated the ellipse. Pole locations for the 5th-order filters of figure 8.11(a) are shown in part (b) of the figure (the Butterworth poles are indicated by asterisks).

Conventional Butterworth and Chebyshev filters are made with passive components—resistors, capacitors, and inductors (although a first-order filter requires only one resistor and one capacitor). The impedances of the signal source and load, and the resistances associated with nonideal capacitors and (especially) inductors, must be taken into account. These matters are covered in most specialist texts on circuits and filters. An attractive alternative, which falls well within the scope of this book, is to use active circuit techniques. For example, we may use the second-order operational amplifier circuit in figure 4.19 as the basis for a whole range of low-pass Butterworth and Chebyshev filters. The idea is quite simple. Each complex-conjugate pole-pair in the overall filter is provided by one of these second-order circuits, and the single real pole (assuming n is odd) by a first-order RC section. Since the input impedance of each section is large, and the output impedance of each active section is very low, we may cascade the various subsystems without significantly affecting their performance.

The approach is illustrated for a 5th-order filter in figure 8.12. Two cascaded active circuits provide the two pairs of complex-conjugate poles. A single RC section provides the real pole. Since the amplifiers are connected as voltage followers, their bandwidth is large. Effective filters with cut-off frequencies up to about 1 MHz may therefore be made in this way, using inexpensive operational amplifiers.

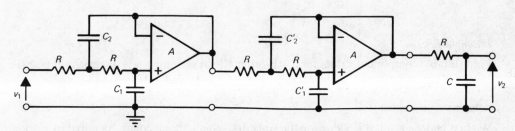

Figure 8.12 Active circuit realisation of a 5th-order low-pass filter.

We defined the relationships between the natural frequency ω_n, the damping factor ζ, and the circuit component values of this type of second-order circuit in equation (4.100). In equation (6.37) we derived the locations of a complex conjugate pair of s-plane poles in terms of ω_n and ζ. This information would be sufficient to estimate suitable values for the resistors and capacitors in figure 8.12, given the s-plane pole locations of the desired filter (these are widely tabulated in the filter literature). However, the reader who wishes to build and test such a filter will probably welcome the information contained in figure 8.13. This is a design table, which indicates component values for a range of Butterworth and Chebyshev low-pass filters. Several different orders of filter are covered, with three different levels of passband ripple (0 dB ripple signifies a Butterworth filter). The table also gives information about the Q-factor and frequency of maximum response ω_m of each second-order subsystem, which is useful for testing the performance of an actual filter. Note also how the cut-off achieved at $2\omega_0$ improves with the filter order, and as more passband ripple is accepted. The use of this table will be illustrated by a worked example.

Filter order (n)	Ripple (dB)	Cut-off at $2\omega_0$ (dB)	circuit 1				circuit 2				circuit 3				First-order s/system
			C_1	C_2	Q	ω_m	C_1	C_2	Q	ω_m	C_1	C_2	Q	ω_m	C
2	0	12	0.707	1.414	0.707	—									
	0.1	13	0.357	0.842	0.767	0.711									
	1.0	14.5	0.497	1.820	0.956	0.708									
3	0	18	0.5	2	1	0.707									1
	0.1	22	0.286	2.063	1.343	1.107									1.031
	1.0	26	0.248	4.044	2.019	0.935									2.022
5	0	30	0.809	1.236	0.618	—	0.309	3.236	1.618	0.901					1
	0.1	40	0.685	2.293	0.915	0.506	0.139	6.000	3.280	1.068					1.855
	1.0	46	0.545	4.266	1.399	0.566	.0905	11.17	5.551	0.986					3.451
7	0	42	0.901	1.109	0.554	—	0.623	1.603	0.802	0.472	0.222	4.493	2.248	0.951	1
	0.1	62	1.028	2.945	0.846	0.316	0.311	4.256	1.849	0.802	.0767	11.92	6.233	1.038	2.653
	1.0	68	0.803	5.400	1.297	0.402	0.196	7.802	3.155	0.788	0.046	21.86	10.89	0.995	4.864

Figure 8.13 A design table for Butterworth and Chebyshev analog low-pass filters.

Example E8.3

Find suitable component values for a 5th-order Chebyshev low-pass filter based upon the circuit of figure 8.12, with a cut-off frequency of 3 kHz and 1 dB passband ripple.

Solution

We first choose a suitable value for the resistors, which are all equal. As noted in worked example E4.8, a value between about 5 kΩ and 500 kΩ is appropriate in most cases. (If the cut-off frequency is very low, it is best to choose a value towards the top of this range, to prevent the capacitors being large and bulky.) In this case let us try 10 kΩ. We must first calculate the *normalised capacitance*, defined as

$$C_0 = \frac{1}{\omega_0 R} = \frac{1}{2\pi(3 \times 10^3)(10^4)}\,\text{F} = 5.305\,\text{nF}$$

We now refer to the relevant row in the design table, multiplying each capacitor value by the normalised capacitance. Using the circuit symbols of figure 8.12, we obtain

$$C_1 = 0.545C_0 = 2.89\,\text{nF}; \quad C_1' = 0.0905C_0 = 0.480\,\text{nF}; \quad C = 3.451C_0 = 0.0183\,\mu\text{F}$$

$$C_2 = 4.266C_0 = 0.0226\,\mu\text{F}; \quad C_2' = 11.17C_0 = 0.0593\,\mu\text{F}$$

These values are sensible—neither so large as to make the capacitors bulky or expensive, nor so small as to run the risk that small stray capacitances in the circuit will affect performance significantly. The filter's frequency response is very dependent on accurate component values, which should therefore be checked on an AC bridge.

8.4.2 *Digital filters*

There are two rather distinct approaches to filtering a discrete-time signal. The first involves estimating its discrete Fourier Transform—generally using the FFT, as described in section 5.3.3. The magnitudes and phases of the various spectral coefficients are then adjusted in accordance with the desired filter characteristics, and the filtered signal found by inverse transformation—again using the FFT. This *frequency-domain* method is very powerful and widely used, and gives great flexibility in the choice of filter characteristics.

The second approach is to work entirely in the *time-domain*. In effect this is done by convolving the signal with the impulse response of the required filter. Whether a time-domain or a frequency-domain method is more appropriate depends on such factors as the amount of storage available in the computer or digital hardware, the duration of the signal, and the complexity of the filter. It also depends on whether or not a strictly *real-time* operation is required. In such an operation, a new output sample value is calculated each time an input sample is delivered. This implies time-domain filtering, because efficient use of the FFT requires the storage and processing of the input signal in substantial blocks.

We focus here on two main classes of time-domain filter. These are the *finite-impulse-response* (FIR) filter, which has a nonrecursive difference equation; and the *infinite-impulse-response* (IIR) filter, with a recursive difference equation. Apart from any poles or zeros at the origin of the z-plane, the transfer function of a FIR filter possesses only z-plane zeros. But the IIR type has one or more z-plane poles. Broadly speaking, we may summarise their relative advantages and disadvantages as follows.

FIR filters, being nonrecursive, are always stable. They may be designed with pure linear-phase characteristics. However, they often involve a large number of recurrence formula terms, and may be computationally expensive.

IIR filters, being recursive, carry the risk of instability if their z-plane poles lie very close to the unit circle. They cannot display pure linear-phase characteristics. But their recurrence formulae often have very few terms, leading to economic filters.

A FIR filter may be thought of as a digital delay line with tapping points and multipliers. It is sometimes referred to as a digital transversal filter. Figure 8.14 shows a hardware version of such a filter. Its impulse response $h[n]$ has sample values equal to the sequence b_0 to b_m. The challenge of designing a FIR filter is to achieve an acceptable performance without specifying too many multiplier coefficients—although 100 or more may be necessary in some cases. A common approach is to start with a desired frequency response, and find the corresponding $h[n]$ by

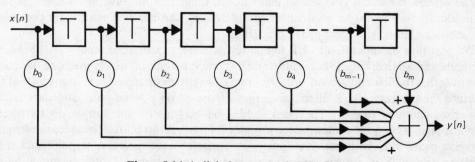

Figure 8.14 A digital transversal (FIR) filter.

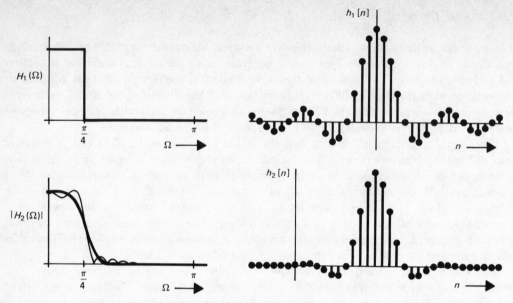

Figure 8.15 The design of a digital FIR filter by the window method.

inverse discrete Fourier transformation. If (as often happens) it contains an unacceptable number of terms, it is truncated using a suitable window function.

This *window method* of FIR filter design is illustrated by figure 8.15. In this example, we have chosen as our starting point an ideal low-pass characteristic $H_1(\Omega)$ with a cut-off at $\Omega = \pi/4$. Assuming $H_1(\Omega)$ is real, the corresponding impulse response $h_1[n]$ is symmetrical about $n = 0$. It is an oscillatory function which continues forever in both directions, implying a noncausal filter. We therefore truncate it and shift it forward to begin at $n = 0$. In this case we have used a 25-point Hanning window, giving an impulse response $h_2[n]$ with 23 finite terms. Transforming back into the frequency-domain, we may find the actual filter response $H_2(\Omega)$. Its magnitude characteristic is shown as a thick line in the lower left part of the figure. Truncation with the Hanning window has clearly caused spreading of the response. This could, of course, be reduced by using a wider window—at the cost of more multiplier coefficients. For comparison, the effect of truncating with a 25-term rectangular window is also shown, by a thin line. We should finally note that since the truncated impulse response $h_2[n]$ is a symmetrical function, our filter will display pure linear-phase characteristics.

The window method is only one of many design techniques for FIR digital filters. We have introduced it here because it is valuable and widely used, and clearly illustrates the possibilities for achieving filters with ideal phase properties.

We next turn our attention to IIR digital filters. Here, too, there are many possible design methods, and we shall have to concentrate on just one valuable and widely used one. We should first note that the first and second-order discrete LTI systems discussed in sections 5.4 and 6.4.3 fall into the category of IIR filters, since they are based on z-plane poles and their impulse responses continue forever. They can indeed be very useful for simple digital filtering applications—as we have demonstrated a number of times in this book. However, we often need a higher-order filter with better frequency response characteristics. A popular and highly effective approach is to convert an analog filter into a digital filter using a *bilinear transformation.* For example we may readily obtain digital versions of the Butterworth and Chebyshev filters described in the previous section.

The basic idea behind a bilinear transformation may be explained by considering the function

$$F(z) = \frac{z - 1}{z + 1} \tag{8.21}$$

This is *bilinear* in the sense that its numerator and denominator are both linear in z. To understand how $F(z)$ may be used to convert an analog filter into a digital one, we need to find its spectrum. Thus

$$F(z)|_{z = \exp(j\Omega)} = F(j\Omega) = \frac{\exp(j\Omega) - 1}{\exp(j\Omega) + 1} = j \tan\left(\frac{\Omega}{2}\right) \tag{8.22}$$

We see that $F(j\Omega)$ is purely imaginary, and periodic in Ω. Now suppose we have an analog filter with a transfer function $H_1(s)$. Wherever s appears in $H_1(s)$, we replace it by $F(z)$, giving us a digital filter transfer function $H_2(z)$. As a simple example, suppose

$$H_1(s) = \frac{1}{(s + \alpha)}, \quad \text{giving } H_2(z) = \frac{1}{\{F(z) + \alpha\}} \tag{8.23}$$

The frequency responses of the two filters are given by

$$H_1(\omega) = \frac{1}{(j\omega + \alpha)}, \quad \text{and} \quad H_2(\Omega) = \frac{1}{\left\{ j \tan\left(\frac{\Omega}{2}\right) + \alpha \right\}} \tag{8.24}$$

Now as ω varies between 0 and ∞, the term $j\omega$ in $H_1(\omega)$ varies between $j0$ and $j\infty$, and the complete frequency response of the analog filter is traced out. But the term $j \tan(\Omega/2)$ in $H_2(\Omega)$ varies between these same limits of $j0$ and $j\infty$ as Ω varies between 0 and π. Therefore the complete frequency response characteristic of the analog filter is compressed into the frequency range $0 < \Omega < \pi$ in the digital filter. In effect, the complete imaginary axis in the s-plane has been compressed into a single revolution around the unit circle in the z-plane.

Figure 8.16 illustrates this important result. Part (a) shows the magnitude response of an analog Chebyshev low-pass filter of 7th-order. Part (b) shows the response of its digital counterpart, obtained with the above bilinear transformation. The analog filter's response falls to zero as $\omega \to \infty$, whereas that of the digital filter reaches zero at $\Omega = \pi$, and then repeats. Although the frequency scale has been compressed, particularly in the region of $\Omega = \pi$, the

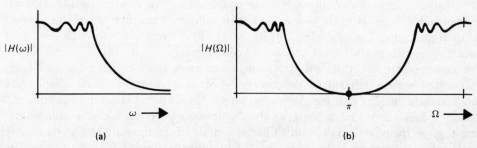

Figure 8.16 (a)A typical Chebyshev analog filter characteristic, and (b) its digital equivalent obtained by bilinear transformation.

equiripple property of the Chebyshev design is preserved. This is a valuable feature of the bilinear transformation.

We have seen that the substitution of $F(z)$ for s in a transfer function is equivalent to replacing ω by $\tan(\Omega/2)$ in a frequency response expression. It follows that digital Butterworth and Chebyshev filters designed in this way must have magnitude characteristics given by modified versions of equations (8.19) and (8.20). Thus

$$|H(\Omega)| = \frac{K_1}{\left\{1 + \left(\dfrac{\tan \Omega/2}{\tan \Omega_0/2}\right)^{2n}\right\}^{1/2}} \quad \text{(Butterworth)} \tag{8.25}$$

and

$$|H(\Omega)| = \frac{K_2}{\left\{1 + \varepsilon^2 C_n^2\left(\dfrac{\tan \Omega/2}{\tan \Omega_0/2}\right)\right\}^{1/2}} \quad \text{(Chebyshev)} \tag{8.26}$$

where K_1 and K_2 are gain factors.

The pole-zero configuration of a typical 4th-order Butterworth low-pass digital filter is shown in figure 8.17(a). Its 4 poles, in two complex-conjugate pairs, lie on a circular locus in the z-plane. Its 4th-order zero at $z = -1$ is responsible for the transmission zero at $\Omega = \pi$. A Chebyshev filter has a similar pole-zero configuration, except that its poles lie along a 'cardioid'

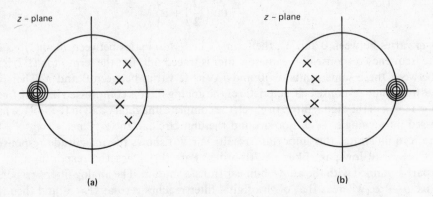

Figure 8.17 Deriving a digital high-pass filter from a low-pass prototype.

locus—neither a circle, nor an ellipse. It is also worth noting that an equivalent high-pass filter may be obtained by reflecting the pole-zero locations about the imaginary axis. This is shown by part (b) of the figure. The only effect this has on the filter's recurrence formula (or difference equation) is to change the sign of some of its coefficients.

We now present a BASIC program which estimates the z-plane poles and zeros of Butterworth low-pass digital filters (program no. 8). Since the program is fairly complicated, we do not comment on it in detail, merely noting that it is based on the bilinear transformation. It is included to help the reader wishing to investigate such filters on a digital computer. For example, given the poles and zeros of a filter, it is quite straightforward to find its recurrence formula, impulse response, and—using the FFT program in section 5.3.3 (program no. 5)—its frequency response. Needless to say, the recurrence formula may also be used to filter an input

```
100 REM ******************** PROGRAM NO.8 ********************
110 REM ***  POLES AND ZEROS OF BUTTERWORTH DIGITAL FILTERS  ****
120 REM
130 DIM RZ(30),IZ(30),RP(30),IP(30)
140 PRINT "ORDER OF LOW-PASS BUTTERWORTH FILTER ?":INPUT N
150 PRINT "CUT-OFF FREQUENCY (DEGREES) ?":INPUT F0
160 W0=PI*F0/360:A=2*SIN(W0)/COS(W0):B=0.25*A^2
170 IF N=1 THEN GOTO 250 ELSE C=N/2:D=INT((N+0.1)/2)
180 IF (C-D)>0.2 THEN GOTO 190 ELSE E=0:GOTO 200
190 E=1
200 F=N+E:G=(3*N+E)/2-1
210 FOR H=F TO G:I=PI*(2*H+1-E)/(2*N):J=1-A*COS(I)+B
220 K=(1-B)/J:L=A*SIN(I)/J:M=(G-H)*2+1
230 RP(M+E)=K:IP(M+E)=L:RP(M+E+1)=K:IP(M+E+1)=-L:NEXT H
240 IF E=0 THEN GOTO 260
250 RP(1)=(1-B)/(1+A+B):IP(1)=0
260 FOR M=1 TO N:RZ(M)=-1:IZ(M)=0:NEXT M:F=N+1
270 FOR M=F TO 30:RZ(M)=0:IZ(M)=0:RP(M)=0:IP(M)=0:NEXT M
280 REM
290 REM ******************** PLOT OPTION ********************
300 CLS:FOR J=1 TO 1001:K=J*2*PI/1000
310 PLOT 300+180*SIN(K),200+180*COS(K):NEXT J
320 PLOT 0,200:DRAW 600,200:PLOT 300,0:DRAW 300,400
330 FOR J=1 TO 100:K=J*2*PI/100:PLOT 120+12*SIN(K),200+12*COS(K)
340 PLOT 120+18*SIN(K),200+18*COS(K):NEXT J
350 FOR J=1 TO N:R=300+180*RP(J):I=200+180*IP(J)
360 FOR K=-5 TO 5:PLOT R+K,I+K:PLOT R+K,I-K:NEXT K:NEXT J
370 PRINT "ENTER ANY NUMBER WHEN PRINT-OUT REQUIRED":INPUT A:CLS
380 REM
390 REM ******************** PRINT OPTION ********************
400 PRINT "REAL AND IMAGINARY PARTS OF Z-PLANE ZEROS:"
410 FOR M=1 TO N:PRINT RZ(M),IZ(M):NEXT M
420 PRINT "REAL AND IMAGINARY PARTS OF Z-PLANE POLES:"
430 FOR M=1 TO N:PRINT RP(M);:PRINT IP(M):NEXT M
440 REM ********************************************************
```

signal! The program includes a plot option and a print option. The former gives a z-plane plot of the filter poles and zeros. When both options are used, line 370 prevents the plot being overwritten as soon as it is produced.

Example E8.4

Using the BASIC program provided (program no. 8), estimate the z-plane poles and zeros of a Butterworth low-pass filter of 5th-order, with a cut-off frequency $\Omega_0 = \pi/5$. Derive the filter's time-domain recurrence formula, and indicate how it may be converted into an equivalent high-pass filter with a cut-off frequency $\Omega_0 = 4\pi/5$.

Solution

The program requests the filter order (5) and cut-off frequency in degrees (36°). Its print option produces the following results:

REAL AND IMAGINARY PARTS OF Z-PLANE ZEROS:

-1	0
-1	0
-1	0
-1	0
-1	0

REAL AND IMAGINARY PARTS OF Z-PLANE POLES:

0.50952545	0
0.684658597	−0.473087455
0.684658597	0.473087455
0.548289733	−0.23414767
0.548289733	0.23414767

As expected, there are 5 zeros (or a 5th-order zero) at $z = -1$. The first pole listed is real, and the other four make up two complex-conjugate pairs. A convenient way of deriving the recurrence formula is to consider the overall filter as a set of cascaded subsystems—in much the same way as we did for analog filters in section 8.4.1 (see figure 8.12). Each second-order subsystem has a pole-pair, and a second-order zero at $z = -1$. Hence its transfer function takes the form

$$H(z) = \frac{Y(z)}{X(z)} = \frac{(z+1)^2}{(z - \alpha + j\beta)(z - \alpha - j\beta)} = \frac{z^2 + 2z + 1}{z^2 - 2\alpha z + (\alpha^2 + \beta^2)}$$

This gives the recurrence formula

$$y[n] = 2\alpha y[n-1] - (\alpha^2 + \beta^2)y[n-2] + x[n] + 2x(n-1] + x[n-2]$$

The first-order subsystem has a single real pole, and a single zero at $z = -1$. Hence

$$H(z) = \frac{Y(z)}{X(z)} = \frac{(z+1)}{(z-\alpha)}$$

giving

$$y[n] = \alpha y[n-1] + x[n] + x[n-1]$$

We now cascade the subsystems as shown in figure E8.4. The intermediate outputs are labelled $v[n]$ and $w[n]$, to avoid confusion. Using the computed pole coordinates in the above recurrence formulae, we readily obtain

$$v[n] = 1.369\,32v[n-1] - 0.692\,57v[n-2] + x[n] + 2x[n-1] + x[n-2]$$

$$w[n] = 1.096\,58w[n-1] - 0.355\,45w[n-2] + v[n] + 2v[n-1] + v[n-2]$$

$$y[n] = 0.509\,53y[n-1] + w[n] + w[n-1]$$

The coefficients are quoted to 5 decimal figures, which is adequate in this case. These equations could be recast as a single equation relating x and y. However, it is quite convenient to use them as they stand. The output $v[n]$ from the first equation feeds the second equation, and $w[n]$ feeds the third equation.

An equivalent high-pass filter, with cut-off frequency $\Omega_0 = \pi - \pi/5 = 4\pi/5$, may be derived by 'reflecting' the poles and zeros about the imaginary axis. In other words, we change the sign of their real parts. The recurrence formulae for second-order and first-order

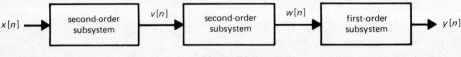

Figure E8.4

subsystems become

$$y[n] = -2\alpha y[n-1] - (\alpha^2 + \beta^2)y[n-2] + x[n] - 2x[n-1] + x[n-2]$$

and

$$y[n] = -\alpha y[n-1] + x[n] - x[n-1]$$

Thus two of the coefficients in each equation change sign.

Problems to chapter 8

Section 8.2

Q8.1. Two signals $x_1(t)$ and $x_2(t)$ have the spectra $X_1(\omega)$ and $X_2(\omega)$ shown in figure Q8.1. The signals are multiplied together, and the resulting function $x_3(t)$ is sampled by a unit impulse train. What is the maximum sampling interval which allows $x_3(t)$ to be recovered from its sampled version with an ideal reconstituting filter?

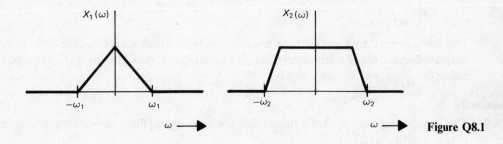

Figure Q8.1

Q8.2. A continuous speech signal with frequency components up to 5 kHz has been sampled at a rate of 20 kHz. It is to be reconstituted using a Butterworth low-pass filter with a nominal cut-off frequency of 5 kHz. If the filter is to reduce all unwanted frequency components by at least 50 dB, what order of filter is required?

Q8.3. A continuous signal $x(t)$ containing frequency components up to 1 MHz is observed and recorded over a time interval of 0.5 ms. A sampled version of its spectrum is then estimated with a spectrum analyser. According to the sampling theorem, what maximum spacing may the samples have, and how many of them are required?

Section 8.3

Q8.4. A radar system transmits a regular train of radio-frequency pulses and measures the time taken for echoes to return from distant aircraft. The system operates at 1000 MHz, the pulse rate is 400 pulses per second, and the pulse duration is 2.5 μs. Sketch the spectrum of the transmitted pulse train. What is the width of the main lobe centred on 1000 MHz, and how would it be affected by a change of pulse length to 1 μs?

Q8.5. Three types of truncation window and their associated spectra have been shown in figure 8.8 of the main text. An alternative function, which is quite often used, is the *Hanning window*. Its discrete-time version is defined by

$$w[n] = 0.54 + 0.46 \cos(\pi n/N_1), \qquad -N_1 \leqslant n \leqslant N_1$$

Use a modified version of the FFT program in section 5.3.3 (program no. 5) to find the spectral magnitude characteristic of a 121-point version of this window. You are recommended to increase frequency-domain resolution by using a 512-point zero-padded FFT. What is the height of the first sidelobe in dB, and how does this compare with the Hanning window?

Section 8.4.1

Q8.6. Find the capacitor values required for a 3rd-order Butterworth low-pass filter based upon the type of active circuit shown in figure 8.12 of the main text. The cut-off frequency is to be 100 kHz and, for reasons external to this problem, all resistors in the circuit are to have the value 1 kΩ.

Q8.7. Using the table in figure 8.13 in the main text, find the *lowest* cut-off frequency which can be achieved with an active 5th-order Butterworth low-pass filter of the type shown in figure 8.12, given that all resistors are 560 kΩ and that no capacitor may be greater than 2 μF.

Q8.8. As explained in the main text, Chebyshev filters have magnitude characteristics based on the so-called *Chebyshev polynomials*. The third-order polynomial is given by

$$C_3\left(\frac{\omega}{\omega_0}\right) = 4\left(\frac{\omega}{\omega_0}\right)^3 - 3\left(\frac{\omega}{\omega_0}\right)$$

Use this information, together with equation (8.20), to make an accurate sketch of the magnitude response of a 3rd-order Chebyshev analog low-pass filter over the frequency range $0 \leqslant (\omega/\omega_0) \leqslant 3$, with $\varepsilon = 1.0$.

Section 8.4.2

Q8.9. The impulse response $h[n]$ of a simple FIR low-pass digital filter has successive sample values (starting at $n = 0$)

$$1, 2, 3, 4, 3, 2, 1, 0, 0, 0, 0 \ldots$$

Find an expression for its frequency response magnitude function $|H(\Omega)|$, and sketch this function over the range $0 < \Omega < 2\pi$. What is the value of $|H(\Omega)|$ at (a) $\Omega = 0$, and (b) $\Omega = \pi$? Why does the filter have a pure linear-phase response?

Q8.10. Use the BASIC program given in section 8.4.2 (program no. 8) to find the z-plane poles and zeros of a 3rd-order low-pass Butterworth digital filter with a cut-off frequency $\Omega_0 = \pi/12$. Make an accurate sketch of the pole-zero configuration, and use it to estimate the approximate peak gain of the filter (assuming the transfer function includes no additional constant, or gain, factor). Why would you expect the peak gain of such filters to increase with the filter order?

Derive the recurrence formula of the filter, expressing it as a pair of equations representing cascaded second and first-order subsystems.

Q8.11. Convert the recurrence formula of the low-pass filter in Q8.10 to that of an equivalent high-pass filter with cut-off frequency $\Omega_0 = 11\pi/12$. Write a computer program to estimate the impulse response $h[n]$, and plot its first 30 values.

Bibliography

A short list of books for further reading.

1. Electronic and electrical circuits

R.L. Boylestad and L. Nashelsky, *Electronic Devices and Circuit Theory*, 3rd edn (New Jersey: Prentice-Hall, 1982).

G.B. Clayton, *Experiments with Operational Amplifiers* (London: Macmillan, 1975).

D.L. Schilling and C. Belove, *Electronic Circuits—Discrete and Integrated* (Tokyo: McGraw-Hill Kogakusha, 1979).

G. Williams, *An Introduction to Electric Circuit Theory* (London: Macmillan, 1973).

2. Systems, transforms, and convolution

C.D. McGillem and G.R. Cooper, *Continuous and Discrete Signal and System Analysis*, 2nd edn (New York: Holt Rinehart and Winston, 1984).

A.V. Oppenheim, A.S. Willsky and I.T. Young, *Signals and Systems* (New Jersey: Prentice-Hall, 1983).

R.E. Ziemer, W.H. Tranter and D.R. Fannin, *Signals and Systems* (New York: Macmillan, 1983).

3. Signal processing

P.A. Lynn, *An Introduction to the Anlaysis and Processing of Signals*, 2nd edn (London: Macmillan, 1982).

T.J. Terrell, *Introduction to Digital Filters* (London: Macmillan, 1980).

M.E. Van Valkenburg, *Analog Filter Design* (New York: Holt Rinehart and Winston, 1982).

Answers to Selected Problems

Chapter 1

Q1.1.   80 Mbit s^{-1}.

Q1.2.   110 Mbit s^{-1}.

Q1.4.   (a) 1.625 Ω, 1.6 Ω;   (b) $\frac{2}{13}$ V;   (c) $\frac{1}{21}$ A.

Q1.5.   (a) 0.461, 62.6°;   (b) $-76.7°$, 796 Hz.

Q1.6. $j\omega CR(3j\omega CR - \omega^2 C^2 R^2 + 1)^{-1}$, 159 Hz.

Chapter 2

Q2.6.   (a) $2u[n-1]$;   (b) $u(2-t)$;

      (c) $1.5\delta(t+1) + 2.0\delta(t-3)$;   (d) $-\delta[n-2]$;

      (e) $2r(t-1)$;   (f) $r[n+4] - r[n] - 2r[n-7] + 2r[n-9]$.

      (There is more than one correct answer to Q2.6(f).)

Q2.8.   (a) periodic, period $= \pi/2$;

      (b) periodic, period $= 14$.

Chapter 3

Q3.1.   (a) $2\delta[n] + 2\delta[n-1] + 2\delta[n-2]$;

      (b) $2\delta[n+2] - \delta[n+1] + \delta[n-1] + 3\delta[n-2] + 2\delta[n-3]$;

      (c) $-0.5\delta(t+0.5) + 0.5\delta(t) + \delta(t-1.0) + 0.3\delta(t-1.8)$.

Q3.3.   (b) $\delta(t) - \exp(-t/CR)/CR$.

Q3.4.   (a) Successive values of $y[n]$, starting at $n = 0$, are: 0, 0, 1, 2, 3, 3, 3, 3, 3, 2, 1, 0, 0,...;

      (b) successive values of $y[n]$, starting at $n = 0$, are: 1, 1, -1.5, -1.0, -0.5, 0.8, 0.3, -0.1,

      0, 0,...;

      (c) $y[n] = \sum_0^n \beta^k \alpha^{n-k}$.

Q3.7.   Successive values of $s[n]$, starting at $n = 0$, are: -0.1, 0.05, -0.2, 0.05, -0.1, 0, 0,....

Q3.10.   (a) 170.67 V, 29.3 mV;   (b) 0.512 V.

Q3.11. (a) $y(t) = 1 - \exp(2 - t)$, $t > 2$; $y(t) = 0$, $t < 2$;

(b) $y(t) = \exp(t) - \exp(t - 1)$, $t < 0$

$\qquad y(t) = 2 - \exp(-t) - \exp(t - 1)$, $0 < t < 1$

$\qquad y(t) = \exp(1 - t) - \exp(-t)$, $t > 1$.

Q3.14. $y(t) = \{\exp(-t) + \sin t - \cos t\}/2$;

final amplitude $= 0.7071$.

Q3.15. (a) $-6.84°C$; (b) $-3.75°C$;

(c) $-1.38°C$; (d) $0°C$.

Q3.16. -9.995 m.

Q3.19. $t \exp(-t/RC)/R^2C^2$.

Chapter 4

Q4.2. 1.5.

Q4.3. $A_0 = 1/2$; $B_k = 0$, all k;

$C_k = -1/k\pi$, all k.

Q4.4. $A_0 = 0$; $B_k = 0$, all k; $C_1 = 8/\pi^2$, $C_3 = 8/9\pi^2$, $C_5 = 8/25\pi^2$.

Q4.7. $A_0 = 0$; $B_k = 0$ and $C_k = 0$, k even.

Q4.9. $x(t) = 1 + 2/j\pi\{\ldots -\frac{1}{3}\exp(-j3\omega_0 t) - \exp(-j\omega_0 t)$

$\qquad\qquad + \exp(j\omega_0 t) + \frac{1}{3}\exp(j3\omega_0 t) + \ldots\}$.

Q4.10. $a_0 = 0.5$; $a_k = 0$, k even;

$a_k = 1/k\pi$, $k = -11, -7, -3, 1, 5, 9, \ldots$;

$a_k = -1/k\pi$, $k = -9, -5, -1, 3, 7, 11, \ldots$

Q4.11. (a) $4 \operatorname{sinc}^2 \omega$, about 1 kHz;

(b) $4 \sin^2(\omega/2)/j\omega$, about 3 MHz.

Q4.12. $(\alpha + j\omega)^{-1}$; $2\alpha(\alpha^2 + \omega^2)^{-1}$.

Q4.15. (a) $2 - \cos \omega t_0 + 2 \cos 2\omega t_0$;

(b) $\{1 + \cos \omega_0 t + 4 \cos 3\omega_0 t\}/2\pi$.

Q4.18. $Q = 10$; (a) $-3.8°$; (b) $-177.9°$.

Q4.20. $y(t) = 4 \exp(-2t) - 2 \exp(-t)$, $t > 0$;

$y(t) = 0$, $t < 0$.

Q4.21. $C_1 = 1.59$ nF, $C_2 = 0.159$ μF.

Q4.22. $2(1 + 0.1j\omega)/(1 + 0.2j\omega)(1 + 0.8j\omega)$.

Chapter 5

Q5.1. (a) $a_0 = 3$, $a_1 = a_7 = 0.5$, $a_2 = -a_6 = -0.5j$, $a_3 = a_5 = 0$, $a_4 = 0$;

(b) $a_1 = (1 - j)/2\sqrt{2}$, $a_3 = (1 + j)/2\sqrt{2}$;

(c) $a_0 = 1.5$, $a_1 = (-0.5 + 0.5j)$, $a_2 = -0.5$, $a_3 = (-0.5 - 0.5j)$.

Q5.3. (a) $3 + 4 \cos \Omega + 2 \cos 2\Omega$;

(b) $1 + \exp(-j\Omega) + \exp(-j2\Omega) - \exp(-j3\Omega) - \exp(-j4\Omega) - \exp(-j5\Omega)$.

Q5.5. 0.518, $75°$.

Q5.8. Computed magnitudes of a_0 to a_8 (to 4 significant figures): 31.25, 26.64, 15.09, 2.195, 6.250, 7.372, 2.589, 3.540, 6.250.

Q5.12. (a) 33.98 dB; (b) 6.02 dB.

Q5.13. $h[n] = \alpha^n u[n]$, $n > 0$ and even;
        $h[n] = 0$, n odd. Peak gain of $(1 - \alpha^2)^{-1}$ occurs at $\Omega = 0$, $\Omega = \pi$.

Q5.14. (b) 15.56 kHz; (c) 15.05 dB, -2.93 dB;
        (d) $+2.83$ per cent.

Q5.15. Magnitude response $= 10$, phase $= 0$.

Chapter 6

Q6.1.   (a) $(s + 1)^{-1}$; (b) $\{1 + \exp(-st_0)\}/s$;
        (c) $\exp(-st_0) - 2\exp(-2st_0)$;
        (d) $(s + \alpha)^{-2}$.

Q6.3.   (a) $0.5\{1 - \exp(-2t)\}u(t)$;
        (b) $\{\cos t + \sin t\}u(t)$;
        (c) $\{1.5 - 2\exp(-t) + 0.5\exp(-2t)\}u(t)$.

Q6.5. $0.37\{\sin(2000\pi t - 1.192) + 0.929\exp(-2500t)\}$;
        (a) 0.370; (b) $-68.3°$; (c) 0.929.

Q6.7.   (a) Pole at $s = (CR)^{-1}$, zero at origin;
        (b) poles at $s = -0.382$ and -2.618, zero at origin.

Q6.9. $H(s) = \alpha^2(s + \alpha)^{-2}$ where $\alpha = 1/CR$; second-order pole at $s = 1/CR$;
        $h(t) = t\exp(-t/CR)/C^2R^2$.

Q6.12. (a) $\{\exp(-t) - \exp(-2t)\}u(t)$;
        (b) $2\{\exp(-t) - \exp(-2t)\}u(t)$;
        (c) $2\exp(-t)u(t)$.

Q6.13. (a) $2/z^2(z - \alpha)$;
        (b) $(z^8 - 1)/z^7(z - 1)$.

Q6.15. $2z^{-1} + 4z^{-2} + 3z^{-3} - z^{-4} - 2z^{-5} - z^{-6}$.

Q6.16. (a) $\{2^{-n/2}\sin n\pi/4\}u[n]$;
        (b) $\{2.5 - 1.5(0.8)^{n-2}\}u[n - 2]$.

Q6.18. Poles at $z = -0.8$ and origin (second order); zeros at $z = 1$, $z = \pm0.8j$.

Q6.20. $H(z) = (z^4 + 2z^3 + 2z^2 + 2z + 1)/z(z^3 - 0.9z^2 + 0.9z - 0.81)$;
        zeros at $z = \pm j$, -1 (second-order);
        poles at $z = \pm0.9487j$, 0.9, and origin.

Q6.23. (a) $(z^2 - z)/(z^2 + 0.5z + 0.5)$;
        (b) $z^2/(z^2 + 0.5z + 0.5)$; $y[-1] = -2$, $y[-2] = 4$.

Chapter 7

Q7.1.   (a) Negative; (b) positive; (c) negative; (d) negative; (e) positive.

Q7.2.   (a) 0.01, 1000; (b) -0.0909, 9091, -0.011 per cent; (c) 50 kHz, 455 kHz, 5 MHz.

Q7.3.   19.74 dB to 20.15 dB.

Q7.4. $\alpha = 0.4$.

Q7.6. $G(\alpha^3 + 6\alpha^2 + 5\alpha + 1)/\{(1 - G)\alpha^3 + 6\alpha^2 + 5\alpha + 1\}$, $\alpha = sCR$;
        pole at $s = -1/5CR$; 0.65 Hz.

Q7.9.   Feedback negative at $\Omega = 0, \pi$; positive at $\Omega = \pi/2$; poles at $z = \pm j0.949$, second-order
        zero at $z = 0$.

Q7.10. $y[n] = 1.99037y[n - 1] - y[n - 2]$, $n > 1$, given that $y[0] = 1$ and $y[1] = 0.995185$.

Chapter 8

Q8.1. $\pi/(\omega_1 + \omega_2)$.

Q8.2.   6th-order.

Q8.5. $-44\,dB$ (approx.).

Q8.7.   0.46 Hz.

Q8.9. $4 + 6\cos\Omega + 4\cos 2\Omega + 2\cos 3\Omega$; 16; 0.

Q8.11.   First few values of impulse response: 1.0, -5.5, 14.5, -26.1, 37.7, -47.6, 54.9, -59.1, 60.2, -58.6, 54.7 etc.

Index